
MATHEMATICS DIVISION VOLUME 18

General Editors W. J. LANGFORD, E. A. MAXWELL, I. N. SNEDDON

A Modern Text-book on Statics

1

A Modern Text-book on Statics

for Students of Applied Mathematics, Physics and Engineering

C. J. ELIEZER
M.A., Ph.D. (Cantab), D.Sc. (London)
Professor of Mathematics in the University of Malaya

PERGAMON PRESS
OXFORD · LONDON · EDINBURGH · PARIS · FRANKFURT
THE MACMILLAN COMPANY
NEW YORK

PERGAMON PRESS LTD. Headington Hill Hall, Oxford
4 & 5 Fitzroy Square, London W.1

PERGAMON PRESS (SCOTLAND) LTD. 2 & 3 Teviot Place, Edinburgh 1

THE MACMILLAN COMPANY 60 Fifth Avenue, New York 11, N.Y.

COLLIER-MACMILLAN CANADA LTD. 132 Water Street South, Galt, Ontario, Canada

GAUTHIER-VILLIERS ED. 55 Quai des Grands-Augustins, Paris 6

PERGAMON PRESS G.m.b.H. Kaiserstrasse 75, Frankfurt am Main

FEDERAL PUBLICATIONS LTD. Times House, River Valley Road, Singapore

SAMCAX BOOK SERVICES LTD. Queensway, P.O. Box 2720, Nairobi, Kenya

First edition 1964

Library of Congress Catalog Card No. 63-21096

Set in 10 on 12 pt. Times New Roman
Printed in Great Britain by Adlard and Son Ltd., Dorking

To

Professor Emeritus F. H. V. Gulasekharam

with gratitude

Contents

Preface

THE POSITION of applied mathematics as a subject of study at school and university has been changing in recent years. When the General Certificate of Education was introduced some years ago, three passes at advanced level were deemed sufficient to provide exemption from the university intermediate examinations which till then had required four subjects of study. A resulting trend has been that many students now have a knowledge of mechanics as a part of physics, rather than as a systematic part of applied mathematics. Furthermore there have also been changes in the contents of courses. Certain portions of what were done previously in the special courses in universities are now completed at general degree level, and elementary parts of university work are now disposed of at school level. The result is that much of the time available is devoted to other topics than to statics. However, the author believes that statics is a valuable subject, and its systematic study provides a good introduction to some of the methods of applied mathematics. This book has been written with a view to helping students to reorganize their knowledge of mechanics learnt as a part of physics, and consolidate it as part of systematic applied mathematics.

This book on statics starts from the beginning and goes on to cover the scope of present-day general degree courses at universities and technical colleges. The book will be of use to students of applied mathematics of the sixth forms, particularly at scholarship level, as well as to students of mathematics, science or engineering at universities and technical colleges. It deals with the statics of rigid bodies, the statics of flexible strings and chains, and certain simple portions of elasticity such as the stretching of bars and bending of beams. Some elementary three-dimensional work has been included. It is necessary that even two-dimensional work should be studied against the background of three dimensions.

The book is divided into nine chapters, and each chapter is followed by exercises, which include questions from various university examination papers. The source is generally indicated at the end of each question, the following abbreviations being used:

MT	Mathematics Tripos Part I
MT II	Mathematics Tripos Part II
PM	Preliminary Examination in Mathematics
NS	Natural Science Tripos Part I
PNS	Preliminary to Natural Science Tripos, Part I
G	General
G II	General (Part II)
S	Special
GCE(S)	General Certificate of Education (Scholarship) level)
CCS(H)	Ceylon Civil Service, Higher Mathematics
CCS(L)	Ceylon Civil Service, Lower Mathematics

I am very grateful to the universities of Cambridge, Oxford, London and Ceylon, the Cambridge Local Examinations Syndicate, the Oxford Delegacy of Local Examinations, and the Public Service Commission of Ceylon for permission to use questions from their examination papers. These bodies, however, are not responsible for the solutions of illustrative examples, these being the responsibility of the author.

My text-book on *Concise Vector Analysis* (Pergamon Press, 1963) is referred to in the text as Reference 1.

It is a pleasure to thank my colleagues and pupils who have encouraged me to write this book. My thanks are also due to Dr. D. Callebaut of the Enrico Fermi Institute (Chicago) for assistance with proof-reading. Suggestions for the corrections of misprints and errors will be gratefully received by the author.

C. J. E.

Kuala Lumpur

Chapter 1

Composition of Forces

1.1. Introduction

STATICS is the branch of mechanics which deals with the study of forces and with the state of rest of bodies under the action of forces.

It is difficult to give a satisfactory concise definition of force. We use here the intuitive idea of force as an agency which, when it acts upon a body, tends to change the state of motion (or rest) of that body, as referred to a particular frame of reference. It is convenient also to simplify the scope of our study by introducing the concepts of a *particle* and of a *rigid body*. By a particle is meant a hypothetical body which is assumed to occupy a geometrical point. By the phrase *force acting at a point* is meant a force which acts upon the particle placed at that geometrical point. A rigid body is a hypothetical body which may be looked upon as an agglomeration of a large number of particles rigidly held together by cohesive forces such that every particle of the body maintains a fixed distance from all the other particles of the body. Actual bodies are of varying degrees of elasticity. The concept of perfect rigidity helps to construct an elementary theory of statics. In what follows, whenever we speak of a body, a rigid body shall be implied unless otherwise stated.

A force acts upon a point of a body and has a magnitude and a direction. It is convenient to indicate a force by a straight line drawn from its point of application, with an arrow to indicate the sense in which the force acts. Symbols such as **F**, **P**, **Q** . . . are generally used to denote forces.

In discussing the effects of a system of forces upon a body, it is useful to reduce the system into an equivalent simpler system. For this purpose there is constructed a theory of forces, based upon certain assumptions. The justification for the assumptions rests eventually upon the agreement of the experimentally obtained results with the calculations from the theory.

An assumption which is generally made is the following:

The introduction of two equal and opposite forces:

(*a*) acting at the same point of a body, or

(*b*) one, say **F**, acting at a point A of the rigid body and the other, $-$**F** at a point B of the body, where the line AB is in the direction of the forces,

will have no effect on the body's state of rest or motion. Such forces are said to balance each other or to be in equilibrium.

A consequence of this assumption is the **principle of transmissibility of force,** according to which a force **F** acting at a point A of a rigid body may be replaced by a force **F** at a point B of the body where the line AB is in the direction of the force **F** without any effect on the state of rest or motion of the body (Fig. 1).

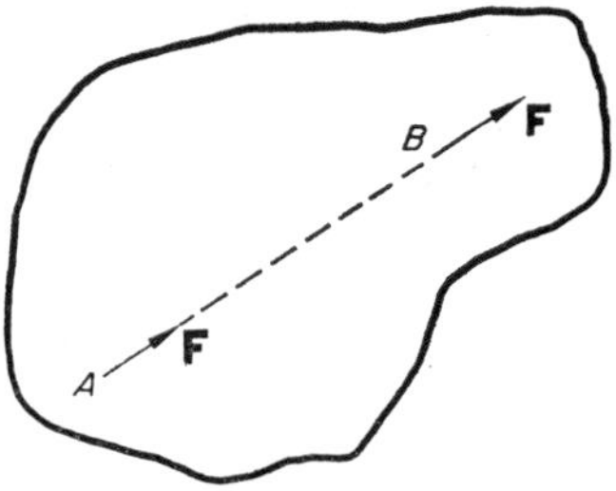

Fig. 1

Hence to consider the effect of a force, the force may be regarded as acting at any point of its line of action. Though we may continue to speak of a force as acting at a point, it may be noted that for determining its effect on a rigid body, it is the line of action (apart from the sense and magnitude of the force), that is necessary to be specified. In a sense, the principle of transmissibility may be regarded as a property of a rigid body, rather than that of a force.

A further practical use of this assumption is that it enables the simplification of a given system of forces by cancelling out forces which balance one another, and sometimes also by adding forces which are in balance, and then compounding the forces according to methods which will be described below.

Two systems of forces are said to be **equivalent** if one can be transformed to the other by the processes of addition or deletion of forces which are in balance among themselves.

A second assumption in the theory of forces is that a force is a vector. That is, it has magnitude and direction, and may be combined with another force by vector addition.

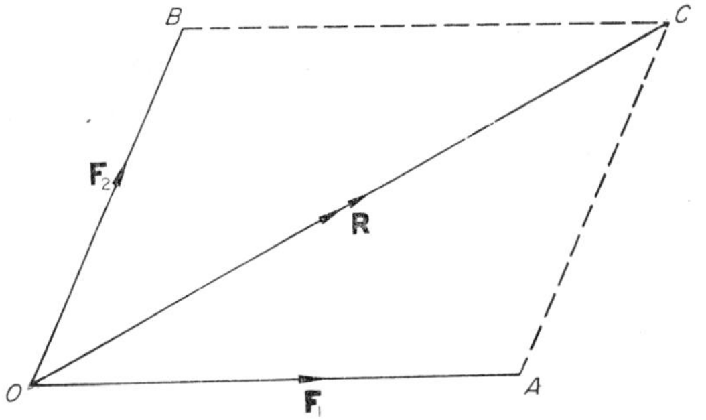

Fig. 2

Thus two forces $\mathbf{F}_1$ and $\mathbf{F}_2$ acting at a point O are combined together to form an equivalent single force $\mathbf{R}$ acting at O, where

$$\mathbf{R} = \mathbf{F}_1 + \mathbf{F}_2,$$

the sign + standing for vectorial addition, that is, addition by the parallelogram law. Figure 2 is a **parallelogram of forces.** The sides OA, OB represent the forces $\mathbf{F}_1$ and $\mathbf{F}_2$. Then the diagonal OC of the parallelogram drawn with OA, OB as edges represents the sum $\mathbf{R} = \mathbf{F}_1 + \mathbf{F}_2$.

$\mathbf{R}$ is called the **resultant** of $\mathbf{F}_1$ and $\mathbf{F}_2$, and $\mathbf{F}_1$ and $\mathbf{F}_2$ are called **components** of $\mathbf{R}$. If θ_{12} is the angle between $\mathbf{F}_1$ and $\mathbf{F}_2$ and θ the angle between $\mathbf{R}$ and $\mathbf{F}_1$ then from the figure we obtain

$$\mathbf{R}^2 = F_1^2 + F_2^2 + 2F_1F_2 \cos \theta_{12} \quad (1)$$

$$\tan \theta = F_2 \sin \theta_{12}/(F_1 + F_2 \cos \theta_{12}). \quad (2)$$

The resultant of three forces $\mathbf{F}_1$, $\mathbf{F}_2$, $\mathbf{F}_3$ acting at a point may be obtained by compounding first two of the forces according to the parallelogram law, and then compounding the result with the third force, also by the parallelogram law. The figure then obtained is called **the parallelepiped of forces** (Fig. 3).

$$\overrightarrow{OA} + \overrightarrow{OB} + \overrightarrow{OC} = (\overrightarrow{OA} + \overrightarrow{OB}) + \overrightarrow{OC} = \overrightarrow{OE} + \overrightarrow{OC}$$
$$= \overrightarrow{OD}.$$

The resultant of forces represented by the edges OA, OB, OC of a parallelepiped is represented by the diagonal OD of the parallelepiped. The magnitude and direction of $\mathbf{R}$ may be calculated from the geometrical properties of the parallelepiped.

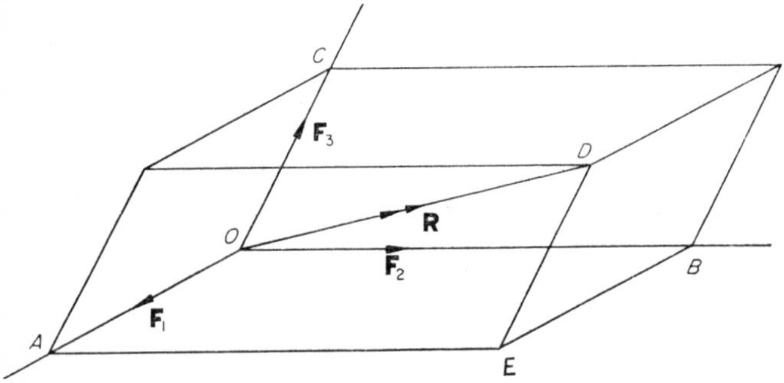

Fig. 3

$$\mathbf{R} = \mathbf{F}_1 + \mathbf{F}_2 + \mathbf{F}_3.$$

An important particular case is when the three forces are mutually perpendicular. The parallelepiped will then be a rectangular figure. Axes of coordinates Ox, Oy, Oz may be taken along the lines OA, OB, OC respectively. Suppose that the forces along the three axes are now denoted by X, Y, Z respectively, and that the direction cosines of the resultant $\mathbf{R}$ are l, m, n. The resultant being represented by the diagonal OD,

$$OD^2 = OA^2 + OB^2 + OC^2$$

gives

$$R^2 = X^2 + Y^2 + Z^2. \qquad (3)$$

Also

$$\left.\begin{aligned} l &= \cos \angle AOD = \frac{OA}{OD} = \frac{X}{R} \\ m &= \cos \angle BOD = \frac{OB}{OD} = \frac{Y}{R} \\ n &= \cos \angle COD = \frac{OC}{OD} = \frac{Z}{R} \end{aligned}\right\} . \tag{4}$$

Hence the resultant of three mutually perpendicular forces X, Y, Z is a force of magnitude $\sqrt{(X^2 + Y^2 + Z^2)}$ acting along a line whose direction cosines are $(X/R,\ Y/R,\ Z/R)$.

Conversely, the force **R** acting along a line whose direction cosines are (l, m, n) may be resolved into components X, Y, Z parallel to the axes where

$$X = Rl, \qquad Y = Rm, \qquad Z = Rn. \tag{5}$$

These components in three perpendicular directions are also called **resolved parts** of **R** along the three directions, X being called the resolved part along the x-axis, and Y, Z similarly along the y- and z-axes.

The resolved part of **R** in any direction, u say, may be obtained by taking mutually perpendicular axes Ox', Oy', Oz' such that Ox' is in the direction of u. The resolved part of R along u is then seen to be, from equation (5),

$$X' = R \cos \theta, \tag{6}$$

where θ is the angle between the direction of **R** and the direction of u.

1.2. Resultant of a general system of forces at a point O

The system of forces $\mathbf{F}_1, \mathbf{F}_2, \ldots, \mathbf{F}_p$, each passing through the point O, is equivalent to a single force **R** also passing through O, where

$$\mathbf{R} = \mathbf{F}_1 + \mathbf{F}_2 + \ldots + \mathbf{F}_p, \tag{7}$$

that is, **R** is obtained by the vectorial addition of the p forces.

If **R** vanishes, then the given system of forces is said to be in **equilibrium.** Given the forces $\mathbf{F}_1$, $\mathbf{F}_2$, . . ., $\mathbf{F}_p$ acting upon a body, the force which, acting along with these forces, keeps the body in equilibrium, is called the **equilibrant** of the system. The equilibrant is equal and opposite to the resultant and is therefore the force $-\mathbf{R}$. The evaluation of **R** may be carried out in different ways. Three methods are described below:

(1) *Analytical Method*

Take rectangular axes Ox, Oy, Oz. Suppose that the forces $\mathbf{F}_r$ have direction cosines (l_r, m_r, n_r), $r = 1, 2, \ldots, p$, and let (l, m, n) be the direction cosines of the resultant **R**, and X, Y, Z the components of **R** parallel to the axes. Then resolving along each axis, and equating the resolved parts of the resultant and of the given system

$$\left.\begin{aligned} Rl &= X = F_1l_1 + F_2l_2 + \ldots + F_pl_p \\ Rm &= Y = F_1m_1 + F_2m_2 + \ldots + F_pm_p \\ Rn &= Z = F_1n_1 + F_2n_2 + \ldots + F_pn_p \end{aligned}\right\}. \tag{8}$$

The magnitude R of the resultant may be obtained by squaring and adding these three equations:

$$\begin{aligned} R^2(l^2 + m^2 + n^2) &= X^2 + Y^2 + Z^2 \\ &= \sum F_r^2(l_r^2 + m_r^2 + n_r^2) + \\ &\qquad + 2 \sum_{r<s}\sum F_rF_s(l_rl_s + m_rm_s + n_rn_s). \end{aligned}$$

That is,

$$R^2 = \sum F_r^2 + 2 \sum_{r<s}\sum F_rF_s \cos \theta_{rs}, \tag{9}$$

where θ_{rs} is the angle between $\mathbf{F}_r$ and $\mathbf{F}_s$.

The direction of the resultant is obtained from

$$l = X/R, \qquad m = Y/R, \qquad n = Z/R. \tag{10}$$

If the forces are coplanar, then axes Ox, Oy may be taken in the plane of the forces. If $\mathbf{F}_r$ makes angle θ_r with the x-axis, and $\mathbf{R}$ makes angle θ with the x-axis, then

$$R \cos \theta = X = \sum F_r \cos \theta_r$$

$$R \sin \theta = Y = \sum F_r \sin \theta_r.$$

R and θ are then obtained from

$$R^2 = X^2 + Y^2 = \sum F_r^2 + 2 \sum_{r<s}\sum F_r F_s \cos \theta_{rs} \tag{11}$$

$$\tan \theta = Y/X. \tag{12}$$

Example 1. Forces P, Q, R, acting at a point O, are parallel to the sides of a triangle ABC. Show that the magnitude of the resultant $\mathbf{F}$ is given by

$$\mathbf{F}^2 = P^2 + Q^2 + R^2 - 2QR \cos A - 2RP \cos B - 2PQ \cos C.$$

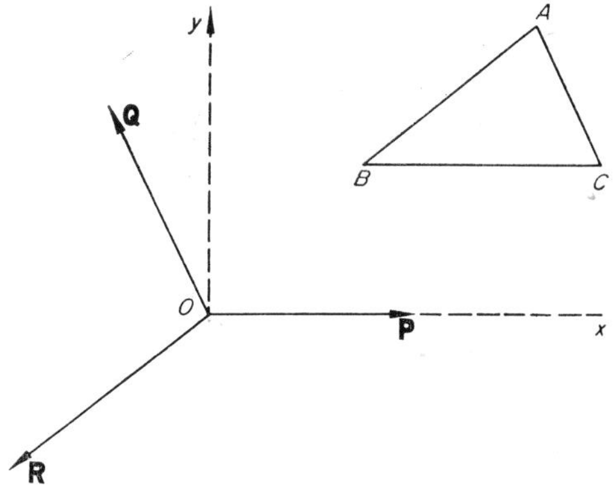

Fig. 4

Take axes Ox, Oy with Ox parallel to the side BC of the triangle, and Oy perpendicular to BC.

$$P\hat{O}Q = 180° - C$$
$$P\hat{O}R = 180° + B$$
$$X = P + Q\cos(180 - C) + R\cos(180 + B)$$
$$= P - Q\cos C - R\cos B$$
$$Y = Q\sin(180 - C) + R\sin(180 + B)$$
$$= Q\sin C - R\sin B$$
$$\mathbf{F}^2 = (P - Q\cos C - R\cos B)^2 + (Q\sin C - R\sin B)^2$$
$$= P^2 + Q^2(\cos^2 C + \sin^2 C) + R^2(\cos^2 B + \sin^2 B) +$$
$$+ 2QR(\cos B\cos C + \sin B\sin C) -$$
$$- 2RP\cos B - 2PQ\cos C$$
$$= P^2 + Q^2 + R^2 - 2QR\cos A - 2RP\cos B -$$
$$- 2PQ\cos C.$$

Example 2. Forces P, $2P$, $4P$, $3P$ act along the edges OA, OB, OC and diagonal OO', respectively, of a cube of side a, shown in Fig. 5. Find the resultant in magnitude and direction.

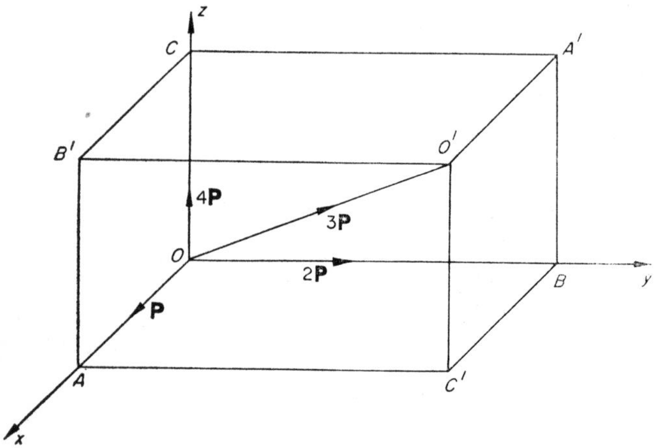

Fig. 5

Take axes Ox, Oy, Oz along OA, OB, OC respectively, the co-ordinates of O' are (a, a, a) and the direction cosines of OO' are

$(1/\sqrt{3}, 1/\sqrt{3}, 1/\sqrt{3})$. Hence

$$X = P + 3P/\sqrt{3} = P(1 + \sqrt{3})$$
$$Y = 2P + 3P/\sqrt{3} = P(2 + \sqrt{3})$$
$$Z = 4P + 3P/\sqrt{3} = P(4 + \sqrt{3}).$$
$$R^2 = X^2 + Y^2 + Z^2 = P^2[(1 + \sqrt{3})^2 + (2 + \sqrt{3})^2 + (4 + \sqrt{3})^2]$$
$$= P^2(30 + 14\sqrt{3}).$$

The resultant $\mathbf{R}$ has magnitude

$$R = P\sqrt{(30 + 14\sqrt{3})}$$

and direction cosines l, m, n where

$$l = \frac{1 + \sqrt{3}}{\sqrt{(30 + 14\sqrt{3})}},$$

$$m = \frac{2 + \sqrt{3}}{\sqrt{(30 + 14\sqrt{3})}},$$

$$n = \frac{4 + \sqrt{3}}{\sqrt{(30 + 14\sqrt{3})}}.$$

(2) *Mass-Centre Method*

Forces acting at a point may also be compounded by using a property of mass-centre, namely that a system of masses, λ_1 at a point A_1, λ_2 at A_2, . . . , λ_p at A_p where $\lambda_1 + \lambda_2 + \ldots + \lambda_p \neq O$, have a centre of mass G which satisfies the relation

$$\lambda_1\overrightarrow{A_1G} + \lambda_2\overrightarrow{A_2G} + \ldots + \lambda_p\overrightarrow{A_pG} = \mathbf{O}. \qquad (13)$$

(See Ref. 1, page 13)

Using this property, it may be shown that

$$\lambda_1\overrightarrow{OA_1} + \lambda_2\overrightarrow{OA_2} + \ldots$$
$$+ \lambda_p\overrightarrow{OA_p} = (\lambda_1 + \lambda_2 + \ldots + \lambda_p)\,\overrightarrow{OG}. \qquad (14)$$

From the addition law for vectors

$$\overrightarrow{OA_1} = \overrightarrow{OG} + \overrightarrow{GA_1}$$
$$\overrightarrow{OA_2} = \overrightarrow{OG} + \overrightarrow{GA_2}$$
$$\cdots\cdots\cdots\cdots\cdots$$
$$\overrightarrow{OA_p} = \overrightarrow{OG} + \overrightarrow{GA_p}.$$

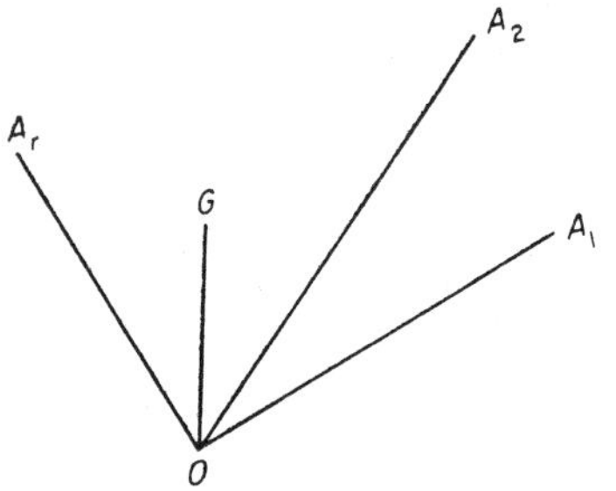

Fig. 6

Multiplying these equations by $\lambda_1, \lambda_2, \ldots, \lambda_p$ respectively, and adding

$$\lambda_1\overrightarrow{OA_1} + \lambda_2\overrightarrow{OA_2} + \ldots + \lambda_p\overrightarrow{OA_p}$$
$$= (\lambda_1 + \lambda_2 + \ldots + \lambda_p)\,\overrightarrow{OG}$$
$$+ (\lambda_1\overrightarrow{GA_1} + \lambda_2\overrightarrow{GA_2} + \ldots + \lambda_p\overrightarrow{GA_p}).$$

The last term in brackets on the right-hand side vanishes, by equation (12), and hence the equation (14) follows. Hence the resultant of the forces $\lambda_1\overrightarrow{OA_1}$, $\lambda_2\overrightarrow{OA_2}$, $\ldots$, $\lambda_p\overrightarrow{OA_p}$ is $(\lambda_1 + \lambda_2 + \ldots + \lambda_p)\,\overrightarrow{OG}$. This result is called *Leibniz's theorem.*

The particular case when $p = 2$ is called *the* (λ, μ) *theorem*, which states that

$$\lambda\overrightarrow{OA} + \mu\overrightarrow{OB} = (\lambda + \mu)\,\overrightarrow{OC}$$

where C is a point on AB such that $\lambda AC = \mu CB$.

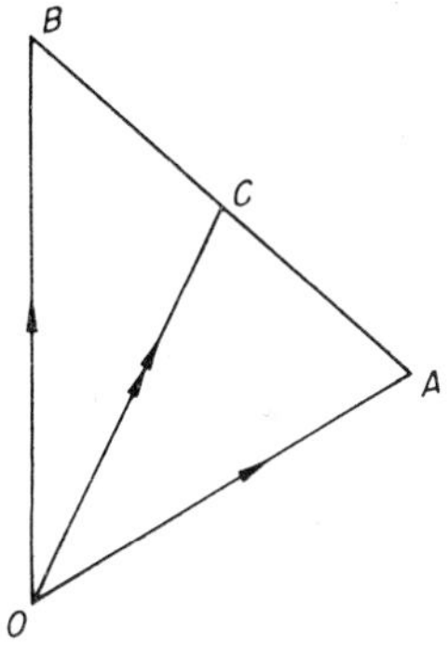

Fig. 7

Example 3. The circumference of a circle of centre C is divided into p equal parts at points $A_1, A_2, \ldots, A_p$ (Fig. 7). If O is any point not necessarily on the plane of the circle, find the resultant of

$$\overrightarrow{OA_1}, \overrightarrow{OA_2}, \ldots, \overrightarrow{OA_p}.$$

Here, we take $\lambda_1 = \lambda_2 = \ldots = \lambda_p = 1$. The mass-centre of 1 at A_1, 1 at A_2, ..., 1 at A_p is by symmetry, the centre of the circle, which is the point C. Hence, applying Leibniz's theorem, the required resultant is $(1 + 1 + \ldots + 1)\,\overrightarrow{OC}$ or $p\overrightarrow{OC}$.

Example 4. Coplanar forces $\mathbf{F}_1, \ldots \mathbf{F}_p$, acting at a point O are in equilibrium. Any transversal l cuts their lines of action in points $A_1, A_2, \ldots A_p$. Show that

$$\Sigma \frac{F_r}{OA_r} = 0$$

where OA_r is positive when it is in the same sense as $\mathbf{F}_r$ and negative otherwise.

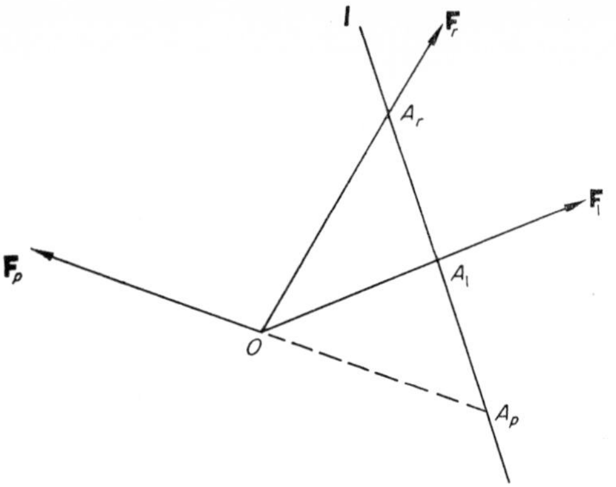

Fig. 8

Suppose that

$$K = \sum \frac{F_r}{OA_r} \neq O.$$

Then

$$\sum \mathbf{F}_r = \sum \left(\frac{F_r}{OA_r}\right) \overrightarrow{OA_r}$$

$$= K\,\overrightarrow{OG}$$

where G is the centroid of masses F_1/OA_1 at A_1, F_2/OA_2 at A_2, ... F_p/OA_p at A_p. Since $A_1, A_2, \ldots A_p$ are on l, the centre of mass G also lies on l. Hence $\overrightarrow{OG}$ cannot vanish and $\sum \mathbf{F}_r = K\,\overrightarrow{OG}$ also cannot vanish. But it is given that the forces are in equilibrium, that is $\sum \mathbf{F}_r = \mathbf{O}$. Therefore the assumption $K \neq O$ does not hold. Hence

$$\sum \frac{F_r}{OA_r} = O.$$

(3) *Graphical Method*

To find the resultant of $\mathbf{F}_1, \mathbf{F}_2, \ldots, \mathbf{F}_p$ shown in Fig. 9(*a*), we take a point A as in Fig. 9(*b*), and draw AA_1 parallel to $\mathbf{F}_1$ and of length such that AA_1 represents $\mathbf{F}_1$ in a suitable scale. From A_1 draw A_1A_2 parallel to $\mathbf{F}_2$ and representing it in the same scale. This process is continued till the point A_p is reached. Then $\overrightarrow{AA_p}$ represents in the same scale the resultant $\mathbf{R}$, and therefore gives the

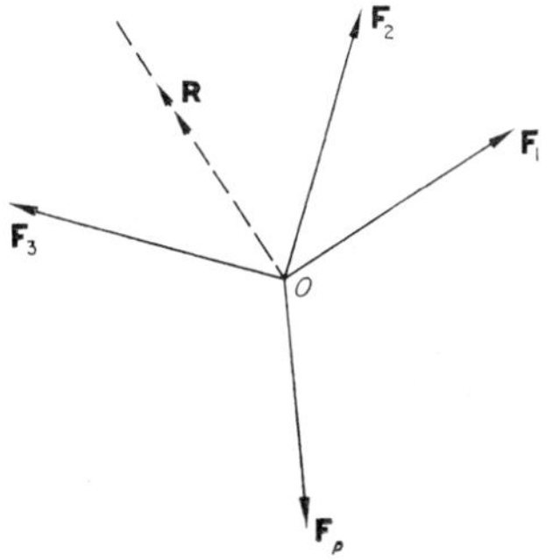

Fig. 9(*a*)

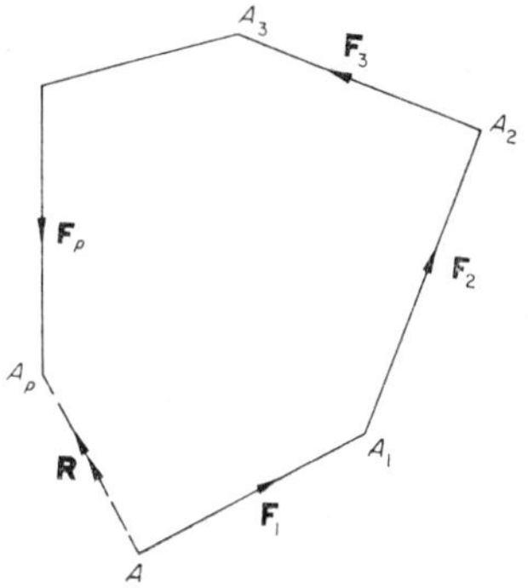

Fig. 9(*b*)

direction and magnitude of $\mathbf{R}$. But since the resultant $\mathbf{R}$ acts at O, $\mathbf{R}$ may be shown in Fig. 9(*a*) by a line through O parallel to $\overrightarrow{AA_p}$ and proportional to it according to the scale.

It may be noted that the polygon $AA_1 \ldots A_p$ need not be a plane polygon. When the forces at O are all coplanar, then the polygon will be a plane polygon.

1.3. Conditions of equilibrium of forces acting at a point

Forces $\mathbf{F}_1, \mathbf{F}_2, \ldots, \mathbf{F}_p$ acting at a point O are in equilibrium (by definition) if and only if their resultant vanishes, that is if and only if

$$\mathbf{R} = \mathbf{F}_1 + \mathbf{F}_2 + \ldots + \mathbf{F}_p = \mathbf{O}. \tag{15}$$

In the analytical method, the equation

$$R^2 = X^2 + Y^2 + Z^2$$

shows that R can vanish if and only if

$$X = Y = Z = 0. \tag{16}$$

If $\mathbf{u}$ is unit vector along any direction, the resolved part of a force $\mathbf{F}$ in that direction is $\mathbf{F} \cdot \mathbf{u}$. From equation (15), taking scalar product with $\mathbf{u}$ gives

$$\mathbf{R} \cdot \mathbf{u} = \mathbf{F}_1 \cdot \mathbf{u} + \mathbf{F}_2 \cdot \mathbf{u} + \ldots + \mathbf{F}_p \cdot \mathbf{u} = 0. \tag{17}$$

Hence a necessary condition for equilibrium is that the sum of the resolved parts of the forces in any direction is zero.

In the mass-centre method, the forces

$$\lambda_1\overrightarrow{OA_1}, \lambda_2\overrightarrow{OA_2}, \ldots, \lambda_p\overrightarrow{OA_p}$$

are in equilibrium if the centre of mass G coincides with O, that is, if O is the centre of mass of λ_1 at A_1, λ_2 at A_2, ..., λ_p at A_p.

In the graphical method, when the polygon $AA_1 \ldots A_p$ is drawn, starting from a point A and with the successive sides representing in magnitude and direction the p forces $\mathbf{F}_1, \ldots, \mathbf{F}_p$, then in the case when $\mathbf{R}$ vanishes, the points A and A_p will coincide, and the polygon will be closed.

We may also consider the conditions of equilibrium according to the number of forces acting:

If two forces acting at O are in equilibrium, they must be equal and opposite.

If three forces, $\mathbf{F}_1$, $\mathbf{F}_2$, $\mathbf{F}_3$ acting at a point O are in equilibrium,

$$\mathbf{F}_1 + \mathbf{F}_2 + \mathbf{F}_3 = \mathbf{O}.$$

One requirement for this to be possible is that the three forces should be coplanar, because the resultant of two of the forces must balance the third force. In Figure 10, $\mathbf{F}_1$ and $\mathbf{F}_2$ are represented by OA_1, OA_2, and $\mathbf{F}_1 + \mathbf{F}_2$ by the diagonal OC of the parallelogram drawn with OA_1, OA_2 as sides.

Since $\mathbf{F}_3 = -(\mathbf{F}_1 + \mathbf{F}_2)$, $\mathbf{F}_3$ may be represented by $\overrightarrow{CO}$.

Thus in the triangle OA_1C, OA_1 represents $\mathbf{F}_1$, A_1C being parallel and equal to OA_2 represents $\mathbf{F}_2$ and CO represents $\mathbf{F}_3$.

Hence when the three forces $\mathbf{F}_1$, $\mathbf{F}_2$, $\mathbf{F}_3$ are in equilibrium, they may be represented by the sides of a triangle taken in order. Such a triangle is called a **triangle of forces.**

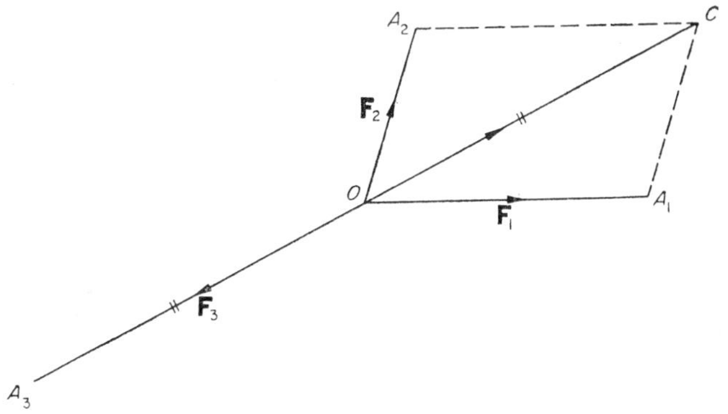

Fig. 10

Any triangle drawn with its sides parallel to the three forces will be a triangle of forces, since the sides of such a triangle will be necessarily proportional to the magnitudes of the corresponding forces.

From the trigonometrical properties of the triangle in Fig. 10 may also be derived

$$\frac{F_1}{\sin A_2\hat{O}A_3} = \frac{F_2}{\sin A_3\hat{O}A_1} = \frac{F_3}{\sin A_1\hat{O}A_2}. \tag{18}$$

Hence if three forces acting at a point are in equilibrium, then the forces are coplanar and each force is proportional to the sine of the angle between the other two. This result is known as **Lami's theorem.**

Vectorially, the conditions of equilibrium of three forces acting at a point may be stated as follows.

Let $\mathbf{a}_1$, $\mathbf{a}_2$, $\mathbf{a}_3$ be unit vectors along the directions of the three forces. Since the three forces are in equilibrium,

$$F_1\mathbf{a}_1 + F_2\mathbf{a}_2 + F_3\mathbf{a}_3 = \mathbf{O}. \tag{19}$$

Scalar product with $\mathbf{a}_2 \times \mathbf{a}_3$ gives

$$F_1[\mathbf{a}_1, \mathbf{a}_2, \mathbf{a}_3] = O, \tag{20}$$

from which it follows that $\mathbf{a}_1, \mathbf{a}_2, \mathbf{a}_3$ are coplanar.

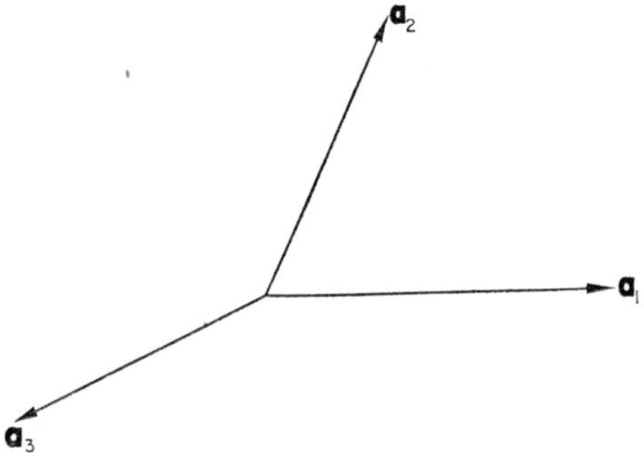

Fig. 11

Vector product of (19) with $\mathbf{a}_3$ gives

$$F_1\mathbf{a}_1 \times \mathbf{a}_3 + F_2\mathbf{a}_2 \times \mathbf{a}_3 = \mathbf{O}$$

from which F_1/F_2 is obtained. Similarly F_2/F_3, F_3/F_1 may also be obtained. The results are then contained in

$$\frac{\mathbf{a}_2 \times \mathbf{a}_3}{F_1} = \frac{\mathbf{a}_3 \times \mathbf{a}_1}{F_2} = \frac{\mathbf{a}_1 \times \mathbf{a}_2}{F_3}. \tag{21}$$

Each force is proportional to the area of the parallelogram formed by unit vectors along the other two. The area of each parallelogram being proportional to the sine of the angle between the vectors, the result agrees with Lami's theorem.

Four Forces Acting at a Point

If four forces $\mathbf{F}_1$, $\mathbf{F}_2$, $\mathbf{F}_3$, $\mathbf{F}_4$ are in equilibrium, and $\mathbf{a}_1$, $\mathbf{a}_2$, $\mathbf{a}_3$, $\mathbf{a}_4$ are unit vectors along the four directions, then

$$F_1\mathbf{a}_1 + F_2\mathbf{a}_2 + F_3\mathbf{a}_3 + F_4\mathbf{a}_4 = \mathbf{O}.$$

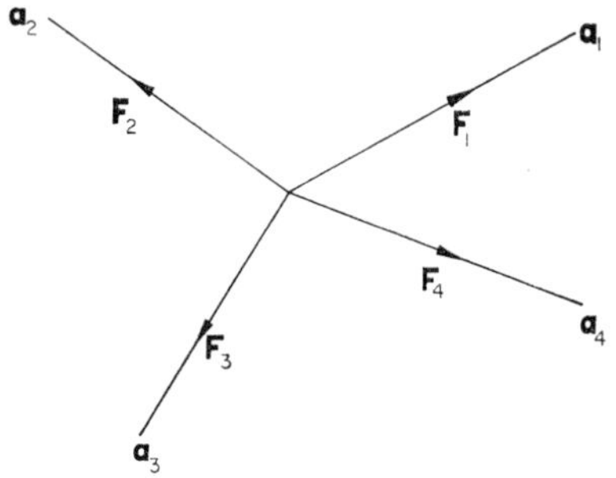

Fig. 12

From this equation one derives

$$\frac{F_1}{[\mathbf{a}_2, \mathbf{a}_3, \mathbf{a}_4]} = \frac{-F_2}{[\mathbf{a}_3, \mathbf{a}_4, \mathbf{a}_1]} = \frac{F_3}{[\mathbf{a}_4, \mathbf{a}_1, \mathbf{a}_2]} = \frac{-F_4}{[\mathbf{a}_1, \mathbf{a}_2, \mathbf{a}_3]}. \qquad (22)$$

Hence each force is proportional to the volume of the parallelepiped formed by unit vectors along the other three.

Polygon of Forces

The extension of the triangle of forces when more than three forces acting at a point are in equilibrium is called the polygon of forces, and states that if forces acting at a point can be represented, in magnitude and direction, by the sides of a polygon taken in order, then the forces are in equilibrium.

There is one difference, however, between the propositions for the triangle and for the polygon, namely that if a number of forces are in equilibrium and a polygon is drawn with sides parallel to the forces it would not necessarily follow that the magnitudes of the forces are proportional to the sides or that this polygon is a polygon of forces. Whereas equiangular triangles are similar, equiangular polygons need not be similar. Hence in the case of the polygon, both directions and magnitudes have to be taken into account.

Example 5. D, E, F are the midpoints of the sides of a triangle ABC. If O is any point on the plane of the triangle, show that the forces

$$\overrightarrow{OA}, \overrightarrow{OB}, \overrightarrow{OC}, \overrightarrow{DO}, \overrightarrow{EO}, \overrightarrow{FO}$$

are in equilibrium.

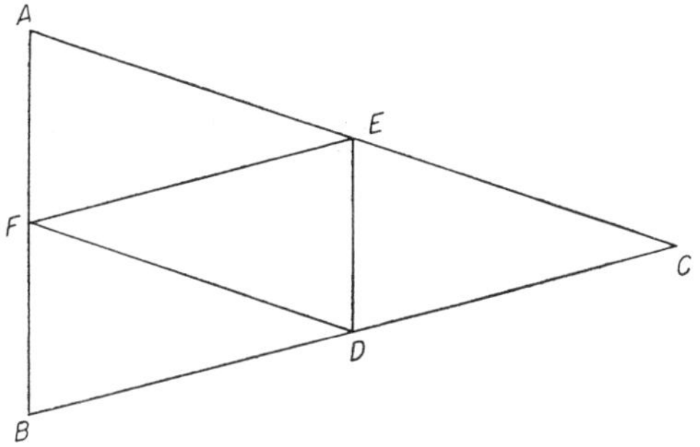

Fig. 13

Applying the mass-centre method

$$\overrightarrow{OA} + \overrightarrow{OB} + \overrightarrow{OC} = 3\overrightarrow{OG},$$

where G is the centroid of the triangle ABC.

Again,

$$\overrightarrow{DO} + \overrightarrow{EO} + \overrightarrow{FO} = 3\overrightarrow{GO}$$

since G is also the centroid of the triangle DEF. Hence the given forces are equivalent to

$$3\overrightarrow{OG} + 3\overrightarrow{GO} = \mathbf{0},$$

and hence are in equilibrium.

Example 6. If forces

$$\alpha\overrightarrow{AB},\ \beta\overrightarrow{CB},\ \gamma\overrightarrow{CD},\ \delta\overrightarrow{AD}$$

acting along the sides of a plane quadrilateral are in equilibrium, show that

$$\alpha\gamma = \beta\delta.$$

We have $$\alpha\overrightarrow{AB} + \delta\overrightarrow{AD} = (\alpha + \delta)\,\overrightarrow{AE}$$

where E is the point on BD such that

$$\alpha BE = \delta ED.$$

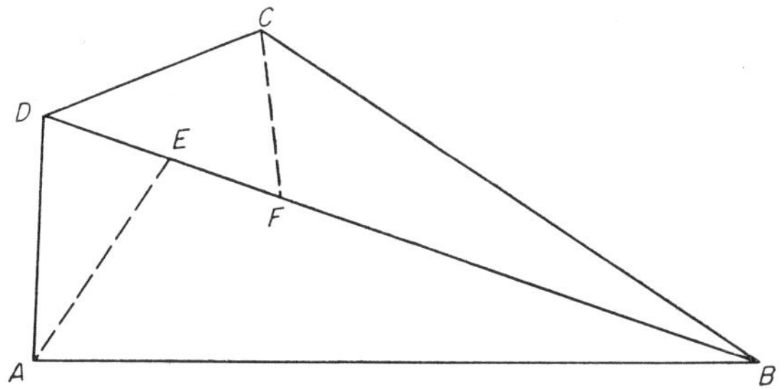

Fig. 14

Also

We have $$\beta\overrightarrow{CB} + \gamma\overrightarrow{CD} = (\beta + \gamma)\,\overrightarrow{CF}$$

where F is the point on BD such that

$$\beta BF = \gamma FD.$$

Since the forces are in equilibrium, the forces along AE and CF must balance one another, which is not possible unless the points E and F coincide with the point of intersection of the two diagonals.

If E and F coincide,

$$\delta/\alpha = BE/ED = BF/FD = \gamma/\beta.$$

Hence,

$$\alpha\gamma = \beta\delta.$$

1.4. Parallel forces, coplanar forces

The composition of forces acting at a point was carried out in the above by vector addition, using the property that a force is a vector. However, a force is not a free vector, but is a *localized vector*. The line of action of a force acting upon a body has an important effect on the body's state of rest or motion. Hence in the composition of forces which do not all act at a point, the positions of the different forces have to be taken into account. We consider first the particular case of two parallel forces.

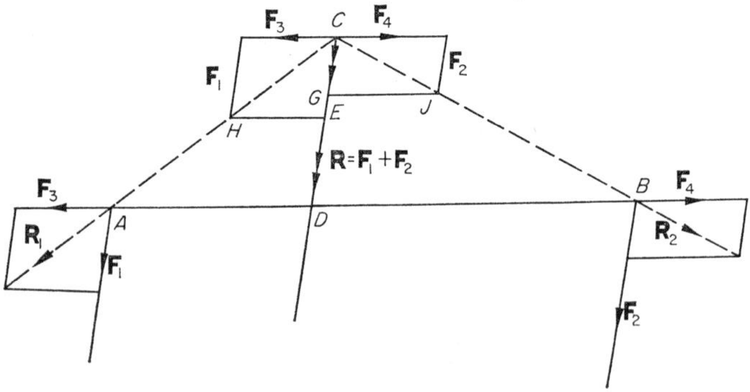

Fig. 15

Given two parallel forces $\mathbf{F}_1$ and $\mathbf{F}_2$, their resultant may be determined in magnitude, direction and location by the method shown in Fig. 15. Suppose A is a point on the line of action of $\mathbf{F}_1$ and B a point on the line of action of $\mathbf{F}_2$. Two equal and opposite forces $\mathbf{F}_3$ at A and $\mathbf{F}_4$ at B are introduced with their lines of action passing through A and B. Since they balance each other, their introduction makes no change. $\mathbf{F}_1$ and $\mathbf{F}_3$ at A may be combined together to have a resultant $\mathbf{R}_1$. $\mathbf{F}_2$ and $\mathbf{F}_4$ at B may similarly be combined to give a resultant $\mathbf{R}_2$. The two forces $\mathbf{R}_1$ and $\mathbf{R}_2$ will intersect (except in the particular case when $\mathbf{F}_1$ and $\mathbf{F}_2$ are equal and opposite, which case will be considered later). Suppose the point of intersection is C. $\mathbf{R}_1$ and $\mathbf{R}_2$ at C may be resolved into $\mathbf{F}_1$, $\mathbf{F}_2$, $\mathbf{F}_3$, $\mathbf{F}_4$ at C. $\mathbf{F}_3$ and $\mathbf{F}_4$ are equal and opposite and cancel out. $\mathbf{F}_1$ and $\mathbf{F}_2$ at C being in the same direction add up to a resultant $\mathbf{R} = \mathbf{F}_1 + \mathbf{F}_2$. Hence the resultant is a force $\mathbf{R}$ at C, and its magnitude is that of $\mathbf{F}_1 + \mathbf{F}_2$. If $\mathbf{F}_1$ and $\mathbf{F}_2$ are in opposite senses, they are called unlike forces, while if they are in the same sense they are called like forces. For unlike forces the magnitude of the resultant is $| \mathbf{F}_1 - \mathbf{F}_2 |$ and its sense is in the sense of the larger force. Thus, the magnitude and direction of $\mathbf{R}$, though not its location, may be obtained by compounding $\mathbf{F}_1$ and $\mathbf{F}_2$ as though they are free vectors.

It is useful to know the position of the point D where the line of action of the resultant intersects AB. The similarity of triangles ACD and HCE gives

$$AD/CD = HE/CE = F_3/F_1,$$

and similarity of triangles BCD and JCG gives

$$BD/CD = JG/CG = F_4/F_2.$$

Hence the point D satisfies the relation

$$AD/BD = F_2/F_1$$

or

$$F_1 \,.\, AD = F_2 \,.\, BD. \tag{23}$$

This gives a rule for determining the point D. When $\mathbf{F}_1$ and $\mathbf{F}_2$ are like forces, the point D will lie between A and B, but when $\mathbf{F}_1$ and $\mathbf{F}_2$ are unlike forces, D will lie outside the range AB.

If the position vector of A is $\mathbf{r}_1$ and that of B is $\mathbf{r}_2$, then since D divides AB in the ratio $F_2 : F_1$, the position vector of D is

$$\frac{F_1\mathbf{r}_1 + F_2\mathbf{r}_2}{F_1 + F_2}. \tag{24}$$

There is one important particular case where the above method of compounding two parallel forces fails, namely when the two forces are equal and unlike, that is, when $\mathbf{F}_1 + \mathbf{F}_2 = \mathbf{O}$. In this case

$\mathbf{R}_1$ and $\mathbf{R}_2$ will be parallel, and there is no finite point C (Fig. 16). The system cannot be reduced to a single resultant force. Such a system is called a **couple.** When a couple acts upon a body it tends to give the body a rotation. A quantitative measure of the tendency of a couple or a system of forces to produce rotation is obtained by introducing the concept of the moment of a force (§ 1.5 below).

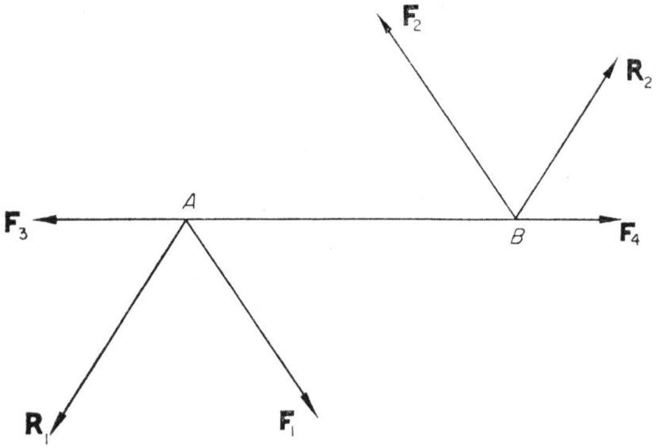

Fig. 16

Coplanar Forces

The above methods of compounding two intersecting forces or two parallel forces enable the determination of the resultant of any system of coplanar forces. The forces may be compounded, step by step, beginning with two forces and compounding their resultant with a third force and so on. It would be necessary to show that the final result is independent of the order in which the forces are taken and added. The resultant system will be a single force or a single couple or be in equilibrium. The direction and magnitude of the resultant force in the first case may be obtained by adding the given forces vectorially as though they are free vectors. The determination of the position of the resultant force is simplified by the concept of *moment* of a force which will be introduced in the next section.

1.5. Moments

Vector Moment of a Force

If P is a point, whose position vector is $\mathbf{r}$, and which lies on the line of action l of a force $\mathbf{F}$, the vector moment of $\mathbf{F}$ about a point P_0 whose position vector is $\mathbf{r}_0$ is defined as the vector

$$\mathbf{M} = \overrightarrow{P_0P} \times \mathbf{F} = (\mathbf{r} - \mathbf{r}_0) \times \mathbf{F}. \tag{25}$$

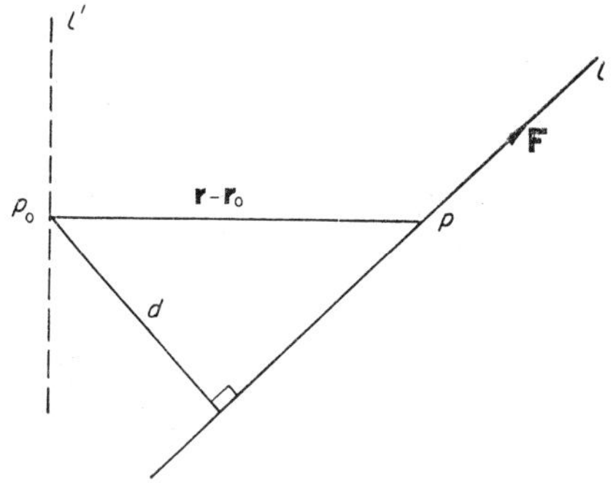

Fig. 17

The vector is normal to the plane formed by the lines P_0P and l, and its sense is in the direction of advance of a right-hand screw when rotated by the force $\mathbf{F}$.

$\mathbf{M}$ does not depend on the particular point P on l. If P is replaced by another point P' which also lies on l, then

$$\overrightarrow{P_0P'} \times \mathbf{F} = (\overrightarrow{P_0P} + \overrightarrow{PP'}) \times \mathbf{F} = \overrightarrow{P_0P} \times \mathbf{F},$$

since PP' and $\mathbf{F}$ are parallel, and their vector product vanishes. The numerical value of $\mathbf{M}$ is Fd where d is the perpendicular distance of the line l from P_0.

It may be noted that the moment of $\mathbf{F}$ about any point on its line of action vanishes, d being zero in this case.

Varignon's Theorem of Moments

If two forces $\mathbf{F}_1$ and $\mathbf{F}_2$ intersect at a point whose position vector is $\mathbf{r}$, and their resultant is $\mathbf{R}$, then the moment of the resultant about any point is equal to the vector sum of the moments of the forces $\mathbf{F}_1$ and $\mathbf{F}_2$ about that point.

Suppose $\mathbf{r}_o$ is the position vector of the point about which the moments are taken. From

$$\mathbf{R} = \mathbf{F}_1 + \mathbf{F}_2$$

taking vector product with $(\mathbf{r} - \mathbf{r}_o)$, we obtain

$$(\mathbf{r} - \mathbf{r}_o) \times \mathbf{R} = (\mathbf{r} - \mathbf{r}_o) \times \mathbf{F}_1 + (\mathbf{r} - \mathbf{r}_o) \times \mathbf{F}_2$$

that is,

$$\mathbf{M} = \mathbf{M}_1 + \mathbf{M}_2, \tag{26}$$

showing that the moment of the resultant of two intersecting forces is the vector sum of the moments of the two forces.

This result may be extended to two parallel forces, by utilizing the results in Fig. 15, particularly the equation (23).

The theorem may then be extended further to a general system of coplanar forces, the moment of the resultant system being the sum of the moments of the individual forces.

Moment about a Line

Suppose $\mathbf{F}$ is a force acting along a line l and that $\mathbf{r}$ is the position vector of a point P on l. Suppose that l' (Fig. 17) is a given line, and that $\mathbf{r}_o$ is the position vector of a point P_o on l'. The moment of the force $\mathbf{F}$ about the line l' is defined as the resolved part along l' of the vector moment $\mathbf{M}$ of the force $\mathbf{F}$ about the point P_o. The moment of a force about a line is a scalar quantity. If $\mathbf{u}$ denotes the unit vector along l and $\mathbf{u}'$ denotes the unit vector along l', then the moment about the line l' of the force $\mathbf{F}$ is

$$\mathbf{M} \,.\, \mathbf{u}' = \{(\mathbf{r} - \mathbf{r}_o) \times \mathbf{F}\} \,.\, \mathbf{u}' = F[\mathbf{r} - \mathbf{r}_o, \mathbf{u}, \mathbf{u}'].$$

The expression

$$[\mathbf{r} - \mathbf{r}_0, \mathbf{u}, \mathbf{u}'] \tag{27}$$

depends only on the two lines l and l' (and not on the particular points P_0 and P taken on them) and is called the mutual moment of the lines l and l'. The roles of l and l' may be interchanged without altering the mutual moment.

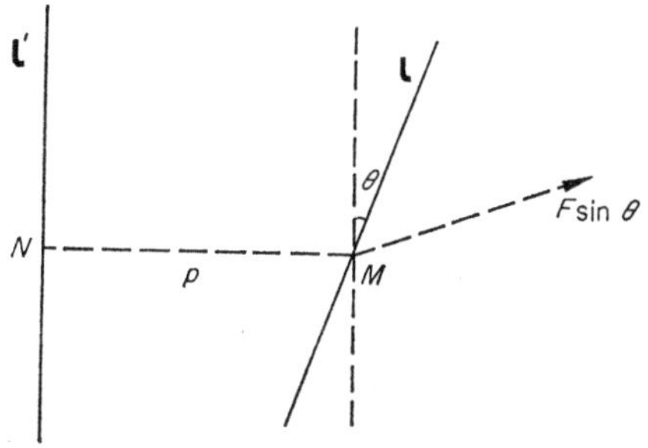

Fig. 18

It is useful to express the moment in terms of the shortest distance and angle between the lines. If MN is the common perpendicular to the two lines l and l' and p is the shortest distance, and θ is the angle between l and l', then the moment of $\mathbf{F}$ about the line l' is

$$Fp \sin \theta. \tag{28}$$

The mutual moment of the two lines is $p \sin \theta$. The moment vanishes if $p = O$ or $\theta = O$, that is, if the force intersects the line or is parallel to it. Conversely if the moment of a force about a line vanishes, we may infer that either the force vanishes or the force is parallel to the line or intersects the line.

Moments about the Axes

Suppose that referred to rectangular Cartesian axes, a force $\mathbf{F}$ with components F_x, F_y, F_z acts at the point P whose position vector

r has components (x, y, z). The moment of the force **F** about the origin O is

$$\mathbf{M} = \mathbf{r} \times \mathbf{F}. \tag{29}$$

The moments about the three axes Ox, Oy, Oz are the components of **M** along the three axes respectively and hence are

$$\left.\begin{aligned} M_x &= yF_z - zF_y \\ M_y &= zF_x - xF_z \\ M_z &= xF_y - yF_x \end{aligned}\right\}. \tag{30}$$

The signs of the moments are such that if one looks from the origin along the positive direction of a coordinate axis, a clockwise rotation gives the positive sense.

When dealing with a system of coplanar forces only, one often speaks of the moment of a force about a point in the plane, meaning by it the expression: force multiplied by the perpendicular distance of the force from the point. This expression is in fact the moment about the line through the point normal to the plane.

Thus if axes Ox, Oy are taken in the plane of the forces, and Oz is normal to the plane, the moment about the lines Ox, Oy, Oz through O of a force $\mathbf{F} = (F_x, F_y, O)$ acting at the point $\mathbf{r} = (x, y, o)$ are

$$M_x = O, \qquad M_y = O, \qquad M_z = xF_y - yF_x. \tag{31}$$

The only non-vanishing component is M_z, and one then refers to M_z simply as the moment about the point O. In the same way, moment of the force **F** about the point (x_1, y_1, O) is

$$(x - x_1) F_y - (y - y_1) F_x. \tag{32}$$

The Moment of a Couple

Suppose that the couple consists of the pair of forces **F** acting at a point $\mathbf{r}_1$ and $-\mathbf{F}$ acting at a point $\mathbf{r}_2$. Taking moments about a point whose position vector is $\mathbf{p}$, the sum of the moments of the two forces is

$$\left.\begin{aligned}(\mathbf{r}_1 - \mathbf{p}) \times \mathbf{F} + (\mathbf{r}_2 - \mathbf{p}) \times (-\mathbf{F}) &= (\mathbf{r}_1 - \mathbf{r}_2) \times \mathbf{F} \\ &= \mathbf{a} \times \mathbf{F}\end{aligned}\right\}. \qquad (33)$$

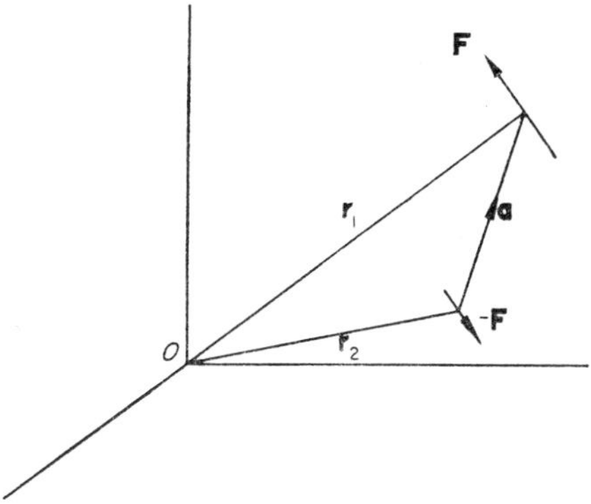

Fig. 19

The moment is thus independent of the point $\mathbf{p}$ about which the moment is taken. Hence we call this moment the moment of the couple, without specifying the point about which the moment is taken, and denote it by the symbol $\mathbf{G}$. The direction of $\mathbf{G}$ is normal to the plane of the forces, and the magnitude of $\mathbf{G}$ is Fd where d is the perpendicular distance between the forces of the couple. The sense of $\mathbf{G}$ is given by the direction of advance of a right-handed screw rotated by the couple.

A couple acting upon a body has no translatory effect, the contribution of the two forces in any direction being the component of $\mathbf{F} + (-\mathbf{F})$, which is zero. A couple has only a rotatory effect. It is sufficient to specify a couple by its moment. The particular values of the force F or the arm d of the couple are not significant but it is the product Fd that determines the effect of the couple. A couple may have its forces rotated through any angle in their plane or translated together to any position without changing its effect.

Two couples in the same or parallel planes are equivalent when their moments are the same, and balance one another when their moments are equal and opposite.

Thus a couple is specified by its vector moment **G**. **G** is a vector but is not a localized vector. It is a free vector. There is no one line along which **G** is specified to act, as in the case of a force. All equal and parallel lines can be used to represent the same couple. A line drawn in the direction normal to the plane of the forces of the couple, with its length proportional to the magnitude of the moment, with the sign convention referred to earlier, is called the **axis of the couple.** The couple **G** is then said to act about its axis.

Two couples **G**, **G**′ may be compounded as vectors according to the parallelogram law. The vector $\mathbf{G} + \mathbf{G}'$ will represent in magnitude and direction the resultant couple that is formed by the addition of the two couples.

The rules given earlier for the composition of forces may therefore be used also for the composition of couples. Thus a couple **G** about a line whose direction cosines are (l, m, n) may be resolved into three couples about the axes, of moments lG, mG, nG respectively. And three couples about the axes, of moments L, M, N respectively, may be combined into a single couple of moment

$$G = \sqrt{(L^2 + M^2 + N^2)}$$

about an axis whose direction cosines are $(L/G, M/G, N/G)$. The moment of this system about a line through O whose direction cosines are (l', m', n') is

$$Ll' + Mm' + Nn'.$$

THEOREM: *A force is equivalent to an equal parallel force together with a couple.*

Suppose that **F** is a given force which passes through a point A (Fig. 20), and it is desired to shift **F** parallel to itself to pass through the point B. At B introduce two equal and opposite forces **F** and —**F**, as shown. These will not alter the effect of the system. The force **F** at A and the force —**F** at B constitute a couple of moment

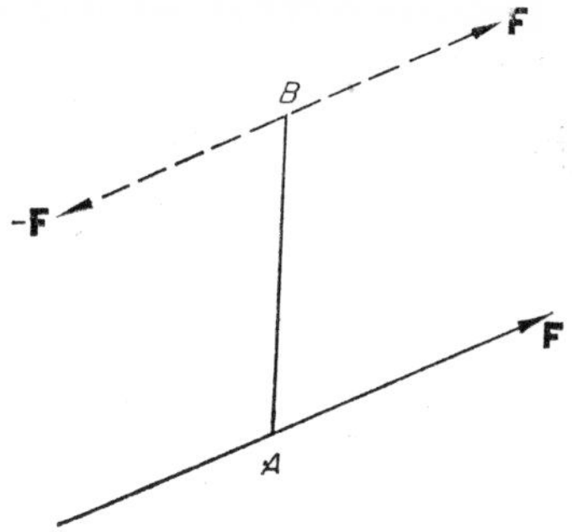

Fig. 20

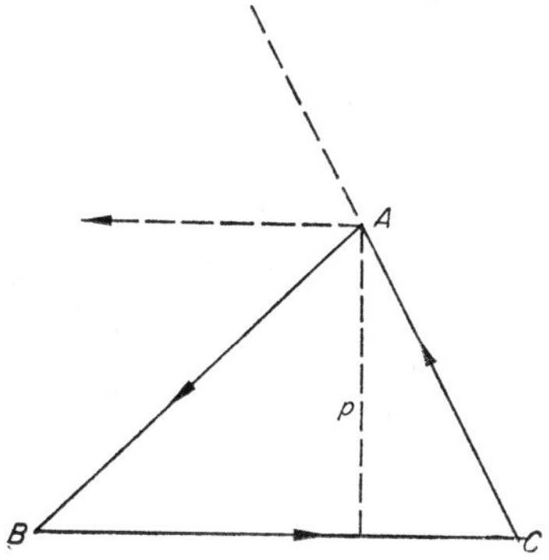

Fig. 21

$\overrightarrow{BA} \times \mathbf{F}$. Hence the original force **F** at A is equivalent to the parallel force **F** at B and the couple of moment $\overrightarrow{BA} \times \mathbf{F}$.

It may be verified that both these systems namely (i) the force **F** at A and (ii) the force **F** at B and the couple of moment $\overrightarrow{BA} \times \mathbf{F}$, have the same force component in any direction and the same moment about any point.

Example 1. Given a triangle ABC, show that forces represented completely by the sides, taken in order, that is, $\overrightarrow{BC}$, $\overrightarrow{CA}$, $\overrightarrow{AB}$ are equivalent to a couple.

$\overrightarrow{CA}$ and $\overrightarrow{AB}$ have a resultant $\overrightarrow{CB}$ acting at A. This resultant and the given force $\overrightarrow{BC}$ are equal, parallel and opposite and therefore are equivalent to a couple. The axis of the couple is normal to the plane of the triangle, and its moment is $p \, . \, BC$ which is twice the area of the triangle.

This result may be generalized, giving the theorem that forces completely represented by the sides of a plane polygon taken in order are equivalent to a couple whose moment is represented by twice the area of the polygon.

Example 2.

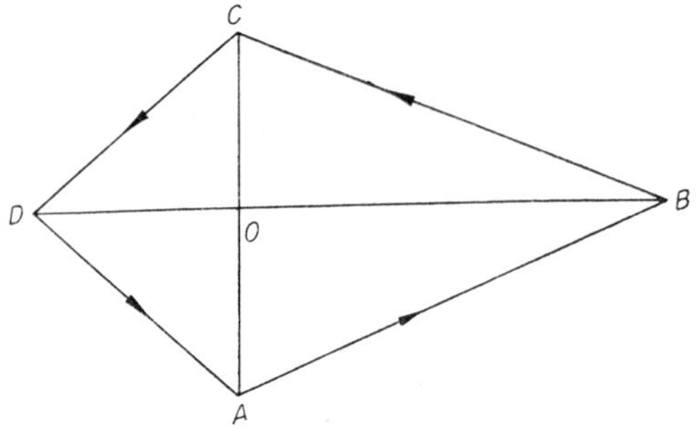

Fig. 22

Forces $\alpha\overrightarrow{AB}$, $\beta\overrightarrow{BC}$, $\gamma\overrightarrow{CD}$, $\delta\overrightarrow{DA}$, act along the sides of a plane quadrilateral $ABCD$ of which O is the point of intersection of AC and BD. If the system is equivalent to a couple, show that

$$OA/OC = (\beta - \gamma)/(\delta - \alpha)$$
$$OB/OD = (\gamma - \delta)/(\alpha - \beta).$$

$\overrightarrow{AB} = \overrightarrow{AO} + \overrightarrow{OB} +$ a couple of moment twice the area of triangle AOB.

Hence

$$\alpha\overrightarrow{AB} + \beta\overrightarrow{BC} + \gamma\overrightarrow{CD} + \delta\overrightarrow{DA}$$
$$= \alpha(\overrightarrow{AO} + \overrightarrow{OB} + \text{couple}) +$$
$$+ \beta(\overrightarrow{BO} + \overrightarrow{OC} + \text{couple}) +$$
$$+ \gamma(\overrightarrow{CO} + \overrightarrow{OD} + \text{couple}) +$$
$$+ \delta(\overrightarrow{DO} + \overrightarrow{OA} + \text{couple})$$
$$= (\delta - \alpha)\,\overrightarrow{OA} + (\alpha - \beta)\,\overrightarrow{OB} +$$
$$+ (\beta - \gamma)\,\overrightarrow{OC} + (\gamma - \delta)\,\overrightarrow{OD} + \text{couple}.$$

Since the resultant is a couple, the two components along the diagonals must vanish.

Hence we deduce

$$(\delta - \alpha)\,\overrightarrow{OA} + (\beta - \gamma)\,\overrightarrow{OC} = \mathbf{O}$$

and

$$(\alpha - \beta)\,\overrightarrow{OB} + (\gamma - \delta)\,\overrightarrow{OD} = \mathbf{O},$$

from which OA/OC, OB/OD are evaluated.

Example 3. The Fig. 23 shows a cube of side a, and four forces P, P, Q, Q. Find their resultant by

(i) adding them as two couples.

(ii) adding the forces directly in pairs and forming a new couple.

(i) The two forces P, P constitute a couple of moment $(0, 0, -Pa)$. The two forces Q, Q constitute a couple of moment $(0, Qa, 0)$. Hence their resultant is a couple. If **G** is the resultant couple and its axis has direction cosines (l, m, n), then

$$Gl = O$$
$$Gm = Qa$$
$$Gn = -Pa.$$

Hence

$$G = a\sqrt{(P^2 + Q^2)}$$

and

$$\frac{l}{O} = \frac{m}{Q} = \frac{n}{-P} = \frac{1}{\sqrt{(P^2 + Q^2)}}.$$

(ii) The forces P and Q at O may be combined into a force $\sqrt{(P^2 + Q^2)}$ at O in the plane YOZ and inclined to Oy at an angle θ where $\tan\theta = Q/P$. Similarly the remaining forces P and Q are equivalent to the opposite force at A. Hence the resultant is a couple of moment $a\sqrt{(P^2 + Q^2)}$, and its axis has direction cosines $(0, \sin\theta, -\cos\theta)$, which agrees with (i).

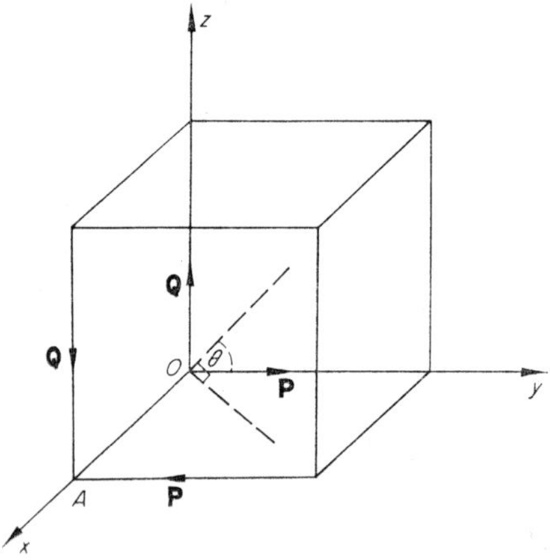

Fig. 23

1.6. The resultant of the general force system

(i) *Three-dimensional System*

Referred to rectangular Cartesian axes, suppose the system of forces consists of $\mathbf{F}_1, \mathbf{F}_2, \ldots, \mathbf{F}_p$ acting at points $P_1, P_2, \ldots, P_p$ whose position vectors are $\mathbf{r}_1, \mathbf{r}_2, \ldots, \mathbf{r}_p$ respectively. Each force may be shifted parallel to itself to act at the origin O by introducing a couple. $\mathbf{F}_i$ at P_i is equivalent to $\mathbf{F}_i$ at O together with a couple of moment $\overrightarrow{OP_i} \times \mathbf{F}_i = \mathbf{r}_i \times \mathbf{F}_i$. When all the p forces have been so transferred to act at O, the forces may be combined together and the couples combined together. The given system is thus equivalent to a force $\mathbf{R}$ with components (X, Y, Z) and a couple $\mathbf{G}$ with moments (L, M, N) where

$$\left.\begin{aligned} \mathbf{R} &= \mathbf{F}_1 + \mathbf{F}_2 + \ldots + \mathbf{F}_p \\ \mathbf{G} &= \mathbf{r}_1 \times \mathbf{F}_1 + \mathbf{r}_2 \times \mathbf{F}_2 + \ldots + \mathbf{r}_p \times \mathbf{F}_p \end{aligned}\right\}. \tag{34}$$

If a different origin is chosen, the force $\mathbf{R}$ will still remain the same, but $\mathbf{G}$ which is the vector sum of the moments of the forces about O will in general depend on the particular origin.

Some particular cases arise:

(*a*) $\mathbf{R} = \mathbf{O},\ \mathbf{G} \neq \mathbf{O}$.

In this case the system is equivalent to a single couple of moment $\mathbf{G}$. The couple $\mathbf{G}$ does not depend on the particular origin.

(*b*) $\mathbf{R} \neq \mathbf{O},\ \mathbf{G} = \mathbf{O}$.
Here the system is equivalent to a single force $\mathbf{R}$ through the origin **O**.

(*c*) $\mathbf{R} = \mathbf{O},\ \mathbf{G} = \mathbf{O}$.
The system is in equilibrium.

(*d*) $\mathbf{R} \neq \mathbf{O},\ \mathbf{G} \neq \mathbf{O},\ \mathbf{G} \cdot \mathbf{R} = O$.

Since the axis of the couple $\mathbf{G}$ is perpendicular to the force, $\mathbf{G}$ and $\mathbf{R}$ together are equivalent to a single parallel force $\mathbf{R}$, in the plane through $\mathbf{R}$ orthogonal to axis $\mathbf{G}$, and acting along a line at distance G/R from O.

The systems (i) and (ii) in Fig. 24 are equivalent. Thus the resultant in this case is a single force $\mathbf{R}$. The equation of the line of action may be obtained from the property that the moment of the resultant about any point on its line of action vanishes. If $\mathbf{r}$ is such a point, then the system (i) has moment

$$\mathbf{G} - (\mathbf{r} \times \mathbf{R})$$

about this point. But the moment about the same point of the equivalent system (ii) vanishes. Hence $\mathbf{r}$ satisfies the equation

$$\mathbf{G} - (\mathbf{r} \times \mathbf{R}) = \mathbf{O}, \tag{35}$$

which is the equation of the line of the action of the resultant. The line of action does not depend on the particular point O taken for origin, but is unique.

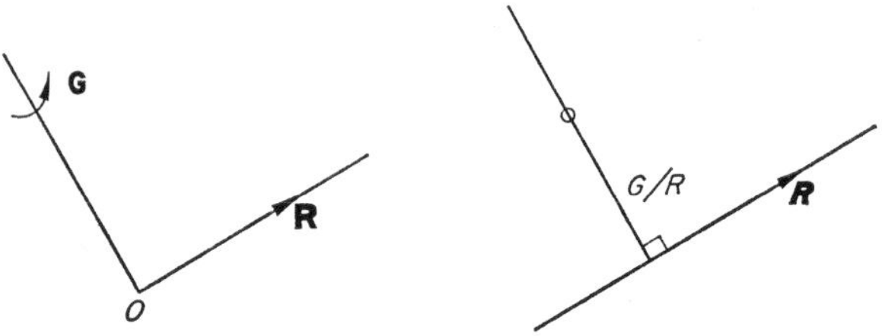

Fig. 24

(*e*) $\mathbf{R} \neq \mathbf{O}$, $\mathbf{G} \neq \mathbf{O}$, $\mathbf{R} \cdot \mathbf{G} \neq O$.

The system may then be reduced to a wrench, that is, a force $\mathbf{R}$ acting on a certain line called the **central axis** and a couple of moment $p\mathbf{R}$ about the same axis.

$$p = \mathbf{G} \cdot \mathbf{R}/ R^2$$

is the pitch of the wrench. The equation of the central axis is

$$\mathbf{G} - (\mathbf{r} \times \mathbf{R}) = p\mathbf{R} \tag{36}$$

which may also be written in the form

$$\mathbf{r} = \frac{\mathbf{R} \times \mathbf{G}}{R^2} + \lambda\mathbf{R} \tag{37}$$

where λ is a scalar parameter (see Ref. I).

In terms of Cartesian components,

$$\left.\begin{array}{ll} X = \sum F_x & L = \sum (yF_z - zF_y) \\ Y = \sum F_y & M = \sum (zF_x - xF_z) \\ Z = \sum F_z & N = \sum (xF_y - yF_x) \end{array}\right\} \tag{38}$$

$R = \sqrt{(X^2 + Y^2 + Z^2)}$, and the direction of $\mathbf{R}$ is given by direction cosines $(X/R, Y/R, Z/R)$. Similarly the couple is

$$G = \sqrt{(L^2 + M^2 + N^2)}$$

and its axis has direction cosines $(L/G, M/G, N/G)$. The equation of the central axis may be written

$$\left.\begin{aligned} \frac{L - yZ + zY}{X} = \frac{M - zX + xZ}{Y} = \frac{N - xY + yX}{Z} \\ = p = \frac{LX + MY + NZ}{X^2 + Y^2 + Z^2} \end{aligned}\right\} . \tag{39}$$

If $\mathbf{R}'$ and $\mathbf{G}'$ are force and couple vectors when system is transferred to origin O', then

$$\mathbf{R}' = \mathbf{R},\ \mathbf{G}' = \mathbf{G} + \overrightarrow{O'O} \times \mathbf{R}$$

It may be see that

$$\mathbf{G}' \,.\, \mathbf{R}' = \mathbf{G} \,.\, \mathbf{R}$$

Hence $\mathbf{R}$ and $\mathbf{G} \,.\, \mathbf{R}$ are **invariants** for different positions of the origin. In terms of Cartesian components

$$X^2 + Y^2 + Z^2 \text{ and } LX + MY + NZ$$

are invariants for different positions of the origin and for different directions of the axes of coordinates.

(ii) *Coplanar Forces*

The same method as in (i) may be applied. It is convenient however to choose axes Ox, Oy to lie in the plane of the forces. Referred to these axes, suppose the forces are $\mathbf{F}_1, \mathbf{F}_2, \ldots, \mathbf{F}_p$ whose directions make angles $\theta_1, \theta_2, \ldots, \theta_p$ with the positive direction of the x-axis, and which act at the points $\mathbf{r}_1 = (x_1, y_1)$, $\mathbf{r}_2 = (x_2, y_2), \ldots,$ $\mathbf{r}_p = (x_p, y_p)$ respectively. Transferring the forces to act at O by the introduction of couples, and combining the forces and combining the couples, the system is seen to be equivalent to a force $\mathbf{R}$ at O, making an angle θ with the x-axis where

$$\left.\begin{aligned} R \cos \theta = X = \sum F_i \cos \theta_i \\ R \sin \theta = Y = \sum F_i \sin \theta_i \end{aligned}\right\} \tag{40}$$

and a couple of moment **G** where

$$G = \sum F_i(x_i \sin \theta_i - y_i \cos \theta_i), \tag{41}$$

and the axis of the couple is normal to the plane of the forces.

Particular cases are the same as (*a*), (*b*), (*c*) and (*d*) above in the case of three-dimensional forces. In case (*d*) the equation of the line of action of the resultant may be written, in terms of the components,

$$G - xY + yX = O. \tag{42}$$

(iii) *Parallel Forces*

A system of parallel forces is a particular case of (i) or (ii). But certain special properties of such a system make it of sufficient interest for separate consideration. Already in section 1.4, the method of compounding two parallel forces has been considered. In Fig. 15, where the resultant of a force F_1 at A and a parallel force F_2 at B was considered, suppose that A has position vector $\mathbf{r}_1$ and B position vector $\mathbf{r}_2$. Then the resultant is the parallel force $\mathbf{F}_1 + \mathbf{F}_2$ acting at the point D, where the position vector of D is

$$\frac{F_1\mathbf{r}_1 + F_2\mathbf{r}_2}{F_1 + F_2}. \tag{43}$$

For unlike forces the same expression may be used with appropriate signs for F_1 and F_2 provided that $\mathbf{F}_1 + \mathbf{F}_2 \neq \mathbf{O}$.

For more than two parallel forces, the same method may be applied step by step, with the resultant of two of the forces being compounded with a third, and so on. The magnitude, direction and position of the resultant should be shown to be independent of the order in which the forces are added.

Suppose that $\mathbf{u}$ is a unit vector in the direction of the forces, and that the system consists of the forces $F_1\mathbf{u}$, $F_2\mathbf{u}$, . . . , $F_p\mathbf{u}$ acting at points $P_1, P_2, \ldots, P_p$ whose position vectors are $\mathbf{r}_1, \mathbf{r}_2, \ldots, \mathbf{r}_p$ respectively and $F_1, F_2, \ldots F_p$ may be positive or negative. The above method of step-by-step addition gives the resultant as the parallel force

$$(F_1 + F_2 + \ldots + F_p)\,\mathbf{u} \tag{44}$$

and that one point G on the line of action of the resultant has position vector

$$\bar{\mathbf{r}} = \frac{F_1\mathbf{r}_1 + F_2\mathbf{r}_2 + \ldots + F_p\mathbf{r}_p}{F_1 + F_2 + \ldots + F_p}. \tag{45}$$

The method breaks down if $\mathbf{F}_1 + \mathbf{F}_2 + \ldots + \mathbf{F}_p = \mathbf{O}$, that is, when the forces are either equivalent to a couple or are in equilibrium. In such a case, the moment of the couple may be found by taking moments about any point, thus determining whether the system is in equilibrium or equivalent to a couple.

When the resultant of parallel forces is a single force, it may be noted that the expression for $\bar{\mathbf{r}}$ depends only on the positions of the points P_1, P_2, . . . P_p and on the relative magnitudes of the forces, and does not depend on the direction of the parallel forces. If the forces are turned about their points of application while they remain parallel to one another, their resultant will continue to pass through the fixed point G. The point G is called **the centre of parallel forces.**

A particular case is provided by the weight of a rigid body. A rigid body may be looked upon as a system of particles, and the weights of all these particles form a set of like parallel forces. These have a resultant force equal to the sum of all the forces, which is the weight of the body. Further there would exist a centre of the parallel forces, that is, the resultant weight will act through a definite point on the body. This point is called the **centre of mass** or **centre of gravity** of the body. From the equation (45), it may be seen that the centre of mass of a system of point masses m_1 at $\mathbf{r}_1$, m_2 at $\mathbf{r}_2$, . . . , m_p at $\mathbf{r}_p$ has position vector

$$\bar{\mathbf{r}} = \frac{m_1\mathbf{r}_1 + m_2\mathbf{r}_2 + \ldots + m_p\mathbf{r}_p}{m_1 + m_2 + \ldots + m_p} = \frac{\sum m\mathbf{r}}{\sum m}. \tag{46}$$

From this may be derived the property of centre of mass in equation (13) above, which was utilized in deriving Leibnitz's theorem.

If a rigid body is a line distribution of line-density λ (that is, λ is mass per unit length) or a surface distribution of surface-density σ (mass per unit area) or a volume distribution of volume-density ρ (mass per unit volume), the position vector of centre of mass is

$$\bar{\mathbf{r}} = \frac{\int \lambda \mathbf{r}\, ds}{\int \lambda ds} \text{ or } \frac{\int \sigma \mathbf{r}\, dS}{\int \sigma dS} \text{ or } \frac{\int \rho \mathbf{r}\, d\Omega}{\int \rho d\Omega},$$

according as the distribution is a line, surface or volume distribution.

Thus the position of the centre of mass of given distributions of mass in curves or areas or volumes may be evaluated by integration. (A text-book on calculus may be consulted for details of calculation.)

Example 1. Six forces P, $2P$, $3P$, $4P$, $5P$, $6P$ act along the sides of a regular hexagon of side $2a$. Show that the resultant is a single force, and find its magnitude and direction, and the distance of its line of action from the centre of the hexagon.

Taking the centre of the hexagon as origin O and axes Ox, Oy as shown in Fig. 25,

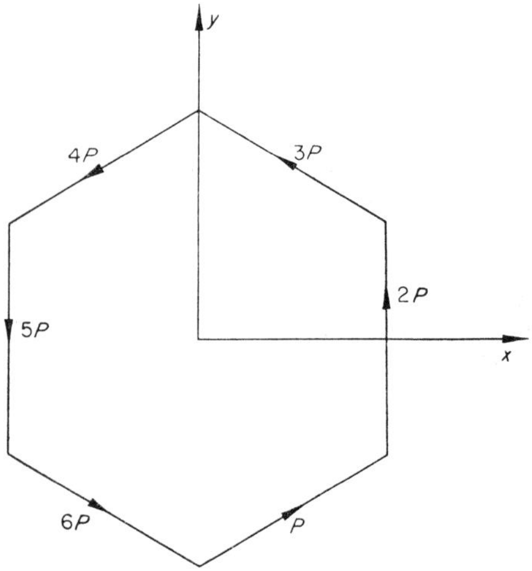

Fig. 25

$$X = P \cdot \frac{\sqrt{3}}{2} - 3P \cdot \frac{\sqrt{3}}{2} - 4P \cdot \frac{\sqrt{3}}{2} + 6P \cdot \frac{\sqrt{3}}{2} = O$$

$$Y = P \cdot \tfrac{1}{2} + 2P + 3P \cdot \tfrac{1}{2} - 4P \cdot \tfrac{1}{2} - 5P - 6P \cdot \tfrac{1}{2} = -6P$$

$$G = (P + 2P + 3P + 4P + 5P + 6P)\,a\sqrt{3} = 21\,aP\sqrt{3}.$$

Hence the resultant is a force $6P$ parallel to the negative direction of the y-axis. Its position is such that the moment of the resultant about O is $21\,aP\sqrt{3}$. The equation of the line of action is

$$G - xY + yX = 0,$$

that is $21\,aP\sqrt{3} + 6Px = 0$, or

$$x = -\frac{7\sqrt{3}}{2}\,a.$$

Example 2. D, E, F are points on the sides BC, CA, AB of a triangle ABC (of area Δ) and divide each side in the ratio $m : n$ in the same sense round. Show that the forces represented by

$$\overrightarrow{AD},\ \overrightarrow{BE},\ \overrightarrow{CF}$$

are equivalent to a couple of moment

$$2\,\frac{n - m}{m - n}\,\Delta.$$

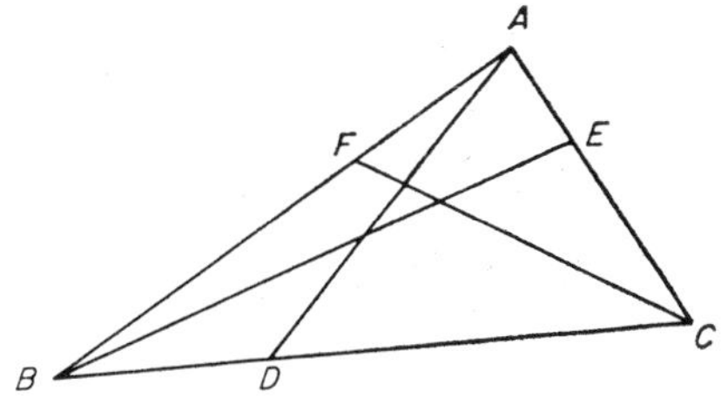

Fig. 26

By the λ, μ theorem, $\lambda\overrightarrow{AB} + \mu\overrightarrow{AC} = (\lambda + \mu)\,\overrightarrow{AD}$ where

$$BD/DC = \mu/\lambda.$$

Hence taking $\lambda = n$, $\mu = m$

$$n\overrightarrow{AB} + m\overrightarrow{AC} = (n + m)\,\overrightarrow{AD}$$

or

$$\overrightarrow{AD} = \frac{n}{m+n}\,\overrightarrow{AB} + \frac{m}{m+n}\,\overrightarrow{AC}.$$

Similarly

$$\overrightarrow{BE} = \frac{n}{m+n}\,\overrightarrow{BC} + \frac{m}{m+n}\,\overrightarrow{BA},$$

$$\overrightarrow{CF} = \frac{n}{m+n}\,\overrightarrow{CA} + \frac{m}{m+n}\,\overrightarrow{CB}.$$

Hence

$$\overrightarrow{AD} + \overrightarrow{BE} + \overrightarrow{CF} = \frac{n-m}{n+m}\,(\overrightarrow{BC} + \overrightarrow{CA} + \overrightarrow{AB})$$

$$= \frac{n-m}{n+m}\text{ . couple of moment } 2\Delta$$

$$= \text{couple of moment } 2\,\frac{(n-m)}{n+m}\,\Delta.$$

Alternatively, suppose **a**, **b**, **c** are the position vectors of A, B, C respectively. Then position vectors of D, E, F are

$$\frac{m\mathbf{c} + n\mathbf{b}}{m+n},\ \frac{m\mathbf{a} + n\mathbf{c}}{m+n},\ \frac{m\mathbf{b} + n\mathbf{a}}{m+n}\ \text{respectively.}$$

Hence

$$\overrightarrow{AD} + \overrightarrow{BE} + \overrightarrow{CF}$$

$$= \left(\frac{m\mathbf{c} + n\mathbf{b}}{m+n} - \mathbf{a}\right) + \left(\frac{m\mathbf{a} + n\mathbf{c}}{m+n} - \mathbf{b}\right) + \left(\frac{m\mathbf{b} + n\mathbf{a}}{m+n} - \mathbf{c}\right)$$

$$= \mathbf{a}\left(-1 + \frac{m}{m+n} + \frac{n}{m+n}\right) + \mathbf{b}\left(\frac{n}{m+n} - 1 + \frac{m}{m+n}\right)$$

$$+\,\mathbf{c}\left(\frac{m}{m+n} - 1 + \frac{n}{m+n}\right) = \mathbf{O}.$$

Hence the system is either in equilibrium or equivalent to a couple.

The moment of the system about the point A is

$$BE \,.\, \text{perpendicular from } A \text{ on } BE - CF \,.\, \text{perpendicular from } A \text{ on } CF = 2 \text{ area of } ABE - 2 \text{ area of } ACF$$

$$= 2\frac{n}{m+n}\Delta - 2\frac{m\Delta}{m+n}$$

$$= 2\frac{n-m}{n+m}\Delta.$$

Hence the resultant is a couple of moment $[2(n-m)/(n+m)]\Delta$.

Example 3. If forces $\alpha\overrightarrow{AB}$, $\beta\overrightarrow{BC}$, $\alpha\overrightarrow{CD}$, $\beta\overrightarrow{DA}$ acting along the sides of a quadrilateral are equivalent to a couple, show that either $\alpha = \beta$ or $ABCD$ is a parallelogram.

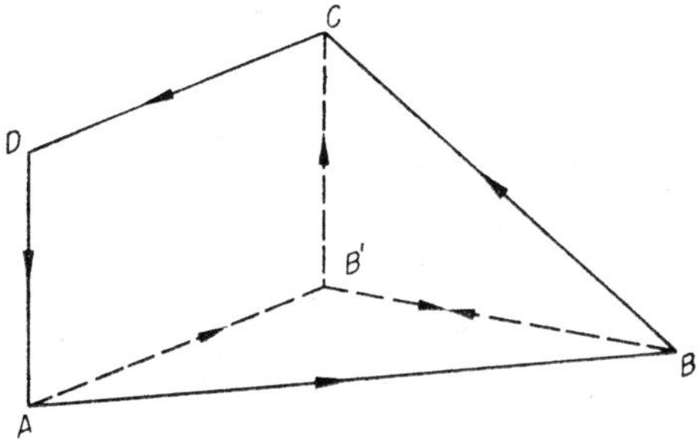

Fig. 27

If $ABCD$ is not a parallelogram, suppose B' is the point such that $AB'CD$ is a parallelogram.

$$\overrightarrow{AB} = \overrightarrow{AB'} + \overrightarrow{B'B} + \text{a couple.}$$

$$\overrightarrow{BC} = \overrightarrow{BB'} + \overrightarrow{B'C} + \text{a couple.}$$

Hence

$$\alpha\overrightarrow{AB} + \beta\overrightarrow{BC} + \alpha\overrightarrow{CD} + \beta\overrightarrow{DA}$$

$$= \alpha(\overrightarrow{AB'} + \overrightarrow{B'B}) + \beta(\overrightarrow{BB'} + \overrightarrow{B'C}) + $$
$$+ \alpha\overrightarrow{CD} + \beta\overrightarrow{DA} + \text{a couple},$$
$$= \alpha(\overrightarrow{AB'} + \overrightarrow{CD}) + \beta(\overrightarrow{B'C} + \overrightarrow{DA}) +$$
$$+ (\alpha - \beta)\,\overrightarrow{BB'} + \text{a couple}$$
$$= \text{a couple} + \text{a couple} +$$
$$+ (\alpha - \beta)\,\overrightarrow{BB'} + \text{a couple}$$
$$= (\alpha - \beta)\,\overrightarrow{BB'} + \text{a couple}.$$

If the given system is equivalent to a couple,

$$(\alpha - \beta)\,\overrightarrow{BB'} = \mathbf{O}.$$

Hence either

$$\alpha = \beta$$

or

$$\overrightarrow{BB'} = \mathbf{O},$$

that is B and B' coincide, in which case $ABCD$ is a parallelogram.

Example 4. Coplanar forces (X_r, Y_r) act at points (x_r, y_r) respectively, where r takes values 1, 2, . . . , p. If each force is rotated about its point of application through an angle θ, show that the resultant passes through a fixed point, for all values of θ. Let

$$X = \sum X_r, \qquad Y = \sum Y_r, \qquad G = \sum (x_r Y_r - y_r X_r).$$

After rotation

$$X' = \sum (X_r \cos\theta - Y_r \sin\theta)$$
$$Y' = \sum (X_r \sin\theta + Y_r \cos\theta)$$
$$G' = \sum \{x_r(X_r \sin\theta + Y_r \cos\theta) - y_r(X_r \cos\theta - Y_r \sin\theta)\}.$$

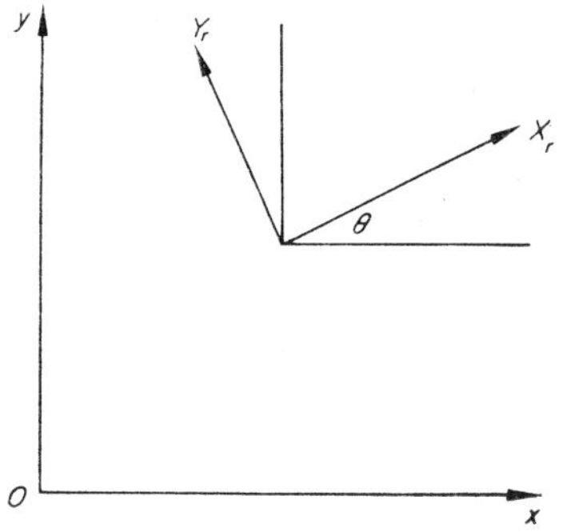

Fig. 28

Then

$$X' = X \cos \theta + Y \sin \theta$$
$$Y' = X \sin \theta + Y \cos \theta$$
$$G' = G \cos \theta + V \sin \theta$$

where

$V = \sum (x_r X_r + y_r Y_r)$, is called the *Virial* of the system.

The equation of the line of action of the resultant is

$$G \cos \theta + V \sin \theta - x(X \sin \theta + Y \cos \theta) + \\ + y(X \cos \theta - Y \sin \theta) = O,$$

that is

$$\cos \theta(G - xY + yX) + \sin \theta(V - xX - yY) = O.$$

Whatever value of θ, the resultant passes through the point which satisfies

$$G - xY + yX = O$$
$$V - xX - yY = O$$

that is, through the point

$$\left(\frac{GY + VX}{X^2 + Y^2}, \frac{VY - GX}{X^2 + Y^2}\right).$$

This point is called the *Astatic Centre.*

Example 5. Show that the moment about the line AB of a force $\mathbf{F}$ acting along the line CD is

$$\frac{6V}{AB\,.\,CD}F$$

where V is the volume of the tetrahedron $ABCD$.

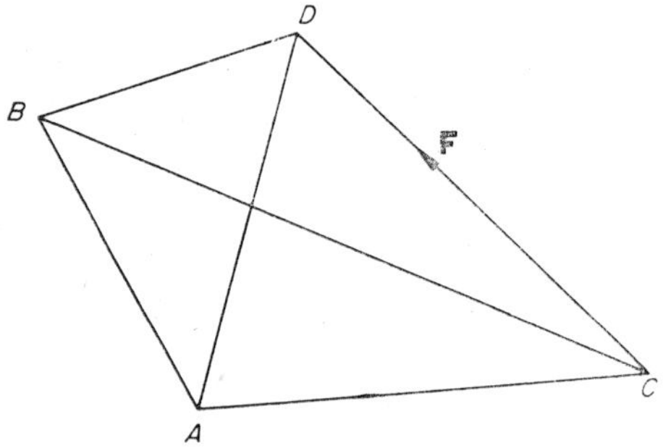

Fig. 29

Suppose that A is taken as origin, and $\mathbf{b}$, $\mathbf{c}$, $\mathbf{d}$, are position vectors of the points B, C, D respectively. Unit vector along AB is $\mathbf{b}/AB$, and unit vector along CD is $(\mathbf{d}-\mathbf{c})/CD$. Vector moment $\mathbf{M}$ of $\mathbf{F}$ about A is

$$\mathbf{c}\times F(\mathbf{d}-\mathbf{c})/CD=\frac{F}{CD}\,\mathbf{c}\times\mathbf{d}.$$

Resolved part of $\mathbf{M}$ along AB is

$$\frac{\mathbf{b}}{AB}\,.\,\mathbf{M}=\frac{F}{AB\,.\,CD}[\mathbf{b},\mathbf{c},\mathbf{d}]=\frac{6V}{AB\,.\,CD}F.$$

Example 6. $OABC$ is a tetrahedron, and a system of forces consists of

$$\alpha\overrightarrow{OA},\ \beta\overrightarrow{OB},\ \gamma\overrightarrow{OC},\ \lambda\overrightarrow{BC},\ \mu\overrightarrow{CA},\ \nu\overrightarrow{AB}$$

acting along the edges of the tetrahedron and are not in equilibrium Show that if

$$\alpha\lambda + \beta\mu + \gamma\nu = O$$

the system is equivalent to a single force or single couple.

Find further conditions for the system to be equivalent to a single couple.

Suppose **a**, **b**, **c** are the position vectors of A, B, C respectively. The system is equivalent to a force **R** at O and a couple **G** where

$$\begin{aligned}\mathbf{R} &= \sum \mathbf{F} = \alpha\mathbf{a} + \beta\mathbf{b} + \gamma\mathbf{c} + \lambda(\mathbf{c} - \mathbf{b}) + \mu(\mathbf{a} - \mathbf{c}) + \nu(\mathbf{b} - \mathbf{a}) \\ &= (\alpha + \mu - \nu)\,\mathbf{a} + (\beta + \nu - \lambda)\,\mathbf{b} + (\gamma + \lambda - \mu)\,\mathbf{c}.\end{aligned}$$

$$\begin{aligned}\mathbf{G} &= \sum \mathbf{r} \times \mathbf{F} \\ &= \lambda\mathbf{b} \times (\mathbf{c} - \mathbf{b}) + \mu\mathbf{c} \times (\mathbf{a} - \mathbf{c}) + \nu\mathbf{a} \times (\mathbf{b} - \mathbf{a}) \\ &= \lambda\mathbf{b} \times \mathbf{c} + \mu\mathbf{c} \times \mathbf{a} + \nu\mathbf{a} \times \mathbf{b}.\end{aligned}$$

$$\begin{aligned}\mathbf{G}.\mathbf{R} &= [(\alpha + \mu - \nu)\,\lambda + (\beta + \nu - \lambda)\,\mu + \\ &\qquad + (\gamma + \lambda - \mu)\,\nu]\,[\mathbf{a}, \mathbf{b}, \mathbf{c}] \\ &= (\alpha\lambda + \beta\mu + \gamma\nu)\,[\mathbf{a}, \mathbf{b}, \mathbf{c}].\end{aligned}$$

If $\alpha\lambda + \beta\mu + \gamma\nu = O$, then $\mathbf{G}.\mathbf{R} = O$, that is, the system is equivalent to a single force or single couple.

If the system is a single couple, then $\mathbf{R} = \mathbf{O}$, which implies

$$\alpha + \mu - \nu = O, \qquad \beta + \nu - \lambda = O, \qquad \gamma + \lambda - \mu = O.$$

Example 7. Two forces, one of which acts along the z-axis, are together equivalent to $(X, Y, Z; L, M, N)$ referred to rectangular Cartesian axes. Show that the magnitude of the force along the z-axis is

$$\frac{LX + MY + NZ,}{N}$$

and find the magnitude and the equations of the line of action of the second force.

Suppose P is the force along the z-axis, and that the second force is equivalent to $(X', Y', Z'; L', M', N')$ when transferred to act at O. Equating the force and couple-components of the two forces and their resultant,

$$X' = X \qquad L' = L$$
$$Y' = Y \qquad M' = M$$
$$Z' + P = Z \qquad N' = N$$

Since X', Y', Z'; L', M', N' are the contributions from a single force.

$$L'X' + M'Y' + N'Z' = 0.$$

Hence

$$LX + MY + N(Z - P) = 0$$

or

$$P = (LX + MY + NZ)/N.$$

Also

$$X' = X,$$
$$Y' = Y,$$
$$Z' = Z - (LX + MY + NZ)/N = -\frac{(LX + MY)}{N}.$$

Hence the magnitude of the second force is

$$\sqrt{\{X^2 + Y^2 + (LX + MY)^2/N^2\}}.$$

The equations of the line of action of this force is from (39)

$$L' - yZ' + zX' = 0,$$
$$M' - zX' + xZ' = 0,$$
$$N' - xY + yX' = 0.$$

Two of these equations would suffice, and we have as the equations of the line of action

$$\left.\begin{array}{r} L + y(LX + MY)/N + zX = 0 \\ M - zX - x(LX + MY)/N = 0 \end{array}\right\}.$$

1.7. Conditions of equilibrium

In the method in which the forces of a general three-dimensional system are transferred to act at a chosen origin O, the resultant is equivalent to a force **R** at O and a couple **G**. Hence when the system is in equilibrium, this force and couple should both vanish. The conditions of equilibrium thus are

$$\mathbf{R} = \sum \mathbf{F} = \mathbf{O}$$
$$\mathbf{G} = \sum \mathbf{r} \times \mathbf{F} = \mathbf{O}.$$

In terms of Cartesian components, these conditions are

$$X = \sum F_x = O \qquad L = \sum (yF_z - zF_y) = O$$
$$Y = \sum F_y = O \qquad M = \sum (zF_x - xF_z) = O$$
$$Z = \sum F_z = O \qquad N = \sum (xF_y - yF_x) = O.$$

There are thus in general six independent equations of equilibrium.

However, for a system of forces in equilibrium, the sum of the resolved parts of the forces along any arbitrary direction is zero, and the sum of the moments about any arbitrary line is zero. Hence any number of valid equations may be written. But these equations would not all be independent of one another.

For any particular system, it is useful to know the number of independent equations which can be written, for this gives the maximum number of unknown quantities which can be found from the equilibrium conditions. Certain statical problems are indeterminate in that the number of independent equations of equilibrium are not enough to determine all the unknown forces, without introducing further hypotheses.

The number of independent equations that are generally available for certain force systems are indicated below:

(i) *General Coplanar System*

Three equilibrium equations may be written. These may be either

(*a*) two force equations and one moment equation, such as

$$X = O, \qquad Y = O, \qquad G = O,$$

or (*b*) one force equation and two moment equations, where the line joining the two points O and O' about which moments are taken is not perpendicular to the direction in which the forces are resolved, e.g.

$$X = O, \qquad G = O, \qquad G' = O$$

where OO' is not perpendicular to the x-axis.

or (c) three moment equations, where the three points O, O', O'' about which the moments are taken are not collinear, e.g.

$$G = O, \qquad G' = O, \qquad G'' = O,$$

where O, O', O'' are not collinear.

(ii) *Three-dimensional Forces Concurrent at a Point O*

Three equations of equilibrium may be derived. These may all be force equations, or moment equations or both force and moment equations, with certain restrictions on the lines about which moments are taken.

(iii) *Three-dimensional General System*

Six independent equations may be written. These may all be moment equations, or made up of moment equations and force equations, but the number of force equations should not exceed three. There will be certain restrictions on the lines about which moments are taken. One set of equations of equilibrium often used is

$$X = O,\ Y = O,\ Z = O;\ L = O,\ M = O,\ N = O.$$

Example 1. A uniform square plate, of sides $2a$ and weight W, is free to turn about an edge of the plate, the two points of trisection of this edge being smoothly hinged to two fixed points P and Q, where PQ is inclined at any angle θ to the vertical, and the length of PQ is $2a/3$. Write down the equations of equilibrium, and determine the reaction at the two hinges as far as they may be determined.

In the equilibrium position, the plane of the lamina is vertical, and the forces acting on the lamina are all in this plane. Taking axes as shown, let (X_1, Y_1) be the reaction at the hinge P and (X_2, Y_2) at Q. There may be written three independent equations of equilibrium. Resolving parallel to Ox,

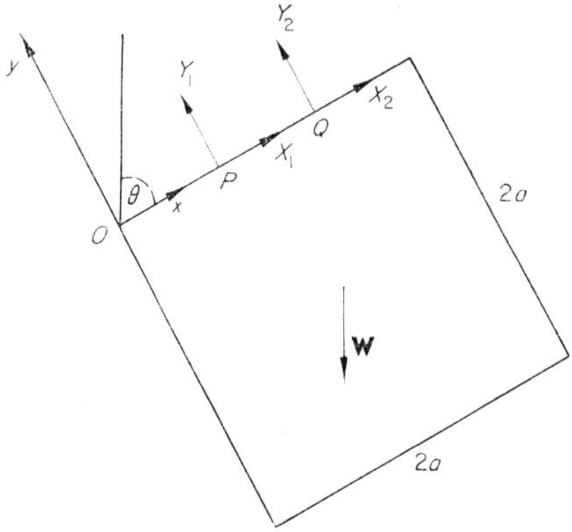

Fig. 30

$$X_1 + X_2 - W\cos\theta = O. \tag{i}$$

Resolving parallel to Oy

$$Y_1 + Y_2 - W\sin\theta = O. \tag{ii}$$

Taking moments about P,

$$\frac{2a}{3}\,Y_2 - W\left(\frac{1}{3}\,a\sin\theta + a\cos\theta\right) = O. \tag{iii}$$

Hence from (iii)

$$Y_2 = \frac{1}{2}\,W(\sin\theta + 3\cos\theta).$$

Substituting in (ii)

$$Y_1 = \frac{1}{2}\,W(\sin\theta - 3\cos\theta).$$

Thus Y_1 and Y_2 are determined. X_1 and X_2, however, occur only in equation (i). They cannot be determined separately. Only their sum is known, that is, $X_1 + X_2 = W \cos \theta$. This is in keeping with the principle of transmissibility of force. The forces X_1 and X_2 act along the same line and cannot be separated.

Example 2. A system of coplanar forces (X_r, Y_r) acting at (x_r, y_r), $r = 1, 2, \ldots p$, are in equilibrium. Find the condition that the system still remains in equilibrium when each force is rotated about its point of application through an angle θ in the same sense.

Since the forces are in equilibrium before rotation,

$$X = \sum X_r = O, \quad Y = \sum Y_r = O, \quad G = \sum (x_r Y_r - y_r X_r) = O.$$

After rotation, the force and couple components would be, as in Example 5 of Section 1.6,

$$X' = X \cos \theta - Y \sin \theta, \qquad Y' = X \sin \theta + Y \cos \theta,$$
$$G' = G \cos \theta + V \sin \theta, \qquad \text{where } V = \sum (x_r X_r + y_r Y_r).$$

Hence, after rotation,

$$X' = 0, \qquad Y' = 0, \qquad G' = V \sin \theta.$$

Hence this system will be in equilibrium for all θ if $V = 0$. Therefore the required condition is

$$V = \sum (x_r X_r + y_r Y_r) = O.$$

When as in this case a system of forces is in equilibrium and is such that when each force is rotated about its point of application through the same angle θ, the system still remains in equilibrium, the equilibrium is said to be *astatic*.

Example 3. Four forces P, Q, R, S acting along the sides of a plane quadrilateral $ABCD$ are in equilibrium. Show that

(i) $$\frac{P/AB}{\Delta DAB\, \Delta ABC} = \frac{-Q/BC}{\Delta ABC\, \Delta BCD} = \frac{R/CD}{\Delta BCD\, \Delta CDA} = \frac{-S/DA}{\Delta CDA\, \Delta DAB}.$$

(ii) $$\frac{P \,.\, R}{AB \,.\, CD} = \frac{Q \,.\, S}{BC \,.\, AD}.$$

Taking moments about A,

Q . (perpendicular from A on BC) +

+ R . (perpendicular from A on CD) = O,

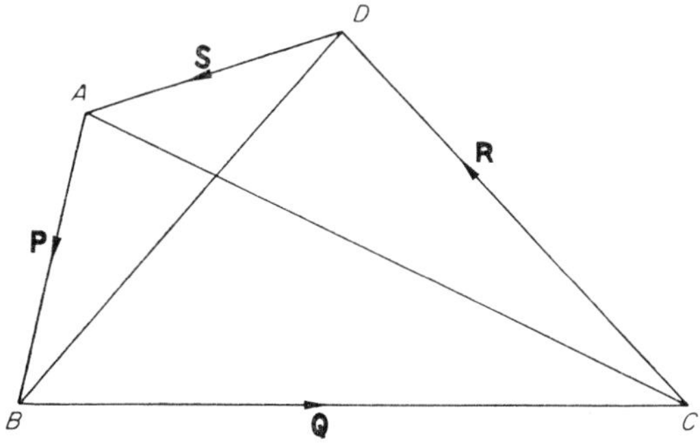

Fig. 31

i.e.

$$Q \cdot \frac{2\Delta\, ABC}{BC} + \frac{R\, 2\Delta\, ACD}{CD} = O.$$

Similarly, moments about B, C, D respectively give

$$R\frac{2\Delta\, BCD}{CD} + S\frac{2\Delta\, BDA}{AD} = O$$

$$S\frac{2\Delta\, CDA}{AD} + P\frac{2\Delta\, CAB}{AB} = O$$

$$P\frac{2\Delta\, DAB}{AB} + Q\frac{2\Delta\, DBC}{BC} = O.$$

From these, (i) may be simply derived.

From (i), by equating the product of the first and third expressions with the product of the second and fourth, there is obtained (ii).

Example 4. Forces $\mathbf{F}_1, \ldots, \mathbf{F}_p$ act along the lines

$$\frac{x - a\cos\theta_r}{a\sin\theta_r} = \frac{y - b\sin\theta_r}{-\,b\cos\theta_r} = \frac{z}{c}, \qquad r = 1, 2, \ldots, p,$$

which are generators of the hyperboloid $x^2/a^2 + y^2/b^2 - z^2/c^2 = 1$.

Show that they are in equilibrium, if they would be in equilibrium when acting at a point in the same directions.

The force and couple components are

$$X = \sum F_r k_r a \sin \theta_r$$
$$Y = \sum - F_r k_r b \cos \theta_r$$
$$Z = \sum F_r k_r c$$
$$L = \sum F_r k_r bc \sin \theta_r = \frac{bc}{a} X$$
$$M = \sum - F_r k_r ca \cos \theta_r = \frac{ca}{b} Y$$
$$N = \sum F_r k_r (- ab \cos^2 \theta_r - ab \sin^2 \theta_r) = - \frac{ab}{c} Z.$$

where $k_r = \sqrt{(a^2 \cos^2 \theta_r + b^2 \sin^2 \theta_r + c^2)}$.

Therefore if $X = O$, $Y = O$, $Z = O$, then L, M, N also vanish. Hence the result.

Exercises 1

1. Forces of magnitude $3P$, $2P$, $-2P$, $-P$, $4P$, $-6P$ act in the sides AB, BC, CD, DE, EF, FA of a regular hexagon $ABCDEF$. Prove that the system is equivalent to a single force through A, and find its magnitude and direction

[Camb. *MT* 1956]

2. ABC is a triangle, G its centroid, O any point *not* in the plane of the triangle. Find the resultant of the forces

$$\mathbf{OA}, \mathbf{OB}, \mathbf{OC}, \mathbf{OG}.$$

Find the condition that the resultant of three forces $p \, . \, \mathbf{OA}$, $q \, . \, \mathbf{OB}$, $r \, . \, \mathbf{OC}$ shall be in a plane parallel to the plane ABC.

[Lond. *GCE*(*S*) 1958]

3. A system of coplanar forces has anticlockwise moments M_1, M_2, M_3 about the point (O, O), (a, O) and (b, c) respectively. If X is the sum of the resolutes of the forces in the positive direction of the x-axis and Y the corresponding sum for the y-axis, obtain the values of X and Y.

Hence find the magnitude of the resultant of the system and the equation of its line of action.

[Lond. *GCE*(*S*) 1957]

4. Show that a system of forces can be replaced by three forces acting along the sides of a given triangle in their plane.

If M_1, M_2, M_3 are the moments in the same sense, of a given system of forces about the vertices A, B, C respectively of a triangle ABC, show that the moment of the system about the centre of the inscribed circle of the triangle is

$$(aM_1 + bM_2 + cM_3)/(a + b + c).$$

[Lond. *G* 1934]

5. L, M, N are the moments of a system of coplanar forces about the vertices of a triangle in their plane. Show that the system can be replaced by forces acting along the sides of the triangle.

P, Q, R, S are the moments of the system about the vertices, taken in order, of a parallelogram in the plane of the forces.

Show that

$$P - Q + R - S = O.$$

[Ceylon *I* 1942]

6. L, M, N are the moments, all in the same sense, of a force P about three points A, B, C respectively which are coplanar with P. If the position of P is varied in such a manner that

$$\lambda L + \mu M + \nu N = O$$

where λ, μ and ν are constants such that $\lambda + \mu + \nu \neq O$, show that the force P will pass through a fixed point.

Determine the ratios $\lambda : \mu : \nu$ in order that this fixed point may bisect the median through the vertex A of the triangle ABC.

[Ceylon *G* 1944]

7. Three forces of magnitudes kBC kCA and kAB act in the plane ABC at the fixed points A, B, C, respectively. If the forces are in equilibrium prove that their lines of action are concurrent and find the locus of the point of intersection.

[Camb. *MT* 1931]

8. $ABCD$ is a plane quadrilateral with $AB = a$, $BC = b$, $CD = c$, $DA = d$ and area Δ. Four forces λa, λb, λc, λd act at the middle points of the corresponding sides. Find the resultant of these forces

(*a*) when they act along the sides, in the sense indicated by the order of the letters,

(*b*) when they act perpendicularly to the sides and directed outwards.

These forces are now transferred so as to act at points L, M, N, P respectively, L being in AB where $AL = 2LB$, M being in BC where $BM = 2MC$, and so on. The forces are directed outwards, each making an angle of 45° with its respective side (λa making an angle of 45° with $\overrightarrow{AB}$ and so on). Prove that there is equilibrium if

$$a^2 + b^2 + c^2 + d^2 = 12\Delta.$$

[Lond. *GCE*(*S*) 1959]

9. Forces (X_r, Y_r) act at the points (x_r, y_r) $r = 1, 2, \ldots n$, on a rigid lamina in the xy-plane. Prove that the algebraic sum G_p of the moments of the forces about the point (a_p, b_p) is given by the equation

$$G_p = G - a_p Y + b_p X,$$

where $G = \Sigma (x_r Y_r - y_r X_r)$, $X = \Sigma X_r$, $Y = \Sigma Y_r$.

The algebraic sum of the moments of a system of coplanar forces about three collinear points (a_1, b_1), (a_2, b_2), (a_3, b_3) are G_1, G_2, G_3 respectively. Prove that the tangent of the angle which the direction of the resultant force makes with the x-axis is

$$\frac{G_1(b_2 - b_3) + G_2(b_3 - b_1) + G_3(b_1 - b_2)}{G_1(a_2 - a_3) + G_2(a_3 - a_1) + G_3(a_1 - a_2)},$$

and find the algebraic sum of the moments of the system about the origin.

[Lond. *G* 1956]

10. Prove that any system of forces in a plane is equivalent to three suitably chosen forces X, Y, Z acting on the sides BC, CA, AB of a given triangle in the plane. Prove that if the system of forces is equivalent to a couple G

$$\frac{X}{BC} = \frac{Y}{CA} = \frac{Z}{AB} = \frac{G}{2\Delta},$$

where Δ is the area of the triangle ABC. D, E, F are the mid-points of the sides BC, CA, AB of the triangle. Forces λEF, μFD, νDE act along EF, FD, DE respectively. Find the equivalent system of forces acting along the sides of the triangle ABC. [Oxf. *I* 1957]

11. Three forces P, Q, R act along the sides BC, CA, AB respectively of a triangle ABC. If the resultant passes through the orthocentre of the triangle show that

$$P \sec A + Q \sec B + R \sec C = O.$$

If the resultant passes through the orthocentre and the incentre, show that

$$P : Q : R = \sec B - \sec C : \sec C - \sec A : \sec A - \sec B,$$

while if the resultant passes through the orthocentre and circumcentre

$$P : Q : R = (b^2 - c^2) \cos A : (c^2 - a^2) \cos B : (a^2 - b^2) \cos C.$$

12. Two coplanar forces act at the points A, B of a rigid body, the forces being represented in magnitude and direction by AA', BB'. Lines through A, B parallel to AB', $A'B$ meet in C, and lines through A', B' parallel to AB', $A'B$ meet in C'. Prove that in general the two given forces are equivalent to a single force acting at C, and represented in magnitude and direction by CC'. [Camb. *MT* 1944]

13. Forces act along the sides BA, BC, DA, DC of a tetrahedron $ABCD$. Each force is in the sense indicated and is inversely proportional to the side along which it acts. Prove that the system is equivalent to a single resultant force if

$$AD \, . \, BC = AB \, . \, CD.$$

When this relation holds show that the resultant meets BD, and find the ratio in which the point of intersection divides BD. [Oxf. *I* 1955]

14. A rigid lamina lying on a smooth horizontal table is acted upon by forces with components (X_r, Y_r) at the points with coordinates (x_r, y_r) referred to rectangular axes in the lamina $(r = 1, 2, \ldots)$. Show that the lamina will be in equilibrium if an additional force $(-X, -Y)$ is applied at any point (x, y) on the line

$$xY - yX - G = O,$$

where $X = \Sigma X_r$, $Y = \Sigma Y_r$, $G = \Sigma (x_r Y_r - y_r X_r)$, and X, Y are not both zero.

The lamina is smoothly pinned to the table at the point at which the above line is intersected by the line

$$xX + yY - H = O,$$

where $H = \Sigma (x_r X_r + y_r Y_r)$. Show that it will remain in equilibrium when the direction of all the forces (X_r, Y_r) are turned through any angle θ, their magnitudes remaining constant. [Lond. *G* 1957]

15. Two coplanar forces, of given magnitudes P, Q are such that their lines of action pass respectively through two fixed points A, B in the plane. If AB is of length c and the lines of action of the forces are inclined to each other at a fixed angle, show that their resultant **R** always passes through a fixed point. Find the distances of this point from A and B. [Lond. *GCE*(*S*) 1959]

16. Forces of fixed magnitude and direction act at assigned points of a rigid body, the whole system of forces being in a plane perpendicular to a fixed axis about which the body can be rotated. Prove that, if in one position of the body the forces are in equilibrium, the resultant in any other position obtained by a rotation θ about the fixed axis is a couple of moment proportional to $\sin \theta$.

Show how for a given set of forces the points of application can be chosen to give equilibrium for all values of θ. [Camb. *MT* 1945]

17. Three coplanar forces P, Q, R act at points A, B, C respectively. If they meet at a point on the circumcircle of the triangle ABC and are such that

$$\frac{P}{BC} = \frac{Q}{CA} = \frac{R}{AB},$$

show that they are in astatic equilibrium.

18. $A_1, A_2, \ldots, A_n$ are n points in a plane and O is a point not in the plane. Forces $\lambda_1 \overrightarrow{OA_1}$, $\lambda_2 \overrightarrow{OA_2}$, $\ldots$, $\lambda_n \overrightarrow{OA_n}$ act through O. Prove that the component of the resultant force along the perpendicular to the plane is

$$(\lambda_1 + \lambda_2 + \ldots + \lambda_n) \overrightarrow{OH}$$

where H is the foot of the perpendicular from O on to the plane.

Forces of magnitude $\mu_2 - \mu_3$, $\mu_3 - \mu_1$, $\mu_1 - \mu_2$ act along the edges AO, BO, CO of a regular tetrahedron $ABCO$ and forces of magnitude μ_1, μ_2, μ_3 along the edges BC, CA, AB, in the senses indicated. Prove that the six forces are equivalent to a couple unless

$$\mu_1 = \mu_2 = \mu_3 = O.$$

[Oxf. *I* 1957]

19. ABC, $A'B'C'$ are two triangles in space. Forces

$$\lambda\overrightarrow{AA'},\ \mu\overrightarrow{BB'},\ \nu\overrightarrow{CC'}$$

act along AA', BB', CC'. Prove that the resultant force is given in magnitude and direction by

$$(\lambda + \mu + \nu)\,\overrightarrow{GG'}$$

where G is the centre of gravity of particles λ, μ, ν at A, B, C and G' is the centre of gravity of particles λ, μ, ν at A', B', C'.

Under what conditions would the resultant be completely represented by $(\lambda + \mu + \nu)\,\overrightarrow{GG'}$? [*CCS*(*H*) 1960]

20. Forces λOA, μAB, νBC, ρCO (λ, μ, ν, ρ not all zero) act along the sides of a skew quadrilateral in the senses indicated. Prove that

(i) the system cannot be in equilibrium;

(ii) if the forces reduce to a couple then $\lambda = \mu = \nu = \rho$ and the plane of the couple is parallel to OB and CA;

(iii) if the system reduces to a single force then $\lambda\nu = \rho\mu$.

[Oxf. *I* 1955]

21. $ABCD$ and $A'B'C'D'$ are opposite faces of a parallelepiped and AA', BB', CC', DD' are parallel edges. Forces $\lambda\overrightarrow{BD'}$, $\mu\overrightarrow{AC}$ and $\nu\overrightarrow{DA'}$ are localized in the corresponding lines. Prove that the system cannot reduce to a couple and that if it reduces to a single force,

$$(\mu + \lambda)\,\nu = \mu\lambda.$$

[Lond. *S* 1947]

22. A force along the line

$$\frac{x}{l} = \frac{y}{O} = \frac{z - c}{O}$$

and a force along another line are together equivalent to a wrench (F; pF) in the axis of y. Prove that the equations of the line of action of the second force are

$$\frac{x}{p} = \frac{y}{-c} = \frac{z}{O}$$

and find the magnitudes of the forces. [Lond. *S* 1932]

23. A number of parallel forces, the direction and magnitude of each force being fixed, act at given points of a rigid body. Show that, if the sum of the forces is not zero, there is a definite point in the body through which the resultant of the forces passes, whatever the orientation of the body.

Find the position of the centre of gravity of a uniform solid hemisphere, and deduce that of an octant of a sphere. [Camb. *MT* 1944]

24. Find the centre of gravity of

(*a*) a circular arc of radius a which subtends an angle 2α at its centre;

(*b*) the area of a circular sector of radius a which subtends an angle 2α at the centre;

(*c*) the area of the ellipse $x^2/a^2 + y^2/b^2 = 1$ in the positive quadrant;

(*d*) a frustum of a uniform solid right circular cone of semi-vertical angle α, made by cutting off $1/n$th of its axis initially of height h.

25. Find the position of the centre of gravity of
(*a*) the area of the loop $r^2 = a^2 \cos 2\theta$;
(*b*) the area of the curve

$$x^{2/3} + y^{2/3} = a^{2/3}$$

lying in the positive quadrant;
(*c*) the semicircular plate of radius a whose mass per unit area at any point varies as $\sqrt{(a^2 - r^2)}$ where r is the distance from the centre;
(*d*) a solid tetrahedron of uniform density.

26. A uniform solid is generated by revolution about the axis of x of the area bounded by this axis and the portion of the curve

$$a^{1/2}y = x^{1/2}(a - x)$$

lying between $x = O$ and $x = a$. Show that the centre of mass of the solid is at a distance $2a/5$ from the origin.

The solid rests in equilibrium on a perfectly rough inclined plane, with its axis parallel to a line of greatest slope of the inclined plane. Find the slope of the plane. [Lond. *G* 1957]

27. The wrench $(P; pP)$ has its axis along the axis of x, and the wrench $(Q; qQ)$ has its axis along the line $y = x \tan \alpha$, $z = O$. Find the resultant.

Prove also that as the magnitudes P and Q vary the surface generated by the axis of their resultant is

$$z(x^2 + y^2) = (q - p)(xy - y^2 \cot \alpha).$$

[Lond. *S* 1947]

28. A solid is formed by rotating about the x-axis through π radians the smaller area bounded by the ellipse $x^2/a^2 + y^2/b^2 = 1$, the line $x = \frac{1}{2}a$ and the x-axis. Prove that the distance of the centre of gravity of this solid from its plane faces are $7a/40$ and $(8\pi - 9\sqrt{3})\, b/10\pi$. [Lond. *S* 1935]

29. A **nul line** of a given system of forces being defined as a line about which the system has zero moment, show that the condition for the line $\mathbf{r} = \mathbf{r}_0 + \lambda\mathbf{t}$ (where $\mathbf{t}$ is a unit vector) to be a nul line is

$$\mathbf{G} \cdot \mathbf{t} + [\mathbf{R}, \mathbf{r}_0, \mathbf{t}] = 0.$$

If a system is such that every tangent to the curve $x = au^3$, $y = au^2$, $r = au$ (where u is a parameter) is a nul line, show that the system is equivalent to a wrench of pitch $\frac{1}{3}a$ along the x-axis.

30. Given a system of forces, show that the nul lines which pass through a point P lie on a plane π (π is called the **nul plane** of P and P the **nul point** of π). Show that if the nul plane of P passes through Q then the nul plane of Q passes through P.

Chapter 2

Problems of Equilibrium

2.1. Types of forces

IT IS USEFUL to discuss briefly some of the different types of forces which have to be taken into account in the practical applications of statics.

(1) *Tension in a String*

Suppose that a body is fastened to one end of a weightless or light string, and that the other end of the string is pulled away from the body. The body then experiences a force, which is the tension exerted in the string. The tension is usually denoted by the symbol T. It vanishes when the string becomes slack. The magnitude of the tension is largest when the string is on the point of breaking. This maximum tension is called breaking tension.

All strings are extensible to some degree, but there are certain cases when the extensibility is very small in practice and so may be neglected. In such cases the string is described as inextensible.

Tension is a passive force which comes into play when the string is taut, and its magnitude comes up to only the extent necessary to preserve equilibrium. The tension in a taut inextensible string lies between zero and the yield point T_0.

When the extensibility cannot be neglected, the string is said to be **elastic.** The tension in an elastic string is found to vary with the extension of the string by a law which was enunciated by Robert Hooke in 1676, on the basis of various experimental studies. This law is called **Hooke's law** and states that the tension in an elastic string is proportional to the extension of length from its natural unstretched state. If a is the natural or unstretched length of the string, and the tension is T when the length of the string in its extended state is x, the extension is $x - a$, and Hooke's law is

$$T = \frac{\lambda}{a}(x - a) \tag{1}$$

where λ is a constant for each string, depending upon the material and thickness of the string, and called the *modulus of elasticity* of the string.

(2) *Stress in a Light Rod*

Suppose that a body is connected to one end of a light thin rod, and that a force is exerted at the other end of the rod. Then the body experiences a force along the line of the rod. This force is due to the stress in the rod, and may be a **tension** or **thrust.** Where the rod is being compressed by the forces at its ends, the stress in the rod is a thrust, tending to restore the natural length of the rod. If the rod tends to be stretched, it exerts a tension.

The rod may be elastic or inextensible. The stress in the elastic rod is given by Hooke's law. In this case, there could be extension as well as compression of the rod, and the corresponding expression T in (1) would be a tension or thrust accordingly.

A light inextensible rod is often used to connect two points in order to limit the freedom of movement in a framework. The stress in such a rod is along the rod, since the rod is in equilibrium under the action of forces at its ends only, and therefore these two forces at the ends should be equal and opposite. This would not necessarily be so if the rod has a weight or if further forces act at some intermediate point of the rod.

It is useful to note the general rule that *when a body is in equilibrium under the action of forces acting at two points P and Q only, then these forces act in the line PQ and are equal and opposite.*

(3) *Reaction between Surfaces*

When the surfaces of two bodies, A and B say, are in contact at a point P, there is a mutual reaction between them. This mutual reaction is also a passive force which comes into play to the extent necessary to preserve equilibrium if this were possible. The action of B upon A is equal and opposite to the action of A upon B, by Newton's third law, which will be elaborated later. The two surfaces will

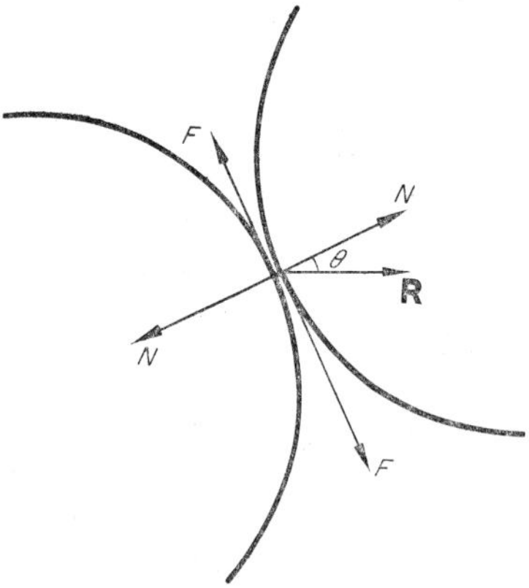

Fig. 32

have a common tangent plane at P, and the plane through P perpendicular to this tangent plane is normal to both surfaces. The reaction **R** between the two bodies will generally have a normal component as well as a component in the tangent plane at P. Suppose θ is the angle between the reaction and the normal (Fig. 32). The normal component of the reaction is $N = R \cos \theta$, and the component in the tangent plane is $F = R \sin \theta$.

The component F prevents or tends to prevent the sliding of one body over the surface of the other. It is called a force of **friction.**

The occurrence of friction is an important factor in nature. For example, if there were no friction between our feet and the floor, it would not be possible for us to walk. Or again if there were no friction, a motor car or locomotive would not be able to move forward, as will be explained later. But in many cases friction causes wastage of effort, and diminishes the efficiency of mechanical devices.

Certain bodies are capable of exerting larger forces of friction than others. It is useful to define certain hypothetical bodies which are such that the frictional forces they are capable of exerting are negligibly small in comparison with other forces acting on the system. Such bodies are said to be **smooth.** The mutual reaction between two smooth bodies is along the common normal at the point of contact. In the above notation, $\theta = 0$ and $\mathbf{F} = 0$.

(4) *Reactions at Smooth Joints*

Bodies are often joined together by a hinge which allows a freedom of movement about the hinge. The arrangement may consist of a rounded end of one body fitting into a hollow in the other, as in a ball and socket joint, or a pin passing through cylindrical holes in the bodies, as in a door hinge.

Suppose that two bodies A and B are smoothly hinged with a pin, that is, each body can turn about the pin without friction. Considering the forces in a plane, the reaction between the pin and either body, at every point of contact, acts in the direction of the normal and thus passes through the centre of the pin.

When the pin is of negligible weight, the equilibrium of the pin under the actions of A and B shows that these actions are equal and opposite. Therefore the action of the pin on the body A is equal and opposite to its action on the body B. It is not necessary to consider the particular form of the joint. It is sufficient to know that when two bodies are smoothly hinged together allowing freedom of rotation about the joint, then the bodies are subject to equal and opposite forces at the joint.

In analysing a problem involving a smooth hinge joining two bodies, the magnitude and direction of the action on each body at the joint are usually unknown. One therefore assumes the action on one body to consist of two unknown components in convenient perpendicular directions. The action of the joint on the other body will be equal and opposite. Figure 33 shows two rods smoothly hinged at a joint A. It is convenient while drawing the figure to leave a gap at A between the two rods, so that the forces may be marked clearly.

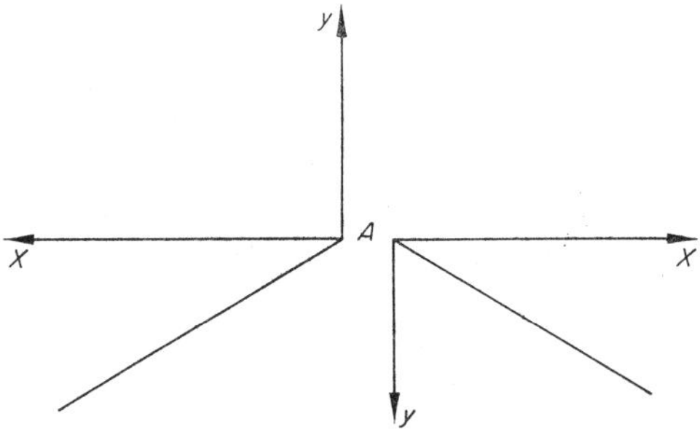

Fig. 33

If three bodies are joined by a smooth pin joint, the three actions of the respective bodies on the pin are in equilibrium, and therefore their magnitudes will satisfy Lami's theorem.

(5) *Field of Force*

This may be defined by a vector, $\mathbf{G}(\mathbf{r})$ say, which acts at every point $\mathbf{r}$ of some region of space. Important particular cases include the gravitational field, electric field and magnetic field. In the following, gravitational fields are considered.

If a point mass M is situated at the origin O, its gravitational field is

$$\mathbf{G} = -\frac{\gamma M \mathbf{r}}{r^3}, \tag{2}$$

which is the force per unit mass on a point mass at the point **r** due to the mass M at O. γ is the constant of gravitation. The total force on a finite body due to the mass M at O may be obtained by dividing the body into small elements, determining the force on a standard element, and integrating over all such elements. The gravitational force between two such bodies may be calculated by an extension of this method.

A particular case is the gravitational attraction due to the earth on bodies at or near the surface of the earth. In the equation (2), if r is very large and the body concerned is in a limited region between $r_0 - \epsilon$ and $r_0 + \epsilon$ where ϵ/r_0 is negligible, the gravitational force at each point in this region may be taken as a constant. At points near the surface of the earth where $r_0 = 4000$ miles approximately, if ϵ is of the order of hundreds of feet or less, **G** is approximately the constant vector **g**, g being the constant acceleration due to gravity in the region considered. The gravitational force due to the earth on a finite body of mass m is then a system of parallel forces and is equivalent to the resultant m**g** acting at the centre of gravity of the body. This force is the weight of the body.

2.2 Isolation of a system

In Chapter 1 there were considered certain standard methods of finding the resultant of a system of given forces. However, in the problems of equilibrium with which one is usually concerned in practice, not all the forces are given or known to begin with. Often what is given is a certain physical situation. It then becomes necessary to investigate the unknown forces that come into play; and to determine these where possible from the conditions of equilibrium.

To apply the conditions of equilibrium, one must, however, isolate a particular body or system of bodies, and apply the condition to this system. In the actions on the system should be included the effects which the rest of the universe has upon this system.

It is useful to distinguish between internal and external forces. An external force is one exerted on the system by a body which is not a part of this system considered. An internal force is exerted on a part of the system by another part of the same system.

It may be noted that a force external to one particular system may be an internal force in another system. The following example may illustrate some of these features:

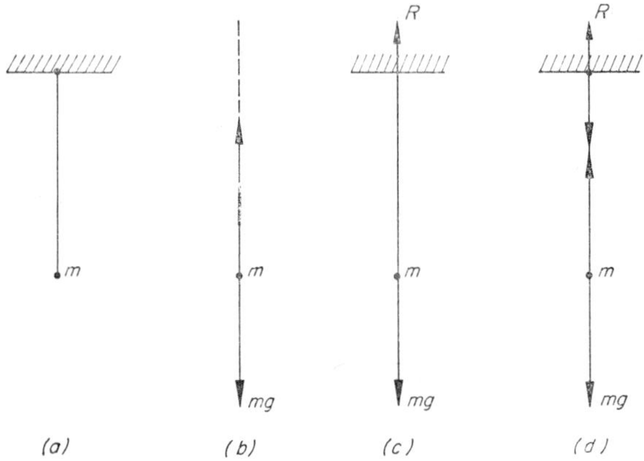

Fig. 34

Suppose that a light string of length a has a particle of mass m attached at one end, and hangs from its other end at a point O. It is necessary to mark the forces which come into action. Diagram (a) of Fig. 34 shows the geometrical configuration without the forces being marked. Diagram (b) shows the external forces upon the system A consisting of the mass m only. Diagram (c) shows the external forces upon the system B consisting of the mass m and the string. Diagrams such as (b) and (c) are called **free-body diagrams.** These show the external forces acting upon the respective systems considered. It is economical however to combine (b) and (c) into the single diagram (d). Here the tension T is an external force as far as system A is concerned, but is an internal force in system B. Though often in practice only the combined diagram (d) would be drawn, it would, however, be useful to have (b) and (c) as mental pictures.

In applying the equations of equilibrium, the number of independent equations for a system is limited, as discussed in §1.7. Suppose that in the system there are two bodies joined together by a string or in contact with one another, so that on each body there is a tension or reaction which is equal and opposite to the tension or reaction acting upon the other body. For each body, the equations of equilibrium may be written, and these would contain the unknown tension or reaction. When the unknown is eliminated, a fewer number of equations would be obtained. But these fewer equations are just those which would be obtained by applying the conditions of equilibrium to the system consisting of the two bodies together. Thus when one is not interested in determining the unknown tension or reaction, the number of equations from which other required quantities may be determined can be reduced. It is helpful to select the system to which the conditions are applied, bearing in mind the information that is being sought.

It is also frequently useful to write down obvious geometrical relations connecting the variables which are used to specify the configuration of a system. Sometimes the equations of equilibrium may be used to derive certain geometrical properties which characterize the equilibrium configuration.

A trigonometrical theorem of use in certain problems of equilibrium under the action of three forces is stated below.

The proof is left to the reader.

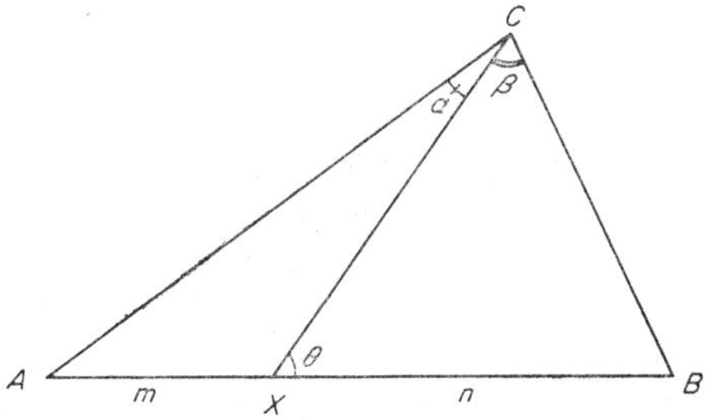

Fig. 35

If X is a point on AB such that $AX : XB = m : n$, and the angles are as shown in the Fig. 35,

$$(m + n) \cot \theta = m \cot \alpha - n \cot \beta \quad (3)$$

$$= n \cot A - m \cot B. \quad (4)$$

Example 1. A particle of weight $2W$ is attached to the end A, and a particle of weight W to the end B, of a light rod AB of length $2a$. The rod hangs from a point O to which it is attached by light strings AO, BO, each of length b. Prove that in equilibrium the inclination of the rod to the horizontal is θ, where

$$\tan \theta = \frac{a}{3\sqrt{(b^2 - a^2)}}.$$

Find the tension in the string AO in terms of a, b and W.

[Camb. MT 1948]

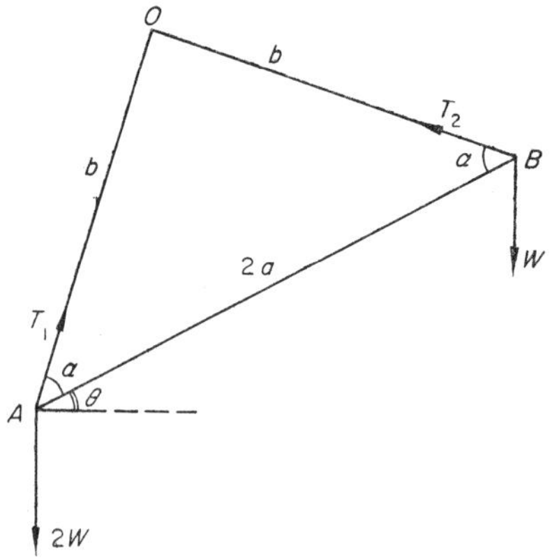

Fig. 36

The triangle AOB is isosceles. Let the angles at A and B be α. Then $b \cos \alpha = a$. Considering the system consisting of the rod AB and the two particles at A and B, the forces acting upon it are the tensions T_1 and T_2 in the strings and the weights W and $2W$. Hence these four forces are in equilibrium, and one may write three independent conditions of equilibrium. Taking moments about A gives

$$T_2 \,.\, 2a \sin \alpha - W \,.\, 2a \cos \theta = 0. \quad \text{(i)}$$

Taking moments about B gives

$$T_1 \,.\, 2a \sin \alpha - 2W \,.\, 2a \cos \theta = 0. \quad \text{(ii)}$$

Resolving horizontally

$$T_1 \cos (\alpha + \theta) - T_2 \cos (\alpha - \theta) = 0. \quad \text{(iii)}$$

From (i) and (ii)

$$T_1 = 2T_2 = 2W \cos \theta / \sin \alpha.$$

Hence from (iii)

$$\frac{\cos (\alpha + \theta)}{\cos (\alpha - \theta)} = \frac{T_2}{T_1} = \frac{1}{2}.$$

Therefore

$$2(\cos \alpha \cos \theta - \sin \alpha \sin \theta) = \cos \alpha \cos \theta + \sin \alpha \sin \theta,$$

from which is obtained

$$\tan \theta = \frac{1}{3} \cot \alpha = \frac{1}{3} \frac{a}{\sqrt{(b^2 - a^2)}}.$$

Also

$$T_1 = 2W \cos \theta / \sin \alpha$$
$$= 6Wb / \sqrt{(9b^2 - 8a^2)},$$

on substituting for $\cos \theta$ and $\sin \alpha$.

Often it is possible to evaluate a trigonometrical expression such as $\tan \theta$ in this case, without writing all the three equations, but by writing a geometrical consequence of the conditions of equilibrium. Thus when a system is acted upon by three non-parallel forces, a geometrical property of equilibrium is that the three forces should meet at a point.

In the example considered, the weight $2W$ at A and W at B can be combined into a weight $3W$ at a point G on AB where $AG/GB = 1/2$, that is, $AG = 2a/3$, $BG = 4a/3$. Hence the system of four forces is equivalent to the three forces T_1, T_2 and $3W$. The lines of action of these three forces should therefore meet at a point. Since T_1 and T_2 meet at O, the weight $3W$ at G must also pass through O. Hence

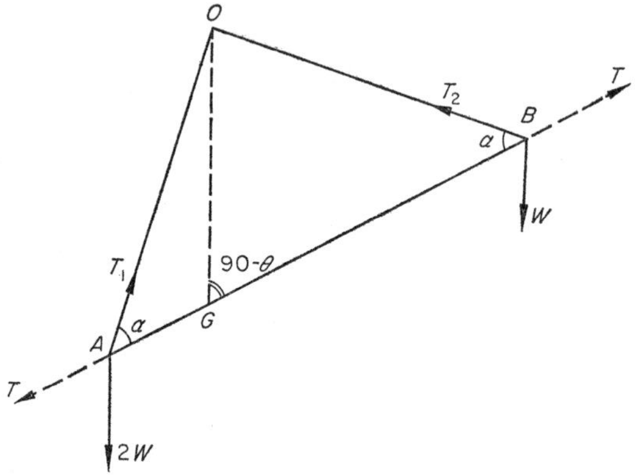

Fig 37

the point G is vertically below O. The angle OGB is then $90 - \theta$. Applying the equation (4) to the triangle OAB

$$2a \cot (90 - \theta) = \frac{4a}{3} \cot \alpha - \frac{2a}{3} \cot \alpha.$$

Therefore

$$\tan \theta = \frac{1}{3} \cot \alpha = \frac{1}{3} \frac{a}{\sqrt{(b^2 - a^2)}}.$$

Thus $\tan \theta$ is evaluated from the geometrical condition of equilibrium.

T_1 may then be determined by applying Lami's theorem at O and obtaining

$$\frac{T_1}{\sin (90 + \alpha - \theta)} = \frac{3W}{\sin (180 - 2\alpha)}$$

or by taking moments about B, obtaining (ii).

Another method of proceeding in the above example is to note that the rod AB exerts a thrust along the line of the rod, T on the mass at A, and an opposite T on the mass at B, as shown in the figure. Considering the equilibrium of the mass at A by itself, it is acted upon by three forces T, T_1 and $2W$. Lami's theorem gives

$$\frac{T_1}{\sin(90-\theta)} = \frac{T}{\sin(90+\theta+\alpha)} = \frac{2W}{\sin\alpha}.$$

Similarly the mass at B is in equilibrium under forces T, T_2 and W, and Lami's theorem gives

$$\frac{T_2}{\sin(90+\theta)} = \frac{T}{\sin(90-\theta+\alpha)} = \frac{W}{\sin\alpha}.$$

From these two sets of equations $\tan\theta$ and T_1 may be obtained as required.

Example 2. Two equal uniform rods AB, AC, each of length $2a$ and weight W, are smoothly jointed together at A and rest symmetrically over a smooth circular cylinder of radius r fixed with its axis horizontal. If the inclination of each rod to the vertical is θ, show that

$$a\sin^3\theta = r\cos\theta.$$

Find the reaction at the joint A.

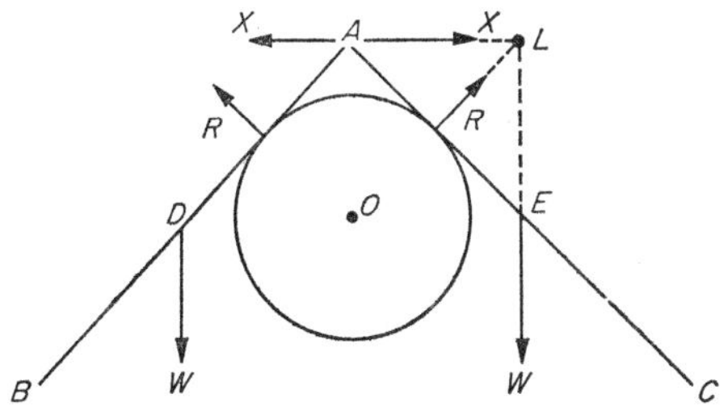

Fig. 38

At the joint A, let the reaction on AC have components (X, Y) as shown in Fig. 39(a). Then the reaction on AB will be equal and opposite.

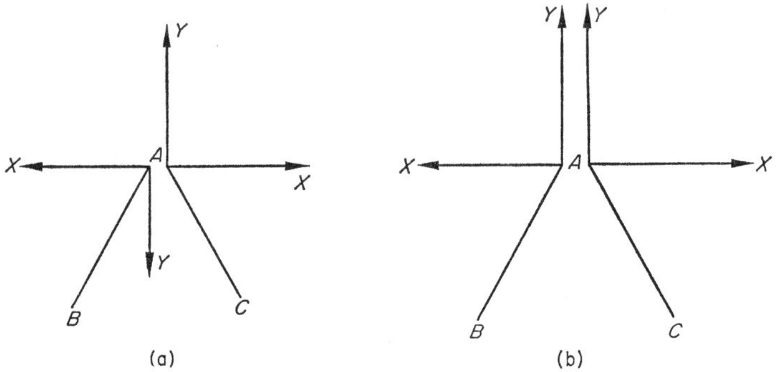

Fig. 39

It may be shown by making use of the property of symmetry that

$$Y = 0.$$

For, if the reaction on AC is (X, Y), as assumed before, then by symmetry the reaction on AB should be as in Fig. 39(b). The vertical through A is a line of symmetry. The left side of the vertical through A should be a mirror image about the line of symmetry of the right side of this vertical.

The situation in the Fig. 39(a) and (b) would simultaneously hold only if $Y = 0$. Hence the reaction at the joint A consists of only the horizontal component X, as shown in Fig. 38.

This property is a particular case of a general property that when a framework (including the forces on it) is symmetrical about a line through a joint, the reaction at that joint is perpendicular to the line of symmetry. *The existence of symmetry helps to reduce the number of unknowns in a system.*

Going back to Fig. 38, the other forces on the rods, beside the reaction at the joint A, are the weights and the reactions of the cylinder. Since the cylinder is smooth, the reaction on each rod is normal to the cylinder and the rod at the point of contact. Let this reaction be R as shown in the figure. Considering the equilibrium of the rod AC, the forces acting upon it are the weight W, the reaction R and the reaction X. Hence their lines of action should meet in a point. Therefore if the lines of action of X and R meet at a point L, then the mid-point E of AC should be vertically below L.

$$AL = OA \cot \theta = r \operatorname{cosec} \theta \cot \theta.$$

AL should also equal $OE \cos (90 - \theta)$.

Hence

$$a \cos (90 - \theta) = r \operatorname{cosec} \theta \cot \theta$$

or

$$\sin^3 \theta \sec \theta = r/a.$$

To find X, one may use Lami's theorem at L, or one may use the property of triangle of forces. The triangle AOL is such that the side AO is parallel to W, OL parallel to R, and LA parallel to X (but in the opposite sense). AOL is therefore a triangle of forces, and

$$\frac{-X}{LA} = \frac{W}{AO}$$

or

$$X = -W \cdot \frac{LA}{AO} = -W \cot \theta.$$

Example 3. A uniform solid right circular cone of semi-vertical angle α and height h, rests with its base area touching a smooth vertical wall, and is supported by a string of length l which joins the vertex to a point on the wall vertically above the centre of the base. Show that

$$l \leqslant h \sqrt{\left(1 + \frac{16}{9} \tan^2 \alpha\right)}.$$

The three forces acting on the cylinder are shown in Fig. 40, and are the weight acting through the centroid G of the cone, the tension T in the string, and the reaction R of the wall, which is normal to the wall since the wall is smooth. Suppose that this reaction acts at a point H on the wall. By symmetry H will lie on the vertical through the centre C of the base. Let $CH = x$, and let the inclination of the string to the vertical be θ. Then $l \sin \theta = h$.

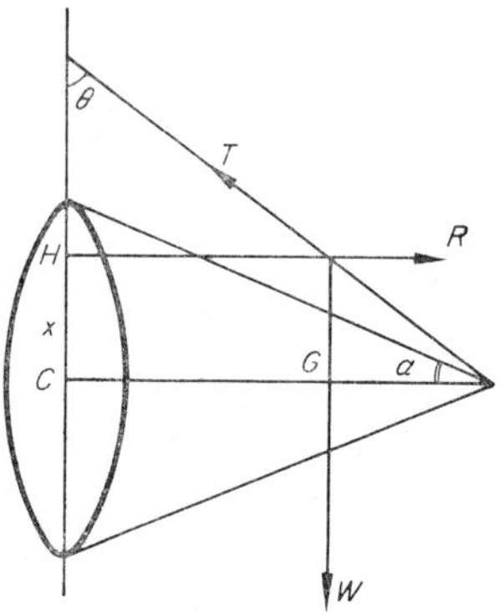

Fig. 40

The reaction R must act within the area of the base as long as there is equilibrium in the position described. Therefore x satisfies the condition that it is less than the radius of the base. That is,

$$x \leqslant h \tan \alpha. \qquad \text{(i)}$$

Now, since the cone is in equilibrium under the action of three forces, these forces should meet in a point. Using this property we obtain from the geometry of the figure

$$x = \tfrac{3}{4}h \cot \theta = \tfrac{3}{4}\sqrt{(l^2 - h^2)}.$$

Hence the condition (i) gives

$$\tfrac{3}{4}\sqrt{(l^2 - h^2)} \leqslant h \tan \alpha.$$

Squaring and rearranging

$$l^2 \leqslant h^2 \left(1 + \frac{16}{9} \tan^2 \alpha\right).$$

Hence the result.

If l is too large to satisfy this equality the cone will slip downwards, and the area of the base will cease to have contact with the wall.

Example 4. A rhombus $ABCD$ consists of four uniform rods, each of length $2a$ and weight W, smoothly jointed at their ends, hangs from the vertex A and is prevented from collapsing by a light rod of length $2a \sin \alpha$ joining the mid-points of the two lower rods. Show that the thrust in the light rod is

$$4W \tan \alpha,$$

and find the reactions at the joints B, C, D. The vertical through A is a line of symmetry. The forces on the left side of the line of symmetry is shown in the Fig. 41.

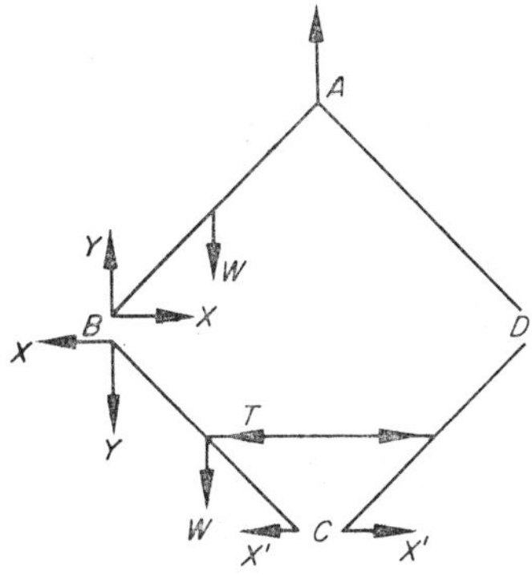

Fig. 41

Considering the equilibrium of the rod AB, and taking moments about the point A (so that the unknown reaction at the joint A does not occur in the equation),

$$X \,.\, 2a \cos \alpha + W \,.\, a \sin \alpha - Y \,.\, 2a \sin \alpha = O,$$

that is,

$$X + \tfrac{1}{2}W \tan \alpha - Y \tan \alpha = O. \qquad \text{(i)}$$

Considering the equilibrium of the rods AB and BC together, and taking moments about A,

$$2W \,.\, a \sin \alpha - T \,.\, 3a \cos \alpha - X' \,.\, 4a \cos \alpha = O$$

or

$$2W \tan \alpha - 3T - 4X' = O. \qquad \text{(ii)}$$

Considering the equilibrium of BC alone, and resolving horizontally and vertically

$$X + T + X' = O. \qquad \text{(iii)}$$

$$Y + W = O. \qquad \text{(iv)}$$

Solving the equations (i), (ii), (iii) and (iv),

$$Y = -W$$

$$X = -\frac{3}{2} W \tan \alpha$$

$$X' = -\frac{5}{2} W \tan \alpha$$

$$T = 4W \tan \alpha.$$

Example 5. A uniform solid hemisphere, of centre O, radius a and weight W, rests with its curved surface on a perfectly rough plane inclined at an angle α to the horizontal. Show that equilibrium is possible only if

$$\sin \alpha \leqslant \frac{3}{8},$$

and that when this condition is satisfied the inclination of the base

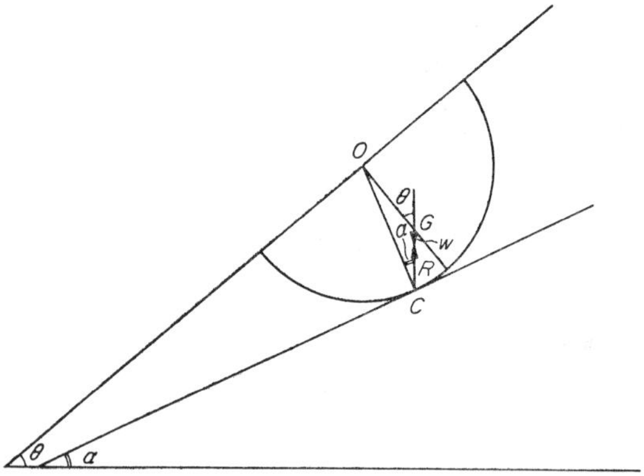

Fig. 42

of the hemisphere to the horizontal is

$$\sin^{-1}\left(\frac{8}{3}\sin\alpha\right).$$

Suppose C is the point of contact between the hemisphere and the plane. The forces acting on the hemisphere are the reaction at the point C and the weight W acting at G the centre of gravity of the hemisphere. Hence these two forces are equal and opposite. The reaction R is a vertical force, and G is vertically above the point of contact C. Suppose θ is the inclination of the base of the hemisphere to the horizontal. In the triangle OCG, the angle OCG is α and angle CGO is $180 - \theta$. Further $OC = a$, $OG = \frac{3}{8}a$. Hence

$$\frac{\sin\theta}{a} = \frac{\sin\alpha}{\frac{3}{8}a},$$

giving

$$\sin\theta = \frac{8}{3}\sin\alpha. \qquad \text{(i)}$$

Since for all real values of θ, $\sin\theta \leqslant 1$, therefore θ given by the equation (i) has a real value only if $\sin\alpha \leqslant 3/8$. The value of θ is then $\sin^{-1}(8\sin\alpha/3)$.

Exercises 2

1. Two uniform rods AO and OB, of equal length and of weight W and nW respectively, are smoothly jointed at O. The ends A and B are smoothly hinged to two fixed points in the same horizontal line. The rods are in equilibrium with O below AB. Prove that the line of action of the force exerted by either rod on the joint at O divides AB externally in the ratio $1/n$.

[Oxf. *GCE*(*S*) 1956]

2. A uniform square lamina of side $2a$ rests with its plane vertical between two smooth pegs which are in the same horizontal level at a distance c apart. Show that the inclination of one of its edges to the horizon is either 45° or

$$\frac{1}{2}\sin^{-1}\frac{a^2 - c^2}{c^2}.$$

3. Two uniform rods AB, BC, each of length l and weight W, are smoothly hinged at B and rest symmetrically over two small smooth pegs at the same

horizontal level and distance c apart. If a particle of weight ω is suspended from B, and θ is the inclination of each rod to the vertical, show that

$$\sin^3 \theta = \left(1 + \frac{\omega}{2W}\right)\frac{c}{l}.$$

4. A square board $ABCD$ rests with its plane perpendicular to the plane of a smooth vertical wall, one corner A of the board being in contact with the wall and the adjacent corner B being tied by a string, equal in length to a side of the square, to a point in the wall. Draw carefully a diagram showing the position of equilibrium of the board under the forces acting upon it and show that in this position the distances of the corners B, C, D from the wall are in the ratio $1:4:3$. [Lond. *G* 1934]

5. AB, BC, CA are uniform rods whose weights are proportional to their lengths which are 5, 4 and 3 units respectively. The rods are freely hinged at their extremities and the whole frame can turn freely in a vertical plane about a fixed horizontal axis through the middle point of AB. Prove that in the position of equilibrium AB is inclined to the vertical at an angle $\tan^{-1} 7$ and find the ratio of the reactions at the joints A and B. [Lond. *G* 1934]

6. The line density of a non-uniform rod AB, of length l, is proportional to the distance from A. Find the position of the centre of gravity G of the rod.

If the rod hangs from a point O by equal light strings OA, OB, each of length l, attached to A and B, find, to within one minute of arc, the inclination to the horizontal at which it rests. [Camb. *MT* 1956]

7. Three equal uniform rods AB, BC, CD are smoothly jointed at B and C. A and D are smoothly hinged to fixed supports so that AB and CD are inclined to the horizontal at angles of 60° and 30° respectively, C being lower than B and D lower than C. Prove that the horizontal reaction at each joint is $W\sqrt{3}$, where W is the weight of each rod, and that BC is inclined to the horizontal at an angle $\tan^{-1}(2/\sqrt{3})$. [Oxf. *GCE(S)* 1958]

8. A rhombus $ABCD$ is formed of four uniform rods, each of length a and weight W, freely jointed at the corners. The system is supported by two vertical strings attached to A and B, so that AB is horizontal. A light inelastic string of length a connects A and C. Find the tensions in the strings attached to A and B.

Prove that there is no horizontal force on the rod BC at either end, and find the tension in the string AC. [Oxf. *GCE(S)* 1960]

9. A framework of five freely jointed rods consists of a rhombus $ABCD$ and its diagonal AC. Two equal rods OB, OD are freely jointed to the framework at B and D and to each other at O, a point external to the framework and in its plane. If the angle $BAD = 2\alpha$, angle $BOD = 2\beta$, and the whole can freely turn about O as a fixed pivot, find the force in AC when forces each of magnitude P are applied symmetrically to the mid-points of OB, OD in directions perpendicular to them. [Lond. *GCE(S)* 1958]

10. A uniform solid hemisphere rests with its curved surface in contact with a rough plane inclined to the horizontal at an angle θ. Show that, for equilibrium to be possible, $\sin\theta \leqslant \frac{3}{8}$, and indicate in a sketch the equilibrium configuration when θ has its extreme value.

Show further that, if the inclination θ of the plane to the horizontal satisfies

$$\sin\theta < \tfrac{3}{8} \leqslant \tan\theta,$$

there are two possible equilibrium configurations with the curved surface of the hemisphere in contact with the plane. Draw a sketch showing roughly the two configurations. [Camb. *GCE(S)* 1954]

11. Four equal uniform rods AB, BC, CD, DA, each of weight W, are freely jointed together and suspended from A. The framework is kept in the form of a square by a light inextensible string which joins the midpoints of AB and BC. Find the horizontal reaction at each joint and the tension in the string.

[Oxf. *GCE(S)* 1957]

12. Four uniform rods, of weight ρ per unit length, are smoothly jointed at their extremities to form a parallelogram $ABCD$, where $AB = a$ and $AD = b$. The framework is suspended from A, and the vertices A and C are joined by a light inextensible string of length $\sqrt{(a^2 + b^2)}$. Find the tension in the string, and prove that the reactions at B and D are each equal to

$$\rho ab/\sqrt{(2a^2 + 2b^2)}.$$

[Oxf. *GCE(S)* 1959]

13. A uniform solid sphere has centre O, and A is a point on its surface. It is divided into two parts by the plane which bisects OA at right angles. The smaller part rests in equilibrium with its curved surface touching a fixed plane inclined at an angle of 30° to the horizontal; the friction is sufficient to prevent it from sliding. Find, to the nearest tenth of a degree, the angle of inclination to the horizontal of its plane face.

Explain why such a position of equilibrium is impossible if the angle of inclination of the inclined plane is 45°. [Oxf. *GCE(S)* 1959]

14. Prove that the centroid of a uniform semicircular lamina of radius a is at a distance $4a/3\pi$ from the centre of the circle.

A uniform solid right circular cone, of height h and base radius a, is cut into two halves along a plane through its axis. One of the halves is suspended freely from the centre of the circle of which the base is half. Prove that its base makes with the horizontal the angle

$$\tan^{-1}(4a/\pi h).$$

[Oxf. *GCE(S)* 1960]

15. Three uniform rods AB, BC, CA of lengths 4, 5, 3 feet and weights 4, 5, 3 lbs, respectively, smoothly jointed at their ends so as to form a triangle ABC, are hinged at A to a fixed point and supported in a vertical plane with BC horizontal and below A, by a couple applied to the rod BC. Find the magnitude of this couple and show that the resultant reaction at the joint B is equal to $\sqrt{17 \cdot 77}$ lbs. [Ceylon *G* 1944]

16. Four equal uniform rods, each of weight W and length $2l$, form a rhombus freely jointed at A, B, C, D. The framework is hung by a cord from A. Show that equilibrium can be maintained, with C vertically below A, and the angle BCD equal to 2θ, by the application of equal and opposite couples $4Wl \sin \theta$ to the rods BC, CD.

Find the horizontal and vertical components of the reactions at B and C.

[Camb. *MT* 1947]

17. Two planes are fixed symmetrically, each at an angle α to the horizon. Two smooth uniform circular cylinders, each of radius a and weight W, touching each other along a horizontal generator, rest symmetrically on the planes and between them, with their axes parallel to the line of intersection of the planes. A third uniform cylinder of radius b and weight P is placed, also with its axis horizontal, so as to touch the other two along generators. Show that, if b is greater than a certain limit l ($= a \operatorname{cosec} \alpha - a$), the two lower cylinders will not separate, however great P may be, and that if $b < l$, the cylinders will separate if

$$\frac{2W}{P} + 1 < \left[\frac{2al + l^2}{2ab + b^2}\right]^{1/2}.$$

[Ceylon *G* 1944]

18. Three uniform rods OA, OB and OC are each of length l and of weight W; they are smoothly jointed together at O and are placed symmetrically over a smooth fixed sphere of radius a, the joint O being vertically above the centre of the sphere and the rods resting on its surface in equilibrium. Show that

$$l \sin^3 \alpha = 2a \cos \alpha,$$

where α is the angle which each rod makes with the downward vertical, and deduce that the rods will be at right angles if (and only if) $l = 3a/\sqrt{2}$.

[Oxf. *I* 1956]

19. A number of uniform planks of length $2a$ are arranged one on top of another so that the top plank projects a distance x_1 beyond the second, the second a distance x_2 beyond the third, and so on. Show that the conditions of equilibrium of successive planks are

$$x_1 \leqslant a, \qquad x_1 + 2x_2 \leqslant 2a, \qquad x_1 + 2x_2 + 3x_3 \leqslant 3a, \; \ldots .$$

If there are $(n + 1)$ planks, show that the greatest overhang

$$x_1 + x_2 + \ldots + x_n$$

of the top plank beyond the bottom plank is

$$a\left(1 + \frac{1}{2} + \ldots + \frac{1}{n}\right).$$

[Oxf. *I* 1957]

20. Three uniform smooth cylinders, each of radius a and weight W, have their axes horizontal and parallel. Two of them lie on a smooth horizontal plane, not touching each other. The third lies symmetrically on top of them, not touching the plane. Equilibrium is preserved by a light endless string, which passes round them. Prove that the length $2\pi a$ of string is in contact with the

cylinders, and hence prove that, if the length of the string is $2\pi a + l$, then

$$6a < l < 8a.$$

Prove that the tension in the string is

$$\tfrac{1}{2}W(l - 4a)/\sqrt{\{l(8a - l)\}}.$$

[Oxf. *GCE(S)* 1957]

21. A regular hexagonal framework *ABCDEF* consists of six equal uniform rods, each of weight ω, and a light rod *CF*, freely jointed at *A* ... *F*. The rod *AB* is fixed horizontally and the framework hangs in a vertical plane. If a weight *W* is suspended from the middle point of *ED*, show that the thrust in the rod *CF* is

$$\sqrt{3}\left(\omega + \frac{W}{3}\right).$$

[Camb. *MT* 1929]

22. Two freely jointed uniform rods of different materials and of lengths $2a$ and $2b$ lie at rest on a smooth horizontal cylinder, of radius r, in a vertical plane normal to the axis of the cylinder. If the rods make angles α, β respectively with the horizontal, show that

$$r(a \sin 2\alpha + b \sin 2\beta) = 4ab \cos \alpha \cos \beta \cos^2 \frac{\alpha + \beta}{2}.$$

[Camb. *MT* 1930]

23. A uniform solid right circular cone of semi-vertical angle α is at rest with its base in contact with a perfectly rough plane whose inclination to the horizontal is $\theta(\theta < \alpha)$. A horizontal force F_1 is applied at the vertex in a vertical plane containing the line of greatest slope and is of such magnitude that the cone is just about to tilt about the lowest point of its base. If a horizontal force F_2 is applied at the vertex, opposite in direction to F_1, the cone is just about to tilt about the highest point of its base. If R_1 and R_2 are the normal components of the corresponding reactions of the plane, prove that

$$R_1/R_2 = \cos(\alpha + \theta)/\cos(\alpha - \theta).$$

[Camb. *MT* 1932]

24. Two equal smooth spheres, each of radius a and weight ω, are placed within a hollow right circular cylinder of weight W and of radius $r(< 2a)$ open at both ends and resting on a horizontal plane. Show that if the cylinder does not upset

$$W \geqslant 2\omega\left(1 - \frac{a}{r}\right).$$

25. Two uniform straight rods *AB* and *BC*, each of length $2l$ and weight W, are smoothly jointed together at *B*; *A* and *C* are joined by a light string of natural length l and modulus of elasticity $\tfrac{1}{2}W$. The rods rest in a vertical plane with *AC* horizontal and *B* above *AC*; they are supported by two smooth pegs at the same

height and at distance l apart. Prove that, if each rod is inclined at an angle θ to the vertical, then

$$2 \sin^2 \theta(\sin \theta + 4 \sin \theta \cos \theta - \cos \theta) = 1.$$

[Camb. *PNS* 1950]

26. A bead of weight ω is threaded on a smooth curved wire which is fixed concave upwards in a vertical plane with its two ends A and B in the same horizontal line and at a distance $2a$ apart. An elastic string of unstretched length $2a$ and modulus ω is threaded through the bead and has its ends fastened at A and B. Prove that the bead is in equilibrium in any position on the wire if the latter has the form determined by the polar equation

$$2ar\,(1 - \sin \theta) = (2a - r)^2 \cot \frac{\theta}{2},$$

A being the pole and AB the line $\theta = O$. [Lond. *S* 1940]

27. A parallelogram $ABCD$ has two opposite sides AB, CD and the two diagonals AC, BD formed of thin rods freely jointed at A, B, C, D, the diagonal rods being free to slide over one another. The rods lie on a smooth horizontal table. Show that if the remaining sides AD, BC are completed by elastic strings at the same tension the system is in equilibrium.

If one of the strings is removed, show that the configuration can be maintained in equilibrium by applying equal and opposite couples to the rods AB, CD, and find the magnitude of the couples in terms of the tension of the remaining string and the dimensions of the parallelogram. [Camb. *MT* 1949]

28. Show that the centre of mass of a uniform solid right circular cone divides the axis in the ratio 3 : 1.

A uniform solid right circular cone is suspended by a light inelastic string which has one end tied to the vertex and the other to a point on the circumference of the base and passes through two small smooth rings fixed at a distance a apart in a horizontal line. The altitude of the cone is $h(h > a)$ and the radius of the base is r. Prove that, if the cone hangs with its axis horizontal, the length of the string is

$$a + \frac{(h - a)\sqrt{(h^2 + 4r^2)}}{h}.$$

[Lond. *G* 1956]

29. Prove that three equal smooth circular cylinders each of radius r can rest in equilibrium with their axes horizontal and parallel, so that each cylinder touches the other two, and two of them touch the inside of a fixed smooth hollow circular cylinder of radius R with axis parallel to the axes of the other cylinders, provided that

$$r(1 + 2/\sqrt{3}) < R < r(1 + 2\sqrt{7}).$$

[Camb. *MT* 1946]

30. A solid cone of uniform density has a circular base of radius a and its vertex is at a perpendicular distance h above the base. The straight line joining the centre of the base to the vertex makes an angle θ with the normal to the base. Prove that, if the cone is placed with its base resting on a horizontal table, it will remain at rest provided that

$$a > \tfrac{1}{4}h \tan \theta.$$

Show also that, if it is placed with its curved surface in contact with the table, it will not tilt over on to its base if

$$h^2 + 4a^2 \cos^2 \theta - 5ah \sin \theta \cos \theta > 0.$$

[Camb. *MT* 1929]

Chapter 3

Friction

3.1. Friction

BRIEF reference was made in §2.1 to the existence of the force of friction. In this section the properties of frictional forces are studied in more detail.

Suppose that two bodies are at rest touching each other, and that the reaction between them has normal component N and frictional component F.

There is a limit to the amount of friction that can be exerted between two bodies. When the equilibrium of a system is such that it is just preserved by the maximum friction coming into play, the system is said to be in **limiting equilibrium,** and the maximum friction thus exerted is called **limiting friction.**

The limiting frictional force has been determined experimentally for different kinds of contact surfaces, and the results may be expressed by a few rules:

(*a*) The limiting friction is independent of the magnitude of the area in contact,

(*b*) The limiting friction bears a constant ratio to the normal component of reaction, that is,

$$F = \mu N \tag{1}$$

where μ is a constant depending on the materials in contact, and is called the **coefficient of static friction.**

For equilibrium which is not limiting, $F < \mu N$. Hence for all cases of equilibrium

$$F \leqslant \mu N. \tag{2}$$

Experimental values for different materials, when the surfaces are dry, are roughly in the following range:

Metal on metal	0·15–0·30
Metal on wood	0·20–0·60
Wood on wood	0·20–0·50
Metal on leather	0·30–0·60
Wood on leather	0·25–0·50.

The values of μ in the above table are all less than unity. There are, however, substances for which μ may be greater than unity. For earth on earth (shingle and gravel) μ may be as high as 1·1.

Angle of Friction

Suppose that an angle λ is defined by the relation

$$\tan \lambda = \mu. \tag{3}$$

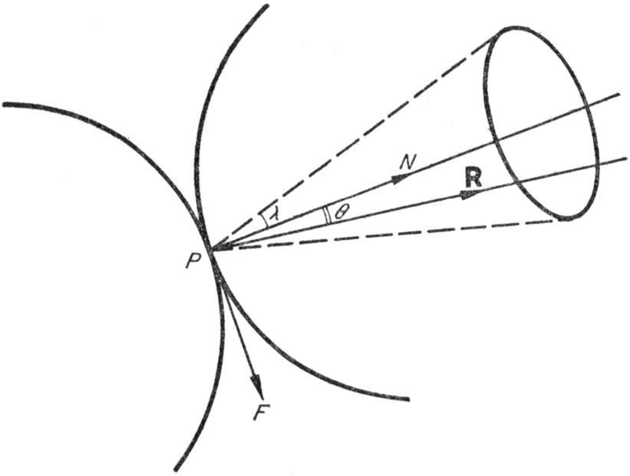

Fig. 43

In Fig. 43,

$$R \cos \theta = N, \qquad R \sin \theta = F$$

Hence

$$\tan \theta = F/N \leqslant \mu,$$

that is,

$$\theta \leqslant \lambda. \tag{4}$$

Hence the angle between the direction of the reaction and the direction of the normal cannot exceed λ. λ is called the angle of friction.

If a cone is drawn with its vertex at the point of contact P, its axis along the common normal at P, and whose semi-vertical angle is λ, the resultant reaction must be within or on the cone, and cannot lie outside the cone. This cone is called the **cone of friction.**

When the maximum friction that a body can exert is not sufficient to preserve equilibrium, and sliding takes place, then during sliding the friction is $F = \mu' N$ where μ' is the **coefficient of kinetic friction.** The direction of friction is such as to oppose the relative motion. μ' is slightly less than the coefficient of static friction between the same two surfaces. In general we may represent the coefficient by the symbol μ, the appropriate coefficient being used in each case.

So far there has been discussed the role of friction when one body slides or tends to slide over another. A brief comment will now be made on the forces which come into play when one body rolls upon another.

When the body A rolls upon B without sliding, the points of each body which are momentarily in contact are at relative rest. Consequently the limiting friction need not be brought into action. The reaction **R** will have normal component N and the frictional component F where

$$F \leqslant \mu N.$$

This is the same inequality as in the case of equilibrium.

When a body A in contact with a fixed body B, is in equilibrium, and a gradually increasing force is applied to the body A, the following possibilities may occur. The equilibrium may continue to be unbroken, however large the impressed force may become; or equilibrium may be broken by the body A sliding on B or equilibrium may be broken by A rolling upon B. Some examples given below will illustrate the properties of frictional forces.

Example 1. Three equal uniform rods AB, BC, CD each of length l are smoothly jointed at B and C. Light rings are attached at A and D and slide on a rough horizontal wire, the coefficient of limiting friction being μ. The system is in equilibrium with BC horizontal. Show that the greatest length of AD is

$$l\left[1+\frac{6\mu}{\sqrt{(9\mu^2+4)}}\right].$$

[Oxf. *I* 1955]

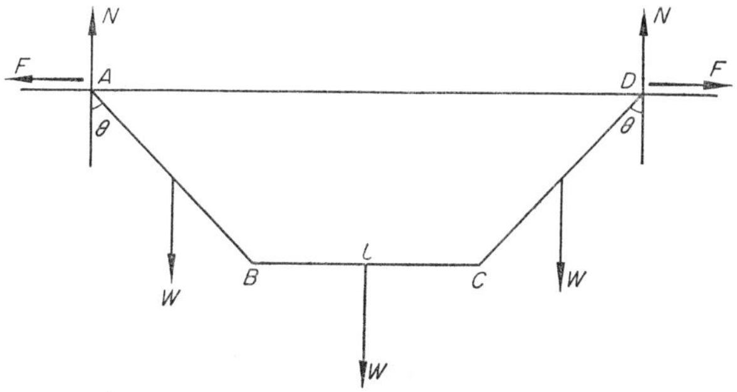

Fig. 44

There is symmetry in the equilibrium position in which BC is horizontal. Hence the inclinations of AB and CD to the vertical are equal, θ say. The reactions at A and D are also equal. Suppose the normal component is N and frictional component F.

Considering the equilibrium of the three rods taken together, and resolving vertically

$$2N - 3W = 0 \text{ or } N = 3W/2.$$

Considering the equilibrium of the rod AB alone, and taking moments about the point B, so that the unknown reaction on AB due to the rod BC does not enter the equation of moments,

$$N \,.\, l\sin\theta - F \,.\, l\cos\theta - W \,.\, \tfrac{1}{2}l\sin\theta = O.$$

Hence

$$F = W\tan\theta.$$

As long as there is equilibrium

$$F/N \leqslant \mu,$$

that is

$$\frac{2}{3}\tan\theta \leqslant \mu.$$

Therefore

$$\theta \leqslant \alpha,$$

where α is the acute angle satisfying

$$\tan\alpha = \frac{3}{2}\mu.$$

Now

$$AD = l(1 + 2\sin\theta) \leqslant l(1 + 2\sin\alpha).$$

That is,

$$AD \leqslant l\left[1 + \frac{6\mu}{\sqrt{(9\mu^2 + 4)}}\right].$$

The expression on the right hand side gives the greatest possible length of AD.

Example 2. The ends of a uniform rod are attached by light rings to a rough uniform wire bent in the form of a circle which is fixed in a vertical plane. The rod subtends an angle 2α at the centre of the circle and the angle of friction between wire and rings is $\lambda(< \pi/4)$. Prove that the angle θ of least possible inclination of the rod to the vertical is given by the equation

$$\tan\theta = \cot 2\lambda + \cos 2\alpha \,.\, \operatorname{cosec} 2\lambda,$$

provided that the expression on the right hand side is positive.

[Camb. *MT* 1946]

Suppose the equilibrium is limiting when the rod is inclined at angle θ to the vertical, as shown in the diagram. The reactions at A and B are R and S and make angles λ with the radii at A and B respectively.

For equilibrium the three forces R, S and weight W through the mid-point of AB meet in a point C, say. The angle BAC is $90 - \alpha - \lambda$ and angle ABC is $90 - \alpha + \lambda$. Hence applying the trigonometrical relation (4) of Chapter 2 to triangle ABC

$$\begin{aligned} 2 \cot \theta &= \cot (90 - \alpha - \lambda) - \cot (90 - \alpha + \lambda) \\ &= \tan (\alpha + \lambda) - \tan (\alpha - \lambda) \\ &= \sin 2\lambda/\cos (\alpha + \lambda) \cos (\alpha - \lambda). \end{aligned}$$

Hence

$$\begin{aligned} \tan \theta &= 2 \cos (\alpha + \lambda) \cos (\alpha - \lambda)/\sin 2\lambda \\ &= (\cos 2\lambda + \cos 2\alpha)/\sin 2\lambda = \cot 2\lambda + \cos 2\alpha \operatorname{cosec} 2\lambda. \end{aligned}$$

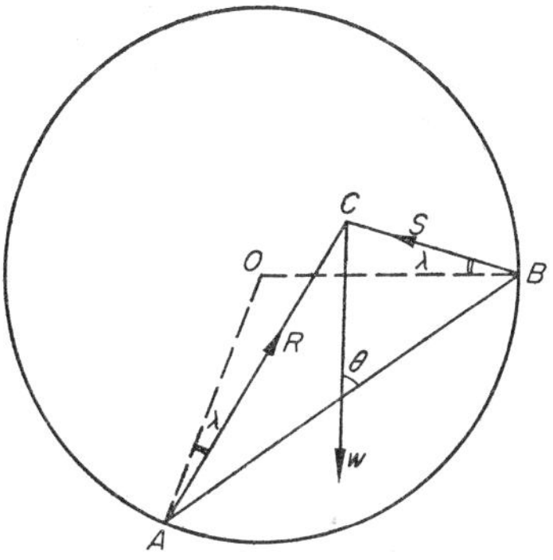

Fig. 45

Example 3. A heavy uniform wire is bent into the form of an equilateral triangle ABC and rests with BC horizontal and supported by a rough peg at its middle point, the vertex A being below BC. A gradually increasing horizontal force is applied at A in the plane of the wire. Show that, as long as the wire does not slip on the peg, when BC is inclined at an angle θ to the horizontal the ratio of the frictional force to the normal reaction at the peg is

$$\frac{2 \tan \theta}{3 + \tan^2 \theta}.$$

Deduce that the wire never slips if the coefficient of friction between the wire and the peg exceeds $1/\sqrt{3}$.

[Lond. *GCE*(*S*) 1956]

When the force applied at A is P, suppose the position is such that BC is inclined at angle θ to the horizontal, and the forces are as shown in Fig. 46.

Considering the equilibrium of the whole wire, taking moments about D gives

$$P \,.\, AD \cos\theta - W \,.\, \tfrac{1}{3} AD \sin\theta = O$$

that is,

$$P = \tfrac{1}{3} W \tan\theta.$$

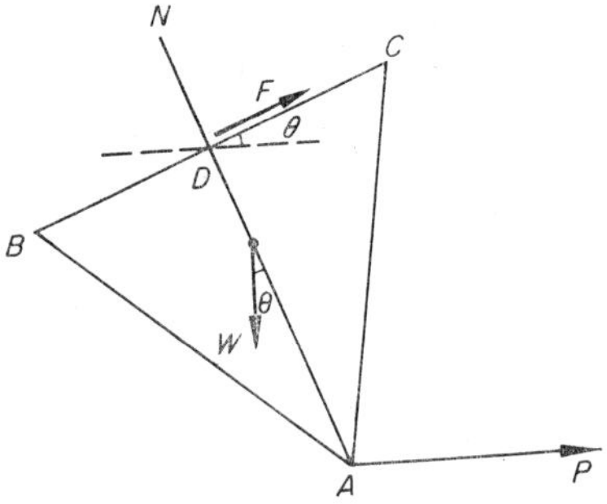

Fig. 46

Resolving along and perpendicular to BC

$$F = W\sin\theta - P\cos\theta = \tfrac{2}{3} W \sin\theta$$
$$N = W\cos\theta + P\sin\theta = W\{\cos\theta + \sin^2\theta/(3\cos\theta)\}.$$

Hence

$$\frac{F}{N} = \frac{2\sin\theta\cos\theta}{3\cos^2\theta + \sin^2\theta} = \frac{2\tan\theta}{3+\tan^2\theta}.$$

The maximum value of F/N may be found by considering the expression

$$\frac{3+\tan^2\theta}{\tan\theta} = \left[\sqrt{\left(\frac{3}{\tan\theta}\right)} - \sqrt{\tan\theta}\right]^2 + 2\sqrt{3}$$
$$\geqslant 2\sqrt{3}.$$

Hence

$$F/N \leqslant \frac{1}{\sqrt{3}}.$$

Therefore if μ, the coefficient of friction between the wire and the peg, exceeds $1/\sqrt{3}$,

$$F/N < \mu$$

and the wire does not slip.

Example 4. Two equal uniform ladders AB, BC, each of length $2l$ and weight W, are smoothly hinged at B, while the ends A and C rest on a rough horizontal plane. The coefficient of friction is μ at A and C, and the angle ABC is 2α. Prove that a man of weight ω can ascend a distance x given by

$$x = \frac{2lW(2\mu - \tan \alpha)}{\omega (\tan \alpha - \mu)},$$

provided that $x < 2l$ and

$$\mu < \tan \alpha < 2\mu.$$

[Lond. *G* 1956]

Consider the forces when the man has ascended a distance x from A. Resolving horizontally for both the rods taken together,

$$F_1 = F_2 \tag{i}$$

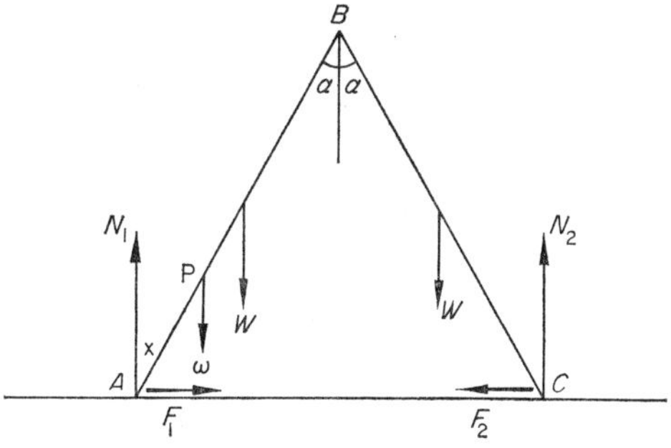

Fig. 47

Take moments about A for both the rods

$$4l \sin \alpha N_2 - 3l \sin \alpha W - l \sin \alpha W - x \sin \alpha \omega = 0$$

that is

$$N_2 = W + \omega x/4l. \tag{ii}$$

Taking moments about C for both the rods

$$4l \sin \alpha N_1 - \omega(4l - x) \sin \alpha - W \,.\, 3l \sin \alpha - Wl \sin \alpha = 0$$

or

$$N_1 = W + \omega\left(1 - \frac{x}{4l}\right). \tag{iii}$$

[(iii) may also be obtained by resolving vertically for both rods, $N_1 + N_2 = 2W + \omega$, and using (ii).]

Taking moments about B for the rod BC alone,

$$N_2 \,.\, 2l \sin \alpha - W \,.\, l \sin \alpha - F_2 \,.\, 2l \cos \alpha = 0,$$

or

$$F_2 = (N_2 - \tfrac{1}{2}W) \tan \alpha = \left(\tfrac{1}{2}W + \frac{\omega x}{4l}\right) \tan \alpha. \tag{iv}$$

For equilibrium

$$F_1/N_1 \leqslant \mu, \qquad F_2/N_2 \leqslant \mu.$$

Since $F_1 = F_2$, and $N_1 > N_2$ (using $x < 2l$), both inequalities are satisfied if $F_2/N_2 \leqslant \mu$, that is

$$\frac{\tfrac{1}{2}(W + \omega x/2l)}{(W + \omega x/4l)} \tan \alpha \leqslant \mu$$

or

$$\frac{\omega x}{Wl}(\tan \alpha - \mu) \leqslant 4\mu - 2 \tan \alpha.$$

If $\tan \alpha$ lies between μ and 2μ, this gives

$$x \leqslant \frac{2lW}{\omega} \frac{2\mu - \tan \alpha}{\tan \alpha - \mu}.$$

The maximum value of x is thus given by the expression on the right hand side.

3.2. Particle on a rough curve or surface

If a particle is constrained to rest on a rough curve or surface under given forces, it is useful to find the condition that slipping may not take place.

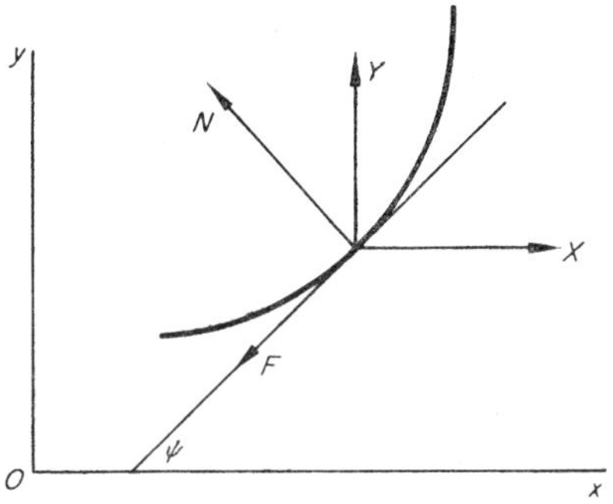

Fig. 48

Suppose that a particle rests upon a plane curve $y = f(x)$, and a force with components (X, Y) acts on the particle. If F, N are the normal and tangential components of the reaction, then

$$N = X \sin \psi - Y \cos \psi \tag{5}$$
$$F = X \cos \psi + Y \sin \psi \tag{6}$$

For equilibrium $| F/N | \leqslant \mu$. Including both positive and negative values of F/N this may be written

$$(F/N)^2 \leqslant \mu^2$$

or

$$(X \cos \psi + Y \sin \psi)^2 \leqslant \mu^2 (X \sin \psi - Y \cos \psi)^2. \tag{7}$$

This may also be expressed as

$$\left(X + Y \frac{\mathrm{d}y}{\mathrm{d}x}\right)^2 \leqslant \mu^2 \left(X \frac{\mathrm{d}y}{\mathrm{d}x} - Y\right)^2 \tag{8}$$

using

$$\tan \psi = \frac{\mathrm{d}y}{\mathrm{d}x}.$$

For a particle on a twisted curve and under the action of a force $\mathbf{P} = (X, Y, Z)$, one may use the condition that the angle between the resultant reaction and the tangent to the curve exceeds $\pi/2 - \lambda$. If $\mathbf{T}$ denotes the unit vector along the tangent, then using the fact that the reaction is equal and opposite to $\mathbf{P}$,

$$\cos^{-1}\left|\frac{\mathbf{P}\,.\,\mathbf{T}}{P}\right| \geqslant \pi/2 - \lambda.$$

or

$$(\mathbf{P}\,.\,\mathbf{T}/P)^2 \leqslant \sin^2\lambda = \mu^2/(1+\mu^2). \tag{9}$$

Suppose a particle rests on a rough surface whose equation is $f(x, y, z) = O$, and is acted upon by given force $\mathbf{P}$. Let $\mathbf{n}$ be unit vector along the normal to the surface. Then $\mathbf{n} = \text{grad} f / |\text{grad} f|$. The reaction balances the force $\mathbf{P}$, and for equilibrium the angle between the reaction and the normal to the surface should be less than λ. Hence

$$\cos^{-1}\left|\frac{\mathbf{P}\,.\,\mathbf{n}}{P}\right| \leqslant \lambda$$

or

$$(\mathbf{P}\,.\,\mathbf{n}/P)^2 \geqslant \cos^2\lambda = 1/(1+\mu^2). \tag{10}$$

Example. A particle rests on the surface

$$xyz = a^3$$

under the action of a constant force parallel to the axis of x. Show that the curve of intersection of the surface with the cone

$$\frac{1}{y^2} + \frac{1}{z^2} = \frac{\mu^2}{x^2}$$

will separate out the part of the surface on which equilibrium is possible.

$$\mathbf{P} = (P, O, O), \qquad \mathbf{n} = \left(\frac{yz}{K}, \frac{zx}{K}, \frac{xy}{K}\right)$$

where $K = \sqrt{(y^2z^2 + z^2x^2 + x^2y^2)}$. Hence the condition (10) gives

$$(yz/K)^2 \geqslant \frac{1}{1+\mu^2}$$

or

$$1 + \mu^2 \geqslant \frac{y^2z^2 + z^2x^2 + x^2y^2}{y^2z^2}$$

or

$$\frac{\mu^2}{x^2} \geqslant \frac{1}{y^2} + \frac{1}{z^2},$$

from which the given result may be inferred.

3.3. Indeterminateness, initial motion

Certain problems of friction are indeterminate, when more friction may be available than is necessary to preserve equilibrium. Consider the Example 2 above of §2.3. Suppose that there is considered a position of the rod AB when it is inclined to the horizontal less than in the limiting case shown in Fig. 45. Draw lines through A inclined at angle λ to AO on either side, and similarly at B lines inclined at angle λ to BO, thus forming the figure $CDEF$.

The reactions at A and B are passive forces with the reaction at A lying within the angle CAF and the reaction at B within the angle EBF, such that these two reactions and the weight W at G keep the

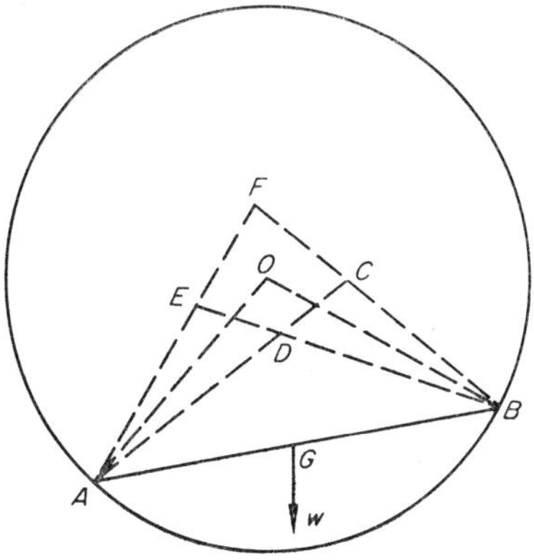

Fig. 49

rod AB in equilibrium. As long as the vertical through G intersects the quadrilateral $CDEF$ to the right of E and left of C, the reactions at A and B can adjust themselves to preserve equilibrium. The reactions at A and B are indeterminate, but lie within the limits indicated, and the vertical through G passes through their point of intersection.

When the inclination of the rod to the horizontal is raised, a stage is reached when the vertical through G passes through C. This is the position shown in Fig. 45. The equilibrium then is limiting, and the maximum friction is called into play at A and B, and the reactions become determinate.

Initial Motion

Suppose that a body A is in contact with one or more bodies, and suppose that a gradually increasing force **P** is applied to the body A. The following possibilities of interest arise. It may happen that the reaction may adjust itself to preserve equilibrium however much **P** is increased. Or it may happen that equilibrium gets broken at some stage or other. The equilibrium may be broken by the body A sliding over the surface of another or rolling upon another. It is useful to investigate the conditions under which these different possibilities hold. A few examples would help to illustrate the principles involved.

Example 1. A square lamina $ABCD$ rests in a vertical plane with AB in contact with a rough horizontal table. The coefficient of friction between the lamina and the table is μ. A gradually increasing force is applied at C in the plane of the lamina in an upwards direction and making an angle α with DC (so that of the line of action of the force lies inside the lamina). Prove that equilibrium is broken as follows:

(i) if $\tan \alpha > 2$ and $\mu > 1/(\tan \alpha - 2)$, by the lamina tilting about A,

(ii) if $\tan \alpha < 2$ and $\mu > 1/(2 - \tan \alpha)$, by the lamina tilting about B,

(iii) if $\mu < 1/ \mid \tan \alpha - 2 \mid$ by the lamina sliding.

[Oxf. *GCE*(*S*) 1959]

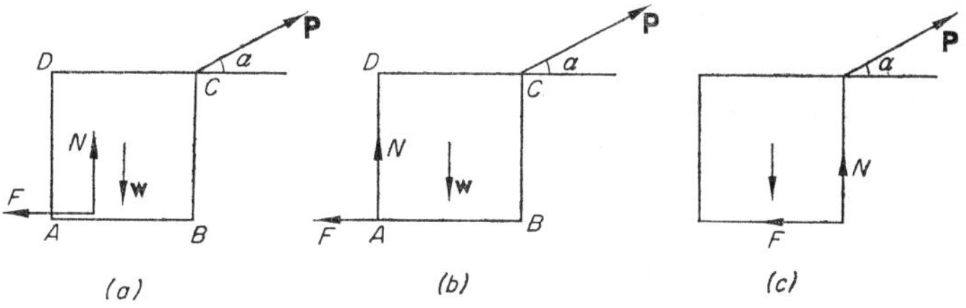

Fig. 50

The general position of equilibrium is shown in Fig. 50(a). The different possible ways in which equilibrium may be broken are, (i) tilting about A, (ii) tilting about B, and (iii) silding at A and B. We assume that (i) takes place, and determine whether the frictional forces for such a motion are consistent with the assumption made. When the body is about to tilt about A, the reaction of the table will act at A, Fig. 50(b). N and F will be such that $F/N < \mu$. Resolving horizontally and vertically

$$P \cos \alpha - F = O$$
$$P \sin \alpha + N = W.$$

Taking moments about A.

$$P \,.\, 2a (\sin \alpha - \cos \alpha) = W \,.\, a.$$

Hence

$$F = \frac{W \cos \alpha}{2(\sin \alpha - \cos \alpha)}, \qquad N = \frac{W(\sin \alpha - 2 \cos \alpha)}{2(\sin \alpha - \cos \alpha)}.$$

For N to be positive, $\tan \alpha > 2$ and

$$\frac{F}{N} = \frac{\cos \alpha}{\sin \alpha - 2 \cos \alpha} = \frac{1}{\tan \alpha - 2} < \mu \text{ for no slipping at } A.$$

Hence if $\tan \alpha > 2$ and $\mu > 1/(\tan \alpha - 2)$, the assumption that tilting at A takes place is not contradicted. If, however, $\tan \alpha > 2$ and $\mu < 1/(\tan \alpha - 2)$, then the assumption is not valid, since $F < \mu N$ is not satisfied, and slipping would not have been stopped.

Now let tilting about B be assumed, and the conditions investigated. The reaction at the table will now be all at B (Fig. 50(c)).

F and N should satisfy $F/N < \mu$. Resolving horizontally and vertically

$$F = P \cos \alpha, \qquad N + P \sin \alpha = W.$$

Taking moments about C:

$$F \,.\, 2a - W \,.\, a = 0, \text{ or } F = W/2$$

$$N = W(1 - \tfrac{1}{2} \tan \alpha). \quad F/N = 1/(2 - \tan \alpha)$$

$$N > 0 \text{ requires } \tan \alpha < 2, \; F/N < \mu \text{ gives } \mu > 1/(2 - \tan \alpha).$$

Hence when $\tan \alpha < 2$ and $\mu > 1/(2 - \tan \alpha)$, the assumption that tilting about B takes place is not contradicted. When $\tan \alpha < 2$ and $\mu < 1/(2 - \tan \alpha)$, then the assumption is not valid. Thus when $\mu < 1/\,|\tan \alpha - 2\,|$, the assumptions (i) or (ii) would not be valid, and equilibrium will therefore be broken by the lamina sliding at A and B.

Example 2. A uniform circular disc of radius a rests in equilibrium in a vertical plane on two rough pegs distant $\sqrt{2}\,a$ apart in a horizontal line; the coefficient of friction between each peg and the cylinder is μ. A gradually increasing force acting in a direction parallel to the line of the pegs is applied to the highest point of the disc; prove that, when equilibrium is first broken, the disc will commence to rotate with its centre fixed, or commence to rotate about one of the pegs according as μ is less than or greater than $\sqrt{2} - 1$.

[Camb. *MT* 1931]

As P increases, there are two possible ways in which equilibrium may be broken. In one the disc turns about the peg at B and in the other, the disc rotates about its centre, thus sliding over the pegs at A and B.

As between the two possibilities, in the second case which is one of sliding, the maximum friction would be called into play while in the first case which is one of rolling the friction need not be limiting. Hence if circumstances permit, the first possibility would generally take place in preference to the second. The disc **would** roll if it **could.**

Let us therefore assume that the disc is on the point of turning about B, and investigate the conditions that may have to be satisfied. The disc is then subject to three forces: the weight W, the force P and

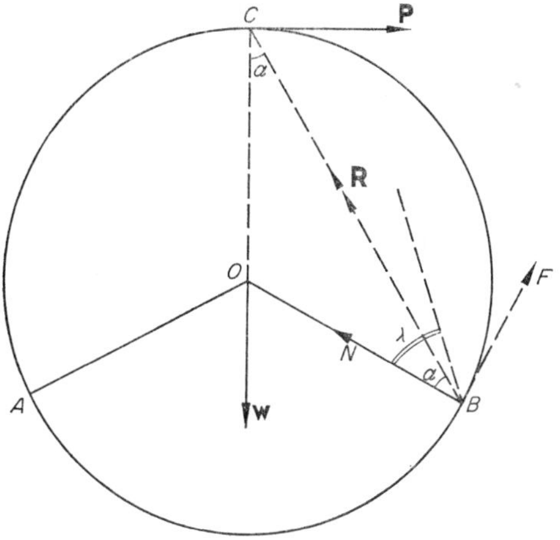

Fig. 51

the reaction at B (the reaction at A vanishes, since contact is on the point of ceasing). These three forces should meet in a point, which clearly is the point C which is the highest point of the disc. The reaction R, however, should not make an angle greater than the angle of friction. Consequently the condition that there is no slipping at C is equivalent to $\alpha < \lambda$.

From the geometry of the figure $\alpha = 22\frac{1}{2}°$. Hence the required condition is $\lambda > 22\frac{1}{2}°$, or $\mu = \tan \lambda > \tan 22\frac{1}{2}$. Now,

$$\tan \alpha = \sqrt{\left(\frac{1 - \cos 2\alpha}{1 + \cos 2\alpha}\right)} = \sqrt{\left(\frac{\sqrt{2} - 1}{\sqrt{2} + 1}\right)} = \sqrt{2} - 1.$$

Hence the required condition is

$$\mu > \sqrt{2} - 1.$$

When this condition is satisfied, the assumption made is not contradicted, and therefore equilibrium is broken by the disc turning about B. If, however, $\mu < \sqrt{2} - 1$, the assumption is contradicted, and hence the only possibility is the second alternative, namely, that the disc turns about its centre.

In some problems where the manner in which equilibrium is broken is under consideration, it may not be possible to state beforehand what the directions of the frictional forces would be. In such cases it would be useful to try to find the instantaneous centre I of the motion that would result when equilibrium is broken. If a position is assumed for I, then the frictional force at any point P is perpendicular to IP. Equations of equilbrium in the limiting position may be used to determine I.

Example 3. A thin, uniform rod of weight P and of length $2l$ rests on a horizontal plane which is equally rough at all points. A gradually increasing, horizontal force is applied perpendicular to the rod at one end. If the coefficient of friction is μ, find the point about which the rod starts to turn, and show that the value of the force when this happens is

$$\mu P(\sqrt{2} - 1).$$

[Lond. *GCE*(*S*) 1959]

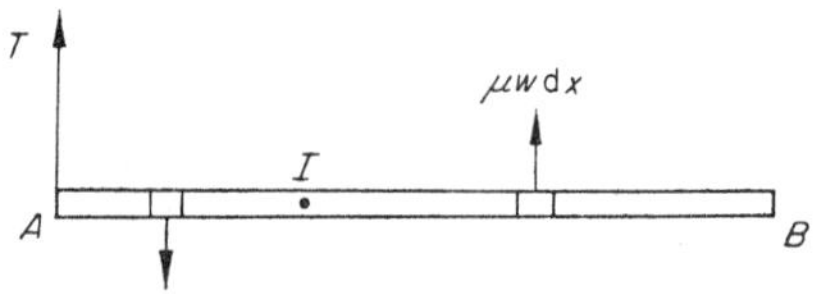

Fig. 52

The Fig. 52 shows the horizontal forces on the rod AB which is acted upon by a gradually increasing force T at the end A. As the rod is about to turn, an element of length dx will experience a frictional force which is μ times the normal reaction on the element. Hence the friction on the element $\mu\omega dx$ where $\omega =$ the weight per unit length $= P/2l$. Suppose the rod turns about the point I. Then it may be seen that I should lie on the line AB, in order that the friction may balance T. Further, I should lie between A and B, for when moments are taken about A, the moments about A of the friction should vanish, and therefore the force of friction should be opposite to T on the part AI of the rod and parallel to T on the part IB.

If $AI = b$, moments about I gives

$$\int_0^b \mu\omega x\mathrm{d}x = \int_b^{2l} \mu\omega x\mathrm{d}x,$$

or

$$\tfrac{1}{2}b^2 = \tfrac{1}{2}(4l^2 - b^2), \text{ i.e. } b = l\sqrt{2}.$$

Further, when the rod is on the point of turning,

$$T = \int_0^b \mu\omega\mathrm{d}x - \int_b^{2l} \mu\omega\mathrm{d}x$$

$$= \mu\omega b - \mu\omega(2l - b) = \mu P(\sqrt{2} - 1).$$

3.4. Rough or rigid hinges or joints

In Chapter II §2.1 there was considered the reaction between two bodies which are jointed together at a smooth hinge which allows a freedom of rotation of each body about the hinge. It was seen that the reaction on the body A due to the hinge is made up of a system of normal reactions which all pass through the centre of the hinge and are therefore equivalent to a single force at the hinge. The reaction on the body B is equal and opposite to the reaction on A.

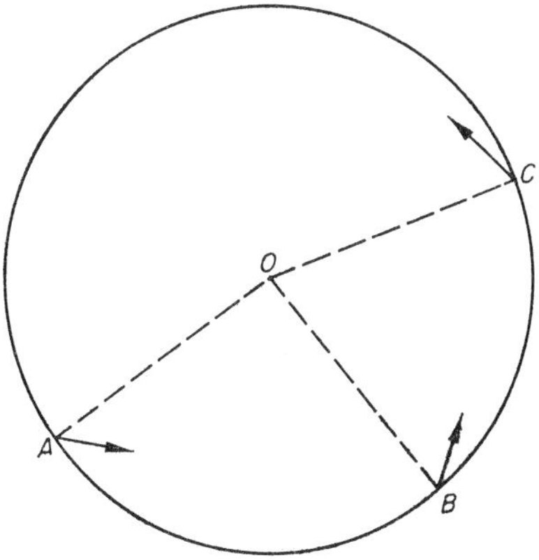

Fig. 53

If the hinge is rough, the reaction at each point of contact will not necessarily be along the normal to the surface of contact, there being in general a frictional component of the reaction (Fig. 53). Each force may however be transferred to pass through the centre O by the introduction of a couple. Hence the system is equivalent to a number of forces at O and a number of couples. These may be compounded into a single force at O and a single couple.

Hence if two bodies A and B are joined together by a rough enough hinge or joint so that relative motion about the hinge or joint does not take place, the reaction on the body A is a force $\mathbf{R}$ at the hinge and a couple $\mathbf{G}$, and the reaction at the hinge on the body B is the force $-\mathbf{R}$ at the hinge and the couple $-\mathbf{G}$. The couple $\mathbf{G}$ in this case is called a friction couple.

Example. Two uniform rods AB, BC, of lengths $2a$ and $2b$ respectively, and each of weight ω per unit length, are rigidly jointed at their ends B so that ABC is a right angle. If the rods are placed in a vertical plane on a smooth horizontal table, determine the reaction at the joint B.

Suppose that the reaction at B on the rod BC consists of force components X, Y and couple G as shown in Fig. 54. The action of the joint on the rod AB will be equal and opposite. The table

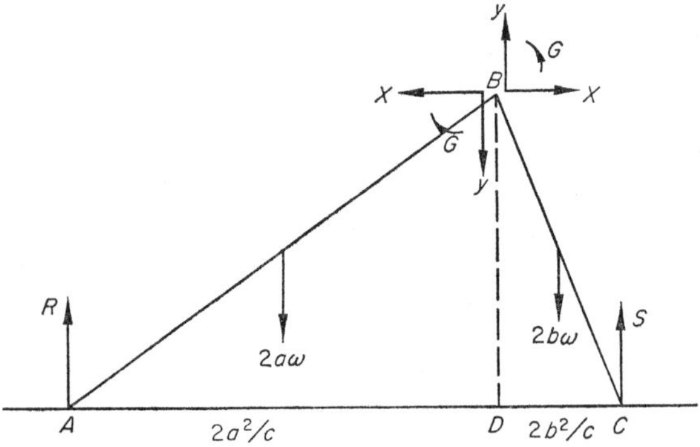

Fig. 54

being smooth, the reactions at A and C are vertical. Suppose that these reactions are R and S respectively.

Let $c = \sqrt{(a^2 + b^2)}$. Then $AC = 2c$, $AD = 2a^2/c$, $CD = 2b^2/c$. Considering the equilibrium of the two rods taken together, resolving vertically

$$R + S = 2(a + b)\,\omega,$$

and taking moments about A

$$S \,.\, 2c = 2b\omega(2c - b^2/c) + 2a\omega \,.\, a^2/c.$$

Hence

$$S = \omega(a^3 + b^3 + 2a^2b)/c^2$$

and

$$R = \omega(a^3 + b^3 + 2ab^2)/c^2.$$

Considering the equilibrium of the rod AB alone, resolving horizontally

$$X = 0;$$

resolving vertically

$$Y = R - 2a\omega = \omega(b^3 - a^3)/(a^2 + b^2);$$

taking moments about B

$$\begin{aligned} G &= 2a\omega \,.\, a^2/c - R \,.\, 2a^2/c \\ &= -\,2\omega(a + b)\,a^2b^2/(a^2 + b^2)^{3/2}. \end{aligned}$$

Thus X, Y and G are determined.

Exercises 3

1. A rough uniform circular cylinder of radius $a \tan \alpha$ and weight W' rests with one generator in contact with a rough horizontal plane. A rough uniform rod, of length a and weight W, rests with one end on the plane and the other end on the cylinder, so that the rod is a tangent to the cylinder. The vertical plane containing the rod bisects the axis of the cylinder perpendicularly. The angle of friction at all contacts is λ. Find all the reactions, and show that the least possible value of λ is α. [Oxf. *GCE*(*S*) 1955]

2. A uniform solid cube is placed on a rough plane inclined to the horizontal at an angle α $(< \frac{1}{4}\pi)$ so that four of its edges are horizontal. The coefficient of friction is $\mu(\tan \alpha < \mu < \cot \alpha)$. A steadily increasing horizontal force **F** is applied at the mid-point of the lower horizontal edge of the face opposite to the face in contact with the plane. The line of action of the force is in the vertical

plane containing the centre of the cube, and the force tends to push the cube up the plane. Prove that the cube begins to slide (if it has not already begun to tilt) when

$$F = W(\sin \alpha + \mu \cos \alpha)/(\cos \alpha - \mu \sin \alpha).$$

Prove that the cube begins to tilt (if it has not already begun to slide) when $F = \frac{1}{2}W(\sin \alpha + \cos \alpha)/(\cos \alpha - \sin \alpha)$. Hence prove that it tilts first or slides first according as

$$\mu \gtrless \frac{2t^2 - t + 1}{t^2 - t + 2}$$

where $t = \tan \alpha$. [Oxf. *GCE*(*S*) 1956]

3. Two planes intersect in a horizontal line l and are inclined at acute angles α, and $\beta (\alpha > \beta)$ to the horizontal, in opposite senses. A rough uniform cylinder, of radius a and weight W, rests with its curved surface touching the planes and its axis parallel to l. A gradually increasing couple C is applied to the cylinder about its axis, in the sense indicated in the diagram, which represents a cross-section. The angle of friction at all points of contact is λ. If $\lambda < \beta$ prove that the cylinder is on the point of moving when

$$C = Wa \sin \lambda \operatorname{cosec} (\alpha + \beta)[\sin (\alpha + \lambda) + \sin (\beta - \lambda)].$$

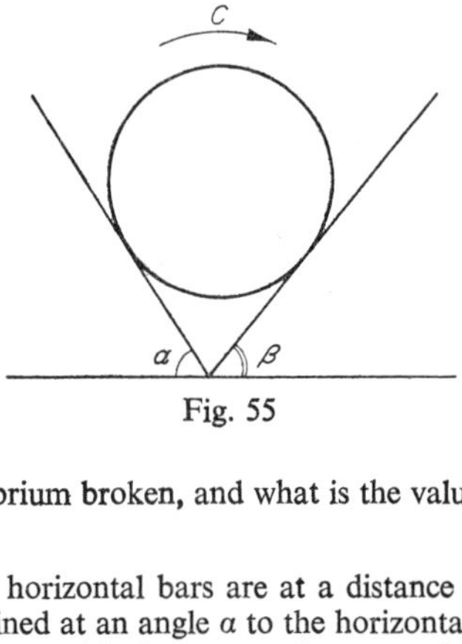

Fig. 55

If $\lambda > \beta$, how is equilibrium broken, and what is the value of C at this instant? [Oxf. *GCE*(*S*) 1957]

4. Two thin parallel horizontal bars are at a distance a apart, and the plane containing them is inclined at an angle α to the horizontal. A thin uniform rod, of length l, rests in contact with the bars, under one and above the other, and is perpendicular to both. If the coefficient of friction between the rod and each bar is μ, prove that the least possible value of μ is

$$a \tan \alpha/(l - a).$$

[Oxf. *GCE*(*S*) 1958]

5. A uniform solid hemisphere rests with its curved surface in contact with a rough horizontal plane. A point on the rim is then pulled by a horizontal force

in a vertical plane through the centre of the hemisphere. If the force is gradually increased and if μ is the coefficient of friction, prove that slipping will occur when the hemisphere has turned through an angle

$$\sin^{-1}\left(\frac{8\mu}{3+8\mu}\right).$$

[Camb. *GCE(S)* 1953]

6. Two particles of weights W_1 and W_2 are connected by a light string and placed on a rough table for which the coefficient of friction is μ. A force P which is less than $\mu(W_1 + W_2)$ is applied to W_1 in a direction directly away from W_2 and its direction is gradually turned in the horizontal plane. It is given that both particles will slip when the direction of P has turned through an angle θ. Prove that

$$\cos\theta = \frac{\mu^2(W_2^2 - W_1^2) + P^2}{2\mu W_2 P}.$$

[Oxf. *I* 1951]

7. A cotton reel rests with its axis horizontal on a rough plane inclined to the horizontal at an angle α. The coefficient of friction between the plane and the reel is μ, where $\tan\alpha > \mu$. The reel is supported by a thread wrapped round it and coming off it in the vertical plane through its centre of gravity at an angle θ to the horizontal. If a is the radius of each end of the reel and b the radius of the middle part, prove that the greatest value of θ consistent with equilibrium is given by

$$\cos\theta = \frac{b}{a}\left(\frac{\sin\alpha}{\mu} - \cos\alpha\right).$$

[Camb. *GCE(S)* 1955]

8. A light rod of length a rests horizontally with its ends on two equally rough fixed planes inclined at angles α and β to the horizontal, the vertical plane containing the rod being at right angles to the line of intersection of the planes. Prove that the length of that part of the rod on which a weight can be placed without disturbing the equilibrium is

$$a\frac{\sin 2\lambda\cos(\alpha-\beta)}{\sin(\alpha+\beta)}$$

where λ is the angle of friction between the rod and a plane.

[Lond. *GCE(S)* 1958]

9. A rough hemisphere of radius a is fixed with its base in contact with level ground. A large, thin, uniform lamina of weight W rests in equilibrium on top of the hemisphere, the angle of friction between the lamina and the hemisphere being λ. Show that the area of the lamina, over which a man of weight w could walk slowly is

$$\pi[a\lambda(W+w)/w]^2.$$

[Lond. *GCE(S)* 1959]

10. A uniform rigid ladder of weight w rests with one end on horizontal ground and the other against a vertical wall, the vertical plane through the ladder

being perpendicular to the wall. The angles of friction at the lower and upper ends are respectively α and β, and the angle made by the ladder with the ground is $\theta(< \frac{1}{2}\pi - \alpha)$. A man of weight W' stands on the lower end and another man, of weight W, slowly ascends the ladder. Show that the second man can reach the top of the ladder before it slips if

$$\frac{2W' + w}{2W + w} \frac{\cos \beta \cos (\alpha + \theta)}{\sin \alpha \sin (\beta + \theta)}.$$

[Lond. *G* 1957]

11. A uniform rod is placed with one end on the floor and the other against a vertical wall, so that the vertical plane containing the rod is perpendicular to the wall. The angles of friction at both contacts are each equal to λ. Show that the rod can rest in equilibrium if its angle of inclination θ to the vertical is less than 2λ.

When $\lambda = \tan^{-1}(2/3)$ and the rod is resting with $\theta = \tan^{-1}(3/4)$, a gradually increasing upward force **P** is applied to the lower end of the rod in the vertical plane through the rod in a direction making an angle α (less than θ and in the same sense as θ) with the upward vertical. Show that equilibrium will be broken in the case

(*a*) $\tan \alpha < 3/10$ by the rod slipping down
(*b*) $3/10 < \tan \alpha < \frac{1}{2}$ by the lower end of the rod rising off the ground
(*c*) $\tan \alpha > \frac{1}{2}$, by the rod slipping upwards.

[Ceylon *S* 1943]

12. The ends A, B of a uniform heavy rod (length $a\sqrt{2}$) are attached to rings which can slide along a rough circular wire (of radius a) in a vertical plane. The coefficient of friction between rings and wire is $\mu = \tan \phi$. Show that the greatest inclination of the rod to the horizontal, when in equilibrium, is 2ϕ.

[Camb. *MT* 1928]

13. A uniform circular cylinder of radius a and weight W rests symmetrically on two fixed equally rough planes each inclined at an angle α to the horizontal, the axis of the cylinder being above and parallel to the line of intersection of the planes.

If μ is the coefficient of friction, prove that the least couple required to rotate the cylinder about its axis is

$$\frac{\mu W a \sec \alpha}{1 + \mu^2}.$$

[Lond. *GCE*(*S*) 1958]

14. Two uniform cubical blocks, each of weight W, are placed symmetrically upon a horizontal table with a pair of parallel vertical plane faces which are nearest at a distance $2x$ apart. Two uniform smooth circular cylinders, each of weight w and radius a, rest with their axes horizontal and parallel to the above plane faces of the blocks so that the lower cylinder is in contact with the table and the face of one block while the upper cylinder rests upon the lower and is in

contact with the plane face of the second block. If μ is the coefficient of friction between the blocks and the table show that the greatest value x can have if the blocks do not slide is

$$a\left\{1+\frac{\mu W}{\sqrt{(w^2+\mu^2W^2)}}\right\}.$$

[Lond. *G* 1934]

15. Two ladders of the same length and negligible weight are smoothly hinged together at their upper ends, and rest upon the ground with an angle 2α between them. They are prevented from slipping by a horizontal rope joining their mid-points. Show that if a man of weight W steps upon the ladders at their vertex, the tension in the rope remains zero if α is less than λ, the angle of friction with the ground, and becomes

$$W(\tan\alpha-\tan\lambda)$$

if α is greater than λ. [Camb. *NS* 1945]

16. A uniform hemisphere is placed with its plane base resting on a rough inclined plane of angle α and is just on the point of slipping. A gradually increasing force which acts in a direction up the plane parallel to a line of greatest slope is then applied to the hemisphere at the point furthest from the plane. Show that the hemisphere will begin to slide if $\tan\alpha$ is less than 8/13, and that otherwise it will tilt. [Camb. *MT* 1956]

17. A uniform plank of length $2l$ rests, with one end on the ground, against a smooth horizontal bar at height h above the ground. If the plank is at right angles to the bar and makes an angle θ with the vertical, prove that

$$\mu h \geqslant l\sin\theta\cos\theta\,(\cos\theta+\mu\sin\theta),$$

where μ is the coefficient of friction with the ground. Taking μ to be 1, find the least height at which the bar must be placed if it is to be used in this way for stacking planks 20 ft long inclined at angles up to 30° with the vertical.

[Camb. *NS* 1946]

18. A heavy table with a square uniform top of side $2a$ has a leg at each corner which is perpendicular to the top and of length h. The table stands on a rough floor and the coefficient of friction between the floor and the legs is μ. Show that if a steadily increasing horizontal force is applied to the top of the table at the mid-point of one of the sides in a direction perpendicular to the side, then static equilibrium will be broken by sliding of the table if $\mu < a/h$ and by toppling of the table if $\mu > a/h$. [Camb. *PNS* 1946]

19. A rough square board, of edge $2l$ and weight W, is freely hinged at its lower edge, which is horizontal, to a rough wall, with which the board makes an angle θ as shown in the diagram (Fig. 56). A light circular cylinder of radius a rests in contact with the board and the wall, and the coefficient of friction at both lines of contact is μ. Equilibrium is maintained by a force T which acts at the mid-point of the upper edge of the board and is perpendicular to the wall. If $\mu > \tan\frac{1}{2}\theta$, show that the cylinder will not slip upwards for any value of T, however great.

If $\mu > \tan \frac{1}{2}\theta$ and $T > \frac{1}{2}W \tan \theta$, find the magnitude of the reaction at the hinge.

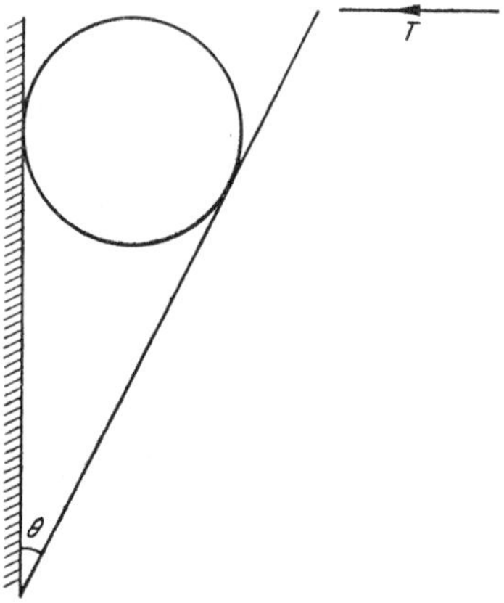

Fig. 56

[Camb. *MT* 1947]

20. Two uniform solid circular cylinders, each of weight w and radius a, lie on a horizontal plane with their axes parallel and at a distance $4a \sin 2\alpha$ apart $(\pi/12 < \alpha < \pi/4)$. A light sphere of radius a rests on the cylinders, and a force W, gradually increasing from zero, is applied to the sphere vertically downwards through its centre. The coefficient of friction between the sphere and either cylinder is μ_1, and the coefficient of friction between either cylinder and the plane is μ_2. Prove that, if μ_1 and μ_2 are both greater than $\tan \alpha$, no slipping occurs for any value of W.

If $\mu_1 = 2 \tan \alpha$ and $\mu_2 = \frac{1}{2} \tan \alpha$, prove that equilibrium is broken when W exceeds $2w$, and explain how the equilibrium is broken.

[Camb. *MT* 1948]

21. Two uniform rough spheres S_B, S_C, of equal mass but unequal size, have centres B, C respectively and rest (without touching each other) on a rough horizontal table. The coefficients of friction between the table and S_B, S_C are μ_B, μ_C respectively. A third uniform rough sphere S_A, also of the same mass, rests supported by both spheres without touching the table; its centre A is in the vertical plane which contains B and C. This sphere has coefficients of friction ν_B, ν_C with S_B, S_C respectively. Show that for equilibrium to be maintained

$$\nu_B \geqslant \tan \beta, \qquad \nu_C \geqslant \tan \gamma,$$

where the lines BA, CA make angles 2β, 2γ respectively with the upward vertical.

If the friction between the top sphere and both lower spheres is limiting, show that the sphere S_B is tending to roll away rather than slide if

$$\frac{1}{\mu_B} < \frac{2}{\nu_B} + \frac{1}{\nu_C}.$$

[Oxf. *I* 1956]

22. Two uniform planks of lengths l_1, l_2 ($l_1 > l_2$) and of weights W_1, W_2 are hinged together at one end and the other ends rest on a rough horizontal plane, the coefficient of friction between the planks and plane being μ. The planks stand at angles α_1, α_2 with the vertical and are on the same side of the vertical line through the hinge. Show that the condition for equilibrium is

$$\mu[W_1(\cot \alpha_2 - 2 \cot \alpha_1) - W_2 \cot \alpha_1] > W_1 + W_2.$$

[Camb. *PNS* 1945]

23. A thin straight rod, AB, not necessarily uniform, with centre of gravity G rests in a horizontal position with its ends supported by two rough horizontal rails. The coefficients of friction at A and B are μ_a and μ_b. A gradually increasing horizontal force is applied at a point P of the rod in a direction perpendicular to that of the rod. Prove that slipping takes place at A or B first according as

$$\frac{\mu_a}{\mu_b} \lessgtr \frac{AG}{GB} \cdot \frac{PB}{AP}.$$

[Camb. *MT* 1952]

24. A car of wheel base l is to be parked on a hill of inclination α to the horizontal. Only the rear wheel brakes are operative, the front wheels being free to rotate and unable to communicate forward forces to the car. The centre of gravity is midway between the axles, a distance h above the ground. Show that the coefficient of friction between the rear wheels and the ground must exceed

$$(\tfrac{1}{2} \cot \alpha + h/l)^{-1}.$$

[Camb. *NS* 1952]

25. A set of rectangular axes Oxy is drawn on a rough horizontal table. A uniform rod AB of weight w and length $2a$ lies on the table along the x-axis between the points $(-a, O)$ and (a, O) pressing uniformly on the table all along its length and μ is the coefficient of limiting friction between the rod and the table. A horizontal force whose components are $n\mu w$, $m\mu w$ acts at the end $B(a, O)$ of the rod and is just sufficient to turn the rod about $(-a, 2a \cot \alpha)$ of the table. Prove that

$$n = \tfrac{1}{2} \cot \alpha \log \frac{1 + \sin \alpha}{1 - \sin \alpha}, \qquad m = \operatorname{cosec} \alpha - \cot \alpha$$

and that

$$\tan \alpha = (1 - n)/m.$$

[Lond. *S* 1940]

26. A uniform rod of weight W and length $2l$ rests in equilibrium with the end A on a horizontal floor and the end B against a vertical wall, the vertical

plane through the rod being normal to the wall. If the coefficient of friction between rod and floor is μ and between rod and wall is μ', and θ is the inclination of the rod to the horizontal, show that

$$\tan\theta \geqslant \frac{1-\mu\mu'}{2\mu}.$$

A gradually increasing force P is applied at B vertically downwards. Show that slipping does not take place if $\mu > \cot\theta$. If $\mu < \cot\theta$, determine the value of P when slipping commences. [*CCS*(*L*) 1952]

27. A uniform rod of weight W rests horizontally on two equally rough planes placed opposite to each other at 45° to the horizon, the vertical plane containing the rod being perpendicular to the line of intersection of the two planes. A gradually increasing downward force P is applied vertically to a point of quadrisection of the rod. Show that if μ, the coefficient of friction at each contact, is less than $2-\sqrt{3}$, the rod will begin to slip when P attains a certain value, and determine this value.

Discuss the case

$$\mu > 2-\sqrt{3}.$$

[*CCS*(*L*) 1949]

28. A uniform disc of mass M and radius a rests on a rough horizontal table. Show that the couple required to turn it about its axis is $\frac{2}{3}\mu Ma$, where μ is the coefficient of friction.

Find the couple required to turn a uniform solid hemisphere about its axis when it rests with its plane face on the table. [*CCS*(*L*) 1960]

29. A uniform triangular plate has three studs at the corners and the plate stands horizontally with the three studs in contact with a rough horizontal plane. A gradually increasing couple is applied to the plate in its own plane. If no angle of the triangle exceeds 120° and all contacts are equally rough, show that the plate will begin to turn about a point inside the triangle, and determine the position of this point.

Prove also that, if the angle at one of the vertices of the triangle exceeds 120°, the plate will begin to turn about the vertex. [Lond. *S* 1949]

Chapter 4

More Problems of Equilibrium

THIS chapter considers some further problems of equilibrium, and includes three dimensional problems or difficult two-dimensional cases. The principles to be applied are the same as those discussed in Chapters 1 to 3. For a three-dimensional system the number of independent equations of equilibrium that may be written is in general six, of which up to three may be obtained by resolving the forces on the system along three directions, and the rest are equations of moments.

Example 1. A gipsy tripod is formed of three light rods OA, OB, OC of lengths l_1, l_2, l_3 which are rigidly connected at O. The feet A, B, C of the rods rest on a rough horizontal plane, the angles at O being such that the centroid of the triangle ABC is vertically below O. A weight W is supported from O. If T_1, T_2, T_3 are the thrusts in OA, OB, OC respectively, prove that

$$\frac{T_1}{l_1} = \frac{T_2}{l_2} = \frac{T_3}{l_3} = \frac{W}{3OG}$$

where $9OG^2 = 3(l_1^2 + l_2^2 + l_3^2) - (a^2 + b^2 + c^2)$ and a, b, c are the sides of the triangle ABC. [Oxf. *I* 1951]

The rod OA being light, it is acted upon by forces at O and A only. Hence these forces must be along OA. If $\mathbf{T}_1$ denotes the thrust in the rod OA, then the reaction at A acts along AO and is of magnitude T_1. Similarly the reactions at B and C are $\mathbf{T}_2$ and $\mathbf{T}_3$ along BO and CO respectively. Considering the equilibrium of the tripod and the weight at O, the forces acting upon it are the reactions at A, B, C and the weight $\mathbf{W}$. These four forces meet in a point, and

$$\mathbf{T}_1 + \mathbf{T}_2 + \mathbf{T}_3 + \mathbf{W} = \mathbf{O}. \tag{i}$$

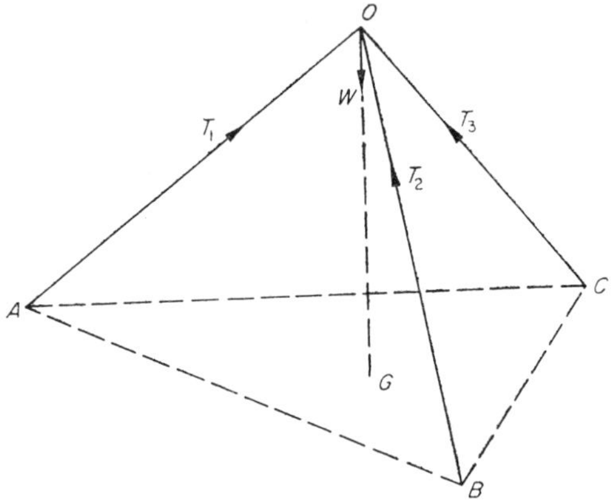

Fig. 57

By applying Leibniz's theorem

$$\mathbf{T}_1 + \mathbf{T}_2 + \mathbf{T}_3 = \frac{T_1}{l_1}\overrightarrow{AO} + \frac{T_2}{l_2}\overrightarrow{BO} + \frac{T_3}{l_3}\overrightarrow{CO}$$

$$= \left(\frac{T_1}{l_1} + \frac{T_2}{l_2} + \frac{T_3}{l_3}\right)\overrightarrow{GO} \tag{ii}$$

where G is the centroid of masses proportional to T_1/l_1, T_2/l_2, T_3/l_3 at A, B, C respectively.

From (i) and (ii),

$$\frac{T_1}{l_1} + \frac{T_2}{l_2} + \frac{T_3}{l_3} = \frac{W}{OG}. \tag{iii}$$

Further because G is given as the centroid of the triangle, and because the centroid of a triangle is the same as that of three equal masses at the vertex

$$\frac{T_1}{l_1} = \frac{T_2}{l_2} = \frac{T_3}{l_3}.$$

Each of these expressions is a third of their sum which is

$$\frac{1}{3}\left(\frac{T_1}{l_1}+\frac{T_2}{l_2}+\frac{T_3}{l_3}\right)=\frac{1}{3}\,.\;W/OG.$$

Hence

$$\frac{T_1}{l_1}=\frac{T_2}{l_2}=\frac{T_3}{l_3}=\frac{W}{3OG}. \qquad \text{(iv)}$$

Again suppose

$$\overrightarrow{OA}=\mathbf{l}_1, \qquad \overrightarrow{OB}=\mathbf{l}_2, \qquad \overrightarrow{OC}=\mathbf{l}_3, \qquad \overrightarrow{OG}=\mathbf{g}.$$

Then

$$\overrightarrow{BC}=\mathbf{l}_3-\mathbf{l}_2, \qquad \overrightarrow{CA}=\mathbf{l}_1-\mathbf{l}_3, \qquad \overrightarrow{AB}=\mathbf{l}_2-\mathbf{l}_1$$

Therefore

$$\begin{aligned} a^2+b^2+c^2 &= (\mathbf{l}_3-\mathbf{l}_2)^2+(\mathbf{l}_1-\mathbf{l}_3)^2+(\mathbf{l}_2-\mathbf{l}_1)^2 \\ &= 2(\mathbf{l}_1^2+\mathbf{l}_2^2+\mathbf{l}_3^2-\mathbf{l}_2\,.\,\mathbf{l}_3-\mathbf{l}_3\,.\,\mathbf{l}_1-\mathbf{l}_1\,.\,\mathbf{l}_2). \qquad \text{(v)} \end{aligned}$$

Also

$$\mathbf{g}=\tfrac{1}{3}(\mathbf{l}_1+\mathbf{l}_2+\mathbf{l}_3),$$

and

$$\begin{aligned} 9OG^2=(3\mathbf{g})^2 &= (\mathbf{l}_1+\mathbf{l}_2+\mathbf{l}_3)^2 \\ &= \mathbf{l}_1^2+\mathbf{l}_2^2+\mathbf{l}_3^2+2(\mathbf{l}_2\,.\,\mathbf{l}_3+\mathbf{l}_3\,.\,\mathbf{l}_1+\mathbf{l}_1\,.\,\mathbf{l}_2). \qquad \text{(vi)} \end{aligned}$$

Adding (v) and (vi),

$$a^2+b^2+c^2+9\,OG^2=3(l_1^2+l_2^2+l_3^2)$$

giving the required result.

Example 2. If forces $\mathbf{F}_1$, $\mathbf{F}_2$, ... $\mathbf{F}_p$ acting at a point O are in equilibrium, and any plane not passing through O intersects their lines of action at points L_1, L_2, ... L_p, then

$$\Sigma\,\frac{k_r F_r}{OL_r}=O, \qquad \text{(i)}$$

where $k_r=+1$ if $\mathbf{F}_r$ and OL_r are in the same sense, and $k_r=-1$ otherwise.

Use this theorem to establish the result (iv) of Example 1 above.

This theorem is an extension to three dimensional forces of the theorem of Example 4 of Chapter 1 which applied to coplanar forces.

The same method of proof may be followed. Alternatively, one may in both cases obtain the result by resolving along the direction ON where N is the foot of the perpendicular from O on to the plane. The component of the force $\mathbf{F}_r$ is $F_r \cos \theta_r$ (where θ_r is the angle between ON and $\mathbf{F}_r$) which has the value $F_r k_r ON/OL_r$. Hence resolving all the forces and dividing by ON, there is obtained

$$\sum k_r F_r / OL_r = O.$$

To apply this result to the problem of the tripod, draw through the point A the plane parallel to the plane formed by OB and OC (Fig. 58). Suppose that this plane through A intersects OG produced in H. The intersections of OB and OC with this plane are points at infinity. Applying the equation (i) to this plane,

$$T_1 \frac{(-1)}{OA} + T_2 \frac{(-1)}{a} + T_3 \frac{(-1)}{a} + W \frac{(+1)}{OH} = 0.$$

Hence

$$\frac{T_1}{l_1} = \frac{W}{OH}.$$

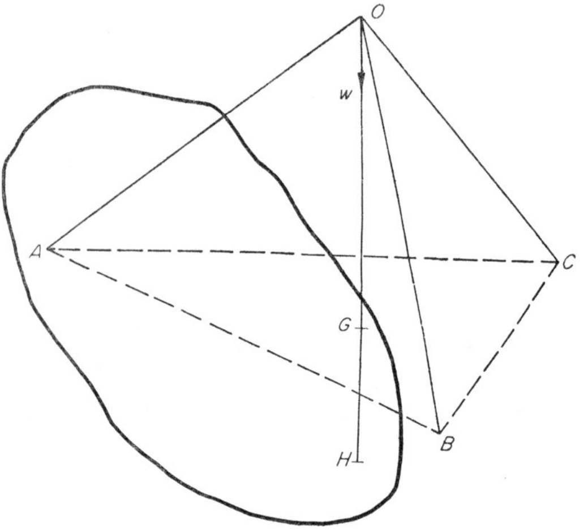

Fig. 58

Since AH is in a plane parallel to OB and OC, the position vector $\overrightarrow{HO}$ will be of the form $\mathbf{l}_1 + \lambda\mathbf{l}_2 + \mu\mathbf{l}_3$ where λ, μ are scalar multipliers and $\mathbf{l}_1$, $\mathbf{l}_2$, $\mathbf{l}_3$ are as in Example 1. But since G lies on OH, and position vector of G is $\frac{1}{3}(\mathbf{l}_1 + \mathbf{l}_2 + \mathbf{l}_3)$, one obtains that the position vector of H is $\mathbf{l}_1 + \mathbf{l}_2 + \mathbf{l}_3$. Hence $OH = 3\ OG$, and $T_1/l_1 = W/3\ OG$. By symmetry the remaining equations may also be obtained.

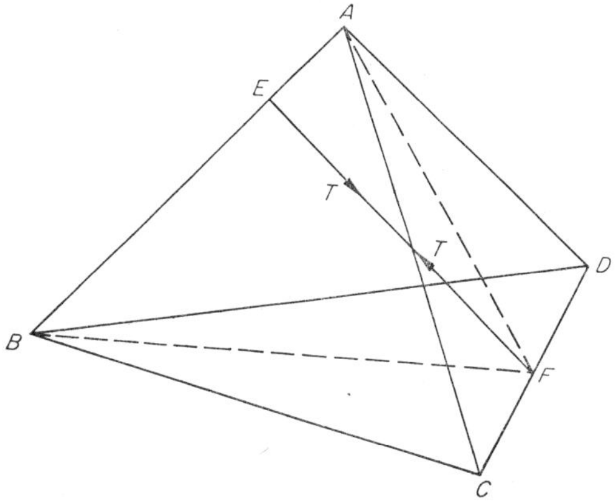

Fig. 59

Example 3. A light tetrahedral framework $ABCD$ consists of six rods, smoothly jointed three by three at A, B, C and D. A light string joins a point E in AB to a point F in CD and is in a state of tension T. Determine the reactions at A and B on the rod AB.

Show that the stress in the rod AC is

$$\frac{T}{EF} \cdot \frac{BE\ .\ DF}{AB\ .\ CD}\ .\ AC.$$

The rods AC, AD, BC, BD are light rods and are acted upon by forces only at their ends. Hence they exert stresses along the rods. Considering the equilibrium of the rod AB, the forces acting upon it are:

(i) at the end A, the stress along CA and the stress along DA;
(ii) at the end B, the stresses along CB and DB;
(iii) the tension T in the string EF.

The resultant of the two forces at A is a force in the plane ACD, and may be seen to lie along FA (for example, by taking moments about the line BF for the forces acting upon AB which are in equilibrium). Suppose this resultant force is $\lambda\overrightarrow{FA}$. Again, considering in the same way the forces at B, they may be seen to have a resultant along FB, $\mu\overrightarrow{FB}$ say. The equilibrium of the forces $\lambda\overrightarrow{FA}$, $\mu\overrightarrow{FB}$ and T shows that T is the resultant of $\lambda\overrightarrow{AF}$ and $\mu\overrightarrow{BF}$. Hence

$$\lambda\overrightarrow{AF} + \mu\overrightarrow{BF} = \mathbf{T} = \frac{T}{EF}\overrightarrow{EF}$$

where

$$\frac{\lambda}{BE} = \frac{\mu}{EA} = \frac{\lambda + \mu}{AB} = \frac{T/EF}{AB}.$$

Hence the reactions at A and B are

$$\frac{T}{EF} \cdot \frac{BE}{AB}\overrightarrow{FA} \text{ and } \frac{T}{EF} \cdot \frac{EA}{AB}\overrightarrow{FB} \text{ respectively.}$$

Also the reaction at A is the resultant of the stress along CA and the stress along DA. If these stresses are denoted by $\alpha\overrightarrow{CA}$, $\beta\overrightarrow{DA}$ respectively,

$$\frac{\alpha}{DF} = \frac{\beta}{FC} = \frac{\alpha + \beta}{CD} = \frac{\lambda}{CD}.$$

Hence the stress along CA is $\alpha \,.\, CA = \lambda(DF/CD)\, CA$, which is

$$\frac{T}{EF} \cdot \frac{BE}{AB} \cdot \frac{DF}{CD}\overrightarrow{CA}.$$

Example 4. Two smooth planes intersect in a horizontal line and are inclined at the same angle $90 - \alpha$ to the vertical. A uniform rod of weight W and length $2a$ is placed between the planes in a horizontal position making an angle θ with their line of intersection. Show that the horizontal couple required to maintain equilibrium is

$$Wa \cos\theta \tan\alpha.$$

Let $\mathbf{i}$, $\mathbf{j}$, $\mathbf{k}$ denote three mutually perpendicular unit vectors such that $\mathbf{k}$ is in the upward vertical direction, $\mathbf{j}$ is parallel to the line of intersection of the planes, and **i** is along a horizontal line and is perpendicular to **i** and **j**. If O is the mid-point of the rod,

$$\overrightarrow{OB} = a(\sin\theta\,\mathbf{i} + \cos\theta\,\mathbf{j}) = \mathbf{r},\ \text{say}$$
$$\overrightarrow{OA} = -\mathbf{r}.$$

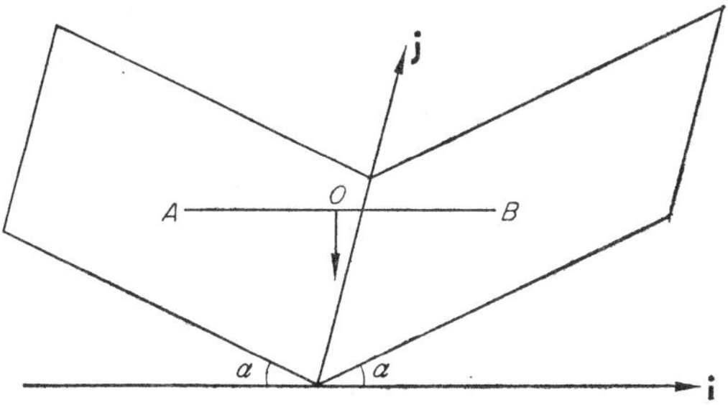

Fig. 60

The forces acting upon the rod are

(i) the weight $-W\mathbf{k}$ at O;

(ii) the reaction **R** at A; this is normal to the plane, and the unit vector along the normal is $\sin\alpha\,\mathbf{i} + \cos\alpha\,\mathbf{k}$;

(iii) the reaction **S** at B. This acts in the direction along which the unit vector is $-\sin\alpha\,\mathbf{i} + \cos\alpha\,\mathbf{k}$.

These forces when reduced to act at the origin are equivalent to a force **F** and couple **G** where

$$\begin{aligned}\mathbf{F} &= -W\mathbf{k} + R(\sin\alpha\,\mathbf{i} + \cos\alpha\,\mathbf{k}) + S(-\sin\alpha\,\mathbf{i} + \cos\alpha\,\mathbf{k})\\ &= (R - S)\sin\alpha\,\mathbf{i} + \{(R + S)\cos\alpha - W\}\,\mathbf{k},\\ \mathbf{G} &= \mathbf{r} \times R(\sin\alpha\,\mathbf{i} + \cos\alpha\,\mathbf{k}) - \mathbf{r} \times S(-\sin\alpha\,\mathbf{i} + \cos\alpha\,\mathbf{k})\\ &= \mathbf{r} \times \mathbf{i}(R + S)\sin\alpha + \mathbf{r} \times \mathbf{k}(R - S)\cos\alpha.\end{aligned}$$

R and **S** are passive forces which will if possible preserve equilibrium. When $R = S = \frac{1}{2}W\sec\alpha$,

$$\begin{aligned}\mathbf{F} = \mathbf{O},\quad \mathbf{G} &= W\tan\alpha\mathbf{r} \times \mathbf{i} = W\tan\alpha(-a\cos\theta)\,\mathbf{k}\\ &= -Wa\cos\theta\tan\alpha\,\mathbf{k}.\end{aligned}$$

Hence if a couple of moment

$$Wa \cos \theta \tan \alpha$$

is applied about the vertical axis, then the force and couple components vanish, and the rod will be in equilibrium.

Example 5. A circular disc of weight W and radius a is suspended horizontally by a number (n) of vertical strings each of length l attached to points at equal intervals round its circumference. A horizontal couple applied to the disc turns it through an angle θ. Find the moment of the couple.

[Lond. *GCE*(*S*) 1958]

In Fig. 61, one of the strings is shown. Initially the string is in the position AB. The turning of the disc will have the effect of raising the level of the disc, so that after the rotation, the string will be in the position AB'. If after rotation the point of the disc vertically below A is D, then $B'\hat{C}'D = \theta$. Let $B'\hat{A}D = \phi$. Then from the

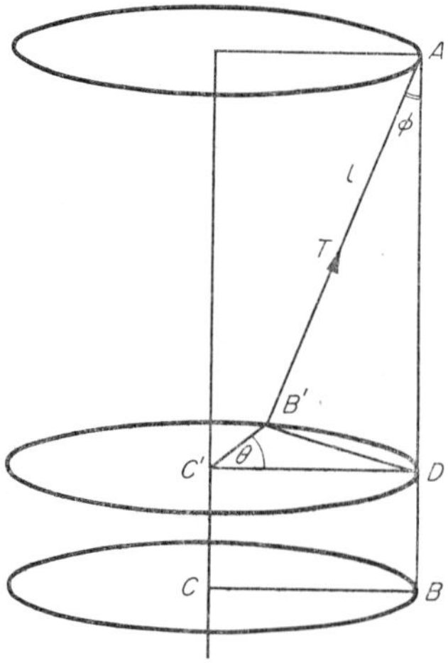

Fig. 61

figure,

$$l \sin \phi = B'D = 2a \sin \theta/2.$$

Considering the forces acting on the disc, since there are n strings, resolving vertically

$$nT \cos \phi = W.$$

If the couple applied to the disc is G, then this couple balances the effect of the sum of the horizontal components of T. Hence taking moments about C'

$$\begin{aligned} G &= nT \sin \phi \,.\, a \cos \theta/2. \\ &= Wa \tan \phi \cos \theta/2 \\ &= \frac{Wa^2 \sin \theta}{\sqrt{\left(l^2 - 4a^2 \sin^2 \dfrac{\theta}{2}\right)}}. \end{aligned}$$

Example 6. A uniform rod AB of length $2a$ free to move about its lower end A, which is fixed, rests in limiting equilibrium with its upper end B against a rough vertical wall. The length of the perpendicular AN from A on the wall is p, and the plane ANB makes an angle θ with the vertical. Supposing that the direction of friction at B is tangential to the circle of centre N and radius NB, show that the coefficient of friction between the rod and the wall is equal to

$$(1/p)(4a^2 - p^2)^{1/2} \tan \theta.$$

Take rectangular axes at A with z-axis vertically upwards, x-axis along AN and y-axis horizontal and perpendicular to x-and z-axes. Let the reaction at A have components (X, Y, Z), and let S be the normal reaction at B. Then the frictional component is μS in a direction along the wall and perpendicular to BN. Let

$$BN = b = \sqrt{(4a^2 - p^2)}.$$

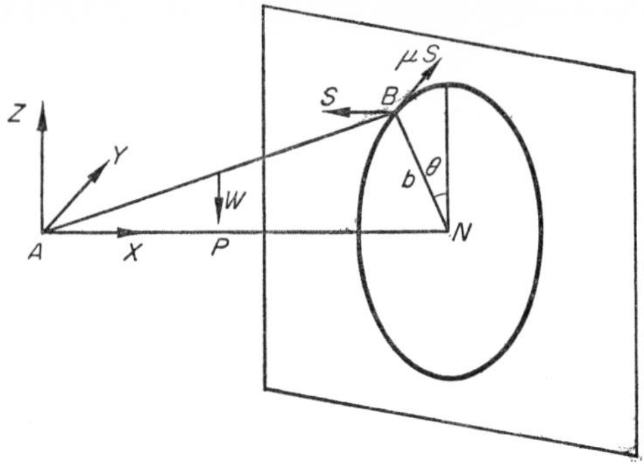

Fig. 62

The forces on the rod are

(i) (X, Y, Z) at $A(O, O, O)$
(ii) $(-S, -\mu S \cos\theta, \mu S \sin\theta)$ at $B(p, b\sin\theta, b\cos\theta)$
(iii) $(O, O, -W)$ at $G(\frac{1}{2}p, \frac{1}{2}b\sin\theta, \frac{1}{2}b\cos\theta)$.

Resolving along the directions of the three axes

$$X - S = O \qquad \text{(i)}$$

$$Y - \mu S\cos\theta = O \qquad \text{(ii)}$$

$$Z - \mu S\cos\theta - W = O. \qquad \text{(iii)}$$

Taking moments about the three axes,

$$\mu bS - \frac{Wb}{2}\sin\theta = O \qquad \text{(iv)}$$

$$-bS\cos\theta - \mu pS\sin\theta + \frac{pW}{2} = O \qquad \text{(v)}$$

$$-p\mu S\cos\theta + bS\sin\theta = O. \qquad \text{(vi)}$$

From (vi),

$$\mu = \frac{b}{p}\tan\theta.$$

From (iv),

[The above method illustrates the method of writing down the six independent equations of equilibrium. There are shorter alternative methods of obtaining the particular results given in the question.

It is of interest to observe that if the above supposition about the direction of the force of friction is not made, and the reaction at B is taken to have the form $(-S, F_1, F_2)$, there are positions of equilibrium with values of $\theta > \theta_1$ where $\tan \theta, = k$ and $k = \mu p\ {}_1b$. We consider the case $k < 1$. It may be shown that in a possible limiting position $\theta = \theta_2\ (> \theta_1)$ where $\sin \theta_2 = k$. From the equations of equilibrium it may be shown that

$$S = \frac{pW}{2b\,(1 - k^2)} \{\cos \theta + \sqrt{(k^2 - \sin^2 \theta)}\}$$

The maximum value of θ consistent with equilibrium is $\theta = \theta_2$ and in this position $F_2 = 0$. This result may also be seen geometrically by considering the cone of friction at B.

Thus the force of friction can suitably accomodate itself to keep the rod in equilibrium for values of θ in the range $\theta_2 \geq \theta \geq \theta_1$. Though these positions are unstable in a sense, nevertheless their existence is of interest. (Thanks are due to Dr. P. Noerdlinger for bringing this solution to the notice of the author).]

Example 7. $Oxyz$ are rectangular axes with Ox horizontal and Oz vertical. A smooth uniform rod, of length $2a$ and weight W, is smoothly hinged at the fixed end O and rests against a smooth fixed rail, whose equations are

$$z = y \tan \alpha, \qquad x = c,$$

being prevented from slipping by a force F acting at A parallel to

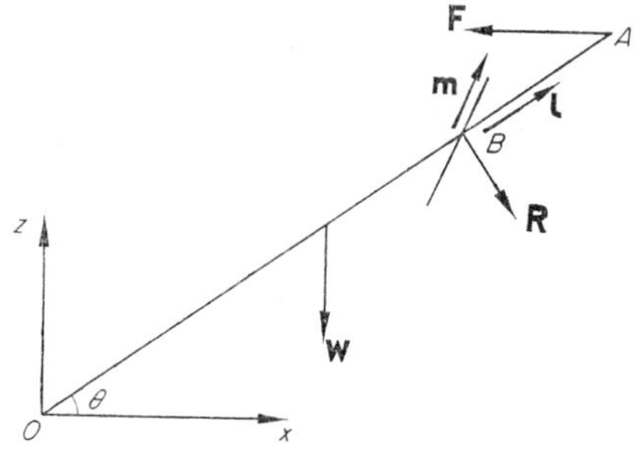

Fig. 63

xO. If the angle between OA and Ox is θ, show that

$$F = \tfrac{1}{2}W \sin \alpha \cot \theta.$$

Determine the magnitude of the reaction at the point of contact between the rod and the rail, and the components of the reaction at the hinge. Let **i**, **j**, **k** be unit vectors along the three axes, and let **l**, **m** be unit vectors along OA and along the rail respectively. From the equations of the rail

$$\mathbf{m} = \cos \alpha \, \mathbf{j} + \sin \alpha \, \mathbf{k}. \qquad \text{(i)}$$

If the point of contact between the rod and the rail is B, then $OB \cos \theta = c$, and B has coordinates $(c, y_1, y_1 \tan \alpha)$ where

$$OB^2 = c^2 + y_1^2 + y_1^2 \tan^2 \alpha = c^2 \sec^2 \theta.$$

Hence $y_1 = c \cos \alpha \tan \theta$, and

$$\mathbf{l} = \cos \theta \, \mathbf{i} + \sin \theta \cos \alpha \, \mathbf{j} + \sin \theta \sin \alpha \, \mathbf{k} \qquad \text{(ii)}$$

The position vector of B is $c \sec \theta \, \mathbf{l}$. The forces acting upon the rod are

(i) Reaction **S** at O

(ii) $-W\mathbf{k}$ at $a\mathbf{l}$

(iii) $-F\mathbf{i}$ at $2a\mathbf{l}$

(iv) Reaction **R** of the rail. **R** is in a direction perpendicular to the rod and to the rail, and unit vector along it is

$$\mathbf{n} = (\mathbf{l} \times \mathbf{m}) / |\, \mathbf{l} \times \mathbf{m} \,| \, .$$

It is seen that $\mathbf{l} \cdot \mathbf{m} = \sin \theta$,

$$\mathbf{l} \times \mathbf{m} = -\sin \alpha \cos \theta \, \mathbf{j} + \cos \theta \cos \alpha \, \mathbf{k},$$

$|\, \mathbf{l} \times \mathbf{m} \,| = \cos \theta$. Hence

$$\mathbf{n} = -\sin \alpha \, \mathbf{j} + \cos \alpha \, \mathbf{k}. \qquad \text{(iii)}$$

The equations of equilibrium, obtained by equating to zero the vector sum of the forces, and the vector sum of the moments about O, are:

$$\mathbf{S} - W\mathbf{k} - F\mathbf{i} + R\mathbf{n} = \mathbf{O} \qquad \text{(iv)}$$

and

$$a\mathbf{l} \times (-W\mathbf{k}) + 2a\mathbf{l} \times (-F\mathbf{i}) + c \sec \theta \, \mathbf{l} \times R\mathbf{n} = \mathbf{O}. \qquad \text{(v)}$$

Scalar product of equation (v) with **n** gives

$$-aW[\mathbf{n}, \mathbf{l}, \mathbf{k}] - 2aF[\mathbf{n}, \mathbf{l}, \mathbf{i}] = \mathbf{O}.$$

On substituting

$$\mathbf{n} \times \mathbf{l} = -\sin \theta \, \mathbf{i} + \cos \alpha \cos \theta \, \mathbf{j} + \sin \alpha \cos \theta \, \mathbf{k},$$

there is obtained

$$- aW \sin \alpha \cos \theta + 2aF \sin \theta = O,$$

that is,

$$F = \tfrac{1}{2} W \sin \alpha \cot \theta.$$

Taking scalar product of equation (v) with $\mathbf{i}$

$$- aW \sin \theta \cos \alpha + c \sec \theta R \sin \theta = O,$$

or

$$R = (aW/c) \cos \alpha \cos \theta.$$

From equation (iv)

$$\begin{aligned} \mathbf{S} &= F\mathbf{i} - R\mathbf{n} + W\mathbf{k} \\ &= F\mathbf{i} + R \sin \alpha\, \mathbf{j} + (W - R \cos \alpha)\, \mathbf{k}. \end{aligned}$$

Hence the components of $\mathbf{S}$ are

$$\left(\tfrac{1}{2} W \sin \alpha \cot \theta,\ \ \frac{aW}{c} \sin \alpha \cos \alpha \cos \theta,\ \ W - \frac{aW}{c} \cos \theta \cos^2 \alpha\right).$$

Exercises 4

1. Six particles each of weight w are suspended from the same point by means of six light inextensible strings each of length a. Every two particles repel each other with a force equal to λ times their distance apart. Show that if the particles are in equilibrium at the vertices of the regular hexagon of side b

$$6a\lambda > w, \qquad w = 6\lambda(a^2 - b^2)^{1/2}.$$

[Ceylon *S* 1947]

2. A light triangular plate ABC is suspended from a point O by strings of lengths l_1, l_2, l_3 attached to the vertices A, B, C respectively. If weights W_1, W_2, W_3 are suspended from the vertices A, B, C, and the tensions in the strings in the equation position are T_1, T_2, T_3 and a, b, c are the sides of the triangle ABC, show that

$$\frac{T_1}{W_1 l_1} = \frac{T_2}{W_2 l_2} = \frac{T_3}{W_3 l_3} = \frac{1}{d},$$

where

$$\begin{aligned} (W_1 + W_2 + W_3)^2 d^2 = (W_1 + W_2 + W_3)(W_1 l_1^2 + W_2 l_2^2 + W_3 l_3^2) - \\ - (W_2 W_3 a^2 + W_3 W_1 b^2 + W_1 W_2 c^2). \end{aligned}$$

[*CCS*(*H*) 1957]

3. A uniform triangular plate, of sides a, b, c, rests with the vertices on the inner surface of a smooth fixed sphere of radius r. If θ is the inclination of the plate to the horizontal and R the circumradius of the triangle, show that

$$\tan^2 \theta = (9R^2 - a^2 - b^2 - c^2)/9(r^2 - R^2).$$

4. A smoothly jointed triangular framework ABC is formed from three light rods, each 1 ft. long. It is hung from a point O by three light strings OA, OB and OC, each 1 ft long. From each of the points A, B and C is hung a weight W. Find the thrust in AB. [Camb. *NS* 1946]

5. A tetrahedron formed of six uniform rods each of weight W and freely jointed at their extremities is suspended from a fixed point by a string attached to the mid-point of one of its edges. Find the thrust in each horizontal rod, and show that these thrusts are both doubled if a weight $3W$ is suspended from the mid-point of the lowest rod. [Camb. *MT* 1951]

6. Six equal heavy uniform rods are smoothly jointed together to form a tetrahedron. The tetrahedron hangs at rest from one vertex. Find the thrust in each of the three horizontal rods. [Camb. *NS* 1950]

7. A triangle ABC, formed of three uniform heavy rods each of length $2a$ and weight W, is suspended by means of three light strings PA, QB, RC each of length $4a$ from three points P, Q, R, which lie in a horizontal plane and form a triangle of side $2a$. The mid-points of the strings are joined in pairs by three other light strings of length a. Find the tensions in this last set of strings. [Camb. *MT* 1952]

8. Three light rods AB, AC, AD, each of length $2a$, are smoothly hinged to a fixed point A. The ends B, C, D are joined by three light elastic strings, each of natural length a and modulus λ. A uniform sphere, of radius a and weight W, touches each of the rods, and the whole system is in equilibrium, with A as the lowest point, each making an angle $\frac{1}{3}\pi$ with the vertical. Prove that $\lambda = W/a\sqrt{3}$. [Oxf. *GCE*(*S*) 1955]

9. Three equal uniform smooth spheres of radius r are placed in contact with each other in a fixed spherical bowl of radius R so that their centres lie in a horizontal plane. A fourth sphere, equal to each of the other three, is gently placed on top of them. Prove that the lower spheres do not separate if

$$R < r(1 + 2\sqrt{11})$$

[Oxf. *GCE*(*S*) 1955]

10. Three uniform rods OA, OB, OC, each of length a and weight W, are freely jointed at a fixed point O. The ends A, B, C are connected by three equal light elastic strings of modulus $\frac{1}{3}W$. There is a position of equilibrium in which A, B, C are above the level of O, and each rod makes an angle of 30° with the vertical. Prove that the natural length of each string is $a/\sqrt{3}$.

A uniform sphere of radius $\frac{1}{4}a$ is placed so that it touches each of the rods. There is now a position of equilibrium in which each rod makes an angle of 60° with the vertical. Prove that the weight of the sphere is

$$\frac{3}{2}(9 - 5\sqrt{3})\,W.$$

(You may assume that the sphere does not touch the strings.) [Oxf. *GCE*(*S*) 1958]

11. Three equal uniform rods AD, BD, CD are freely jointed at D, and the ends A, B, C rest on a smooth horizontal plane. Equilibrium is maintained by three strings, attached to A, B, C respectively, whose other ends are attached to fixed points of the plane. Prove that the lines in which these strings lie all pass through the circumcentre of the triangle ABC. Prove that the reaction of the plane at A is $\frac{1}{4}W(5 - 3 \cot B \cot C)$ and that the tension in the string attached to A is $\frac{3}{4}W \tan \alpha\,(1 - \cot B \cot C)$ where W is the weight of the rod, α is the angle which each rod makes with the vertical, and the angles B and C refer to the triangle ABC. [Oxf. *GCE*(*S*) 1957]

12. Three equal spheres each of radius $3a$ are placed on a smooth horizontal plane and fastened together by an inextensible string which surrounds them in the plane of their centres and is just not tight. A fourth sphere of weight $3W$ is placed on top touching all three of the lower spheres. If the string will break when its tension reaches the value W, show that the radius of the upper sphere cannot be less than a without breaking the string. [Lond. *S* 1949]

13. Two particles A and B of weights W and $W \cot \theta$ respectively ($0 < \theta < \pi/2$), attached to the ends of a light inextensible string of length a, lie at rest at the distance a apart on a rough plane inclined at an angle α to the horizon. The string makes angle θ with the line of greatest slope, and the particle A is at a higher level than B. A gradually increasing force is applied at A in the sense of the upward line of greatest slope. If the coefficient of friction is $\mu(> \tan \alpha)$ at both A and B, show that equilibrium will be broken by A and B slipping simultaneously if

$$\mu < \tfrac{1}{2} \tan \alpha \sec \theta.$$

[Ceylon *S* 1946]

14. Three equal hemispheres having their bases downwards are placed in contact with each other on a rough horizontal table; if a smooth sphere of the same radius and made of the same substance is placed upon them, show that these will be in equilibrium or not according as the coefficient of friction between the hemisphere and the table be greater or less than $\sqrt{2}/5$.

[Camb. *PNS* 1948]

15. The cone

$$z^2 = ax^2 + by^2, \qquad (0 < b < a)$$

whose inner surface is smooth, is fixed with the z-axis vertical and vertex downwards. A thin rod of length $2l$ and weight W is placed with its ends resting on the inner surface of the cone and kept in equilibrium in a horizontal position in which it intersects the z-axis at a height h above the vertex, by the application of a couple acting in the horizontal plane through the rod. Show that the magnitude of the couple is

$$(W/h)\{(al^2 - h^2)(h^2 - bl^2)\}^{1/2},$$

and that the rod is subject to a thrust equal to $hW/2l$.

[Ceylon *S* 1943]

16. A uniform rod AB of weight W and length $2a$, resting on horizontal ground at one end, leans at an inclination of 60° to the horizontal across the edge of a horizontal table. The vertical plane containing the rod is perpendicular to the edge of the table and the point of contact C between the rod and the table is at a distance na from the end B that is resting on the ground. A gradually increasing force P is applied to the upper end of the rod parallel to the edge of the table against which it rests. Show that equilibrium will be broken by slipping taking place at C only, if μ the coefficient of friction, assumed to have the same value at B and C, satisfies the conditions

$$\mu^2(5n-3)(3n+1) > 3.$$

[*CCS*(*H*) 1949]

17. A uniform rod AB of length a and weight W rests with its upper end B against a rough vertical wall (at which the coefficient of friction is μ) and the lower end attached by a smooth universal joint to a point on the ground, the length of the perpendicular AC from A on the wall being c. If the rod rests in limiting equilibrium with the plane ABC inclined at an angle θ to the vertical, show that $\tan\theta = \mu c/(a^2 - c^2)^{1/2}$. Evaluate the reaction at the joint A.

[Ceylon *S* 1947]

18. Ox, Oy, Oz are a set of right-handed axes, the plane xOz being vertical and xOy horizontal. A uniform rod of length l and weight $2w$ rests against the vertical plane at the point (a, O, c), the coefficient of friction there being μ_1. Its lower end rests on the plane xOy at the point (O, b, O) the coefficient of friction there being μ_2. Show that the equations for the reactions at the ends give indeterminate values and obtain the general solution in the form

$$(ka, -kb, w+kc), \qquad (-ka, kb, w-kc),$$

where k is an arbitrary constant.

Show that for equilibrium to be possible there must be negative values of k which satisfy both of the inequalities

$$k^2\{l^2 - (1+\mu_1^2)b^2\} + 2kcw + w^2 < O$$

and

$$k^2\{l^2 - (1+\mu_2^2)c^2\} + 2k\mu_2^2 cw - \mu_2^2 w^2 < O.$$

Show that if

$$(1+\mu_1^2)b^2 < l^2 \text{ and } a > \mu_1 b$$

no equilibrium is possible. [Camb. *PM* 1945]

19. A uniform rod of weight $2W$ rests in equilibrium with its lower end A on a rough horizontal plane and its upper end B touching a rough vertical wall. The rod makes an angle α with the horizontal plane, and the vertical plane containing the rod makes an angle β with the wall, the coefficients of friction at A and B are μ_1 and μ_2. Prove that, if the friction at A is of magnitude $(1/n)W$, the vertical reaction at A is $(1 + (1/n)\tan\alpha)W$. Find the friction and normal reaction at B. Deduce that

$$\mu_2 \sin\beta \geqslant \cos\beta, \qquad \sqrt{(\mu_2^2\sin^2\beta - \cos^2\beta)} + 2\tan\alpha \geqslant 1/\mu_1.$$

[Camb. *MTII* 1953]

20. A rigid body is acted on by a force **F** at a point O and a couple **G**. For a given point P, show that if there is at least one line through P about which the moment of the system does not vanish then there is a place which contains all the lines through P about which the moment of the system vanishes. If no such plane exists show that **F** is perpendicular to **G**. [Oxf. *I* 1961]

21. A smooth uniform rod AB of length l and weight W is pivoted freely at a fixed point A. The rod rests on a smooth horizontal rail not vertically above A and is prevented from slipping by a force **F** parallel to the rail applied at B. The distance from A of the point of contact is d and the rod makes an angle α with the vertical and an angle β with the rail. Find the magnitude of **F** and the reaction between the rod and rail. [cf. Oxf. *I* 1962]

22. The end A of a uniform heavy rod AB of length l can move freely on a smooth straight vertical wire and the end B can move along a rough straight horizontal wire, the shortest distance apart of the wires being $a(< l)$ and the coefficient of friction at the end B being μ. If $l > a\sqrt{(1 + \mu^2)}$, and the end A is higher than the end B, show that equilibrium is only possible if

$$\sin^{-1}\left(\frac{a}{l}\right) \leqslant \theta \leqslant \cos^{-1}\left\{\frac{l^2 - a^2(1 + \mu^2)}{l^2(1 + 4\mu^2)}\right\}^{1/2}$$

where θ is the angle AB makes with the downward vertical.

[Oxf. *I* 1959]

Chapter 5

Graphical Statics

5.1. Bow's notation

In §1.2 there was discussed a graphical method for determining the resultant of a system of forces $\mathbf{F}_1, \mathbf{F}_2, \ldots, \mathbf{F}_p$ acting at a point. The method consists of drawing a polygon of forces

$$AA_1, A_1A_2, \ldots, A_{p-1}A_p$$

in which the side $A_{r-1}A_r$ of the polygon represents the force $\mathbf{F}_r$, that is, $A_{r-1}A_r$ is parallel and proportional to $\mathbf{F}_r$. The resultant is then represented by the side AA_p.

In this chapter this graphical method is extended to the determination of the resultant of a general system of coplanar forces, and to investigate various problems of equilibrium, in particular the determination of stresses in frameworks.

It is helpful to introduce a notation known as Bow's notation. The following simple example is given to illustrate the method.

Example 1. Given that the forces acting at a point O, and shown in Fig. 64(i) are in equilibrium, show how to determine graphically the values of P and Q.

Since the forces are in equilibrium, the force-polygon is a closed one. Starting from an arbitrary point, a line is drawn to represent 20 lb, followed by a line to represent 10 lb. Since $\mathbf{P}$ and $\mathbf{Q}$ are not known in magnitude, the sides corresponding to them cannot be drawn immediately. The directions of $\mathbf{P}$ and $\mathbf{Q}$ being known, lines parallel to them may be drawn, and their point of intersection obtained, thus completing the force polygon, shown in the Fig. 64(ii). From this figure the values of $\mathbf{P}$ and $\mathbf{Q}$ may be obtained by measurement or by calculation. The Fig. 64(i) is known as a **space-diagram,** and 64(ii) as a **force-diagram.**

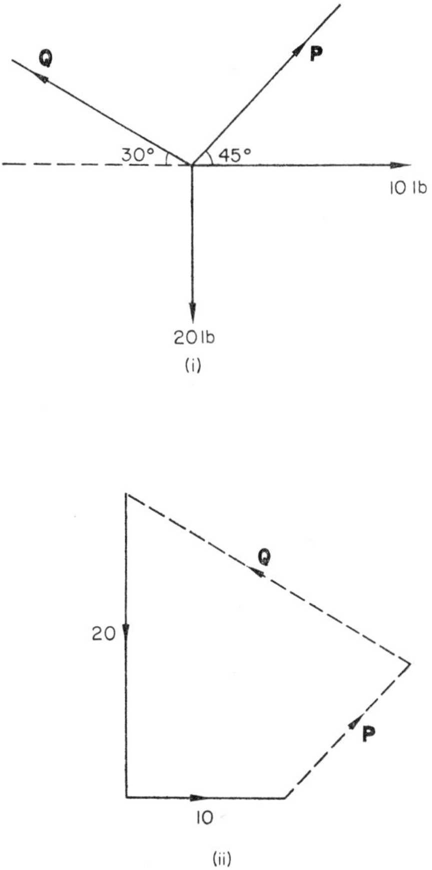

Fig. 64

In Bow's notation, the spaces between the forces, in the space diagram, are indicated by letters or numbers. In the example considered, there are four spaces between the forces, the line of action of each force being imagined to be produced indefinitely. Let these spaces be denoted by the symbols A, B, C, D as shown in Fig. 65(i).

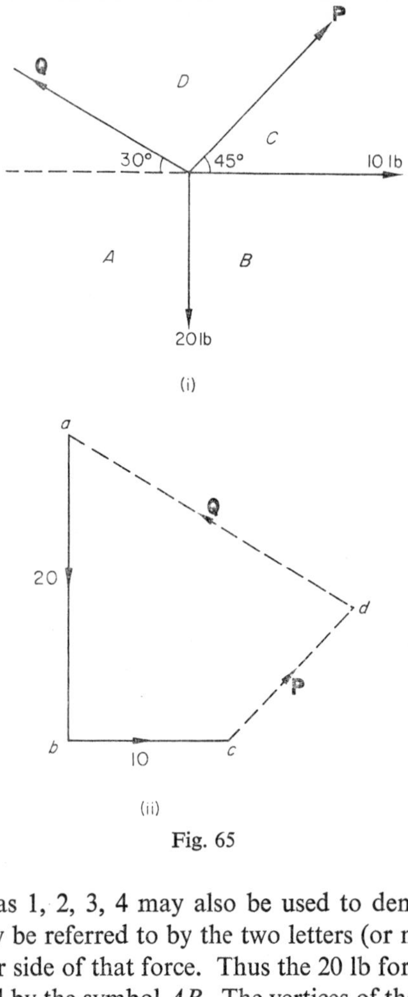

Fig. 65

Symbols such as 1, 2, 3, 4 may also be used to denote the spaces. Each force may be referred to by the two letters (or numbers) of the spaces on either side of that force. Thus the 20 lb force in the above may be denoted by the symbol *AB*. The vertices of the force polygon are denoted by letters *a*, *b*, *c*, *d* (or by numbers 1, 2, 3, 4) so that the side *ab* represents the force *AB* (or the 20 lb force), *bc* the force *BC* (the 10 lb force), *cd* the force *CD* (*P*) and *da* the force *DA* (*Q*).

In the construction of the force diagram, one starts with the arbitrary point a, then finds the point b such that ab represents 20 lb force, then the point c so that bc represents the 10 lb force, and then lines cd and ad are drawn, parallel to **P** and **Q** respectively, to meet at the point d. The force polygon $abcd$ is thus constructed.

5.2. Funicular polygon

If particles of weights $W_1, W_2, \ldots, W_p$ are attached to different points of a light cord, and the ends of the cord are attached to two fixed points, the figure formed by the chord is called a funicular polygon.

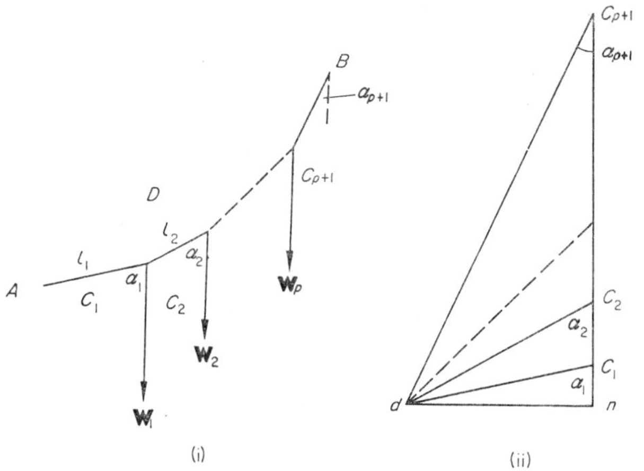

Fig. 66

Figure 66(i) shows the cord attached to the fixed points A and B, and $\alpha_1, \alpha_2, \ldots, \alpha_{p+1}$ are the inclinations to the vertical of the different portions of the string which are of lengths

$$l_1, l_2, \ldots, l_{p+1}.$$

Let $T_1, T_2, \ldots, T_{p+1}$ be the tensions in these portions, and let the spaces between the forces be marked $C_1, C_2, \ldots, C_{p+1}, D$. Considering the equilibrium of each particle in succession, and resolving horizontally and vertically,

$$T_1 \sin \alpha_1 = T_2 \sin \alpha_2 = \ldots = T_{p+1} \sin \alpha_{p+1} = X, \qquad (1)$$

say

$$\left.\begin{aligned} T_2 \cos \alpha_2 - T_1 \cos \alpha_1 &= W_1 \\ T_3 \cos \alpha_3 - T_2 \cos \alpha_2 &= W_2 \\ \cdots\cdots\cdots\cdots \\ T_{p+1} \cos \alpha_{p+1} - T_p \cos \alpha_p &= W_p \end{aligned}\right\} \quad (2)$$

Also if h, k are the horizontal and vertical distances of B from A,

$$l_1 \sin \alpha_1 + l_2 \sin \alpha_2 + \ldots + l_{p+1} \sin \alpha_{p+1} = h \quad (3)$$

$$l_1 \cos \alpha_1 + l_2 \cos \alpha_2 + \ldots + l_{p+1} \cos \alpha_{p+1} = k. \quad (4)$$

There are thus $2p + 2$ equations connecting the $2p + 2$ variables

$$\alpha_1, \ldots, \alpha_{p+1}, \qquad T_1, \ldots, T_{p+1}.$$

Substituting for $T_1, \ldots, T_{p+1}$ from (1) in (2)

$$\left.\begin{aligned} \cot \alpha_2 - \cot \alpha_1 &= W_1/X \\ \cot \alpha_3 - \cot \alpha_2 &= W_2/X \\ \cdots\cdots\cdots\cdots \\ \cot \alpha_{p+1} - \cot \alpha_p &= W_p/X \end{aligned}\right\}. \quad (5)$$

If the weights are equal, the cotangents of the angles increase in arithmetical progression.

Graphical Method: From a point d draw a line parallel to the different portions of the string, and intersecting a vertical line in points $c_1, c_2, \ldots, c_{p+1}$ [Fig. 66(ii)]. Let n be the foot of the perpendicular from d on this vertical line. Then dn represents X, the horizontal component of each tension, c_2c_1 represents W_1, c_3c_2 represents $W_2, \ldots$, and $c_{p+1}c_p$ represents W_p. $dc_{r+1}c_r$ is the triangle of forces for the particle of weight W_r, with qa_r representing T_r.

If the angles $\alpha_1, \ldots, \alpha_{p+1}$ are given, then the ratios of the weights may be obtained from the force diagram. Or if the weights and the directions of two portions of the string are given, then the force-diagram may be constructed, and the directions of the rest of the cords determined.

5.3. Resultant of coplanar forces

The general method of determining graphically the resultant of a system of coplanar forces may be illustrated by considering the case of three coplanar forces **P**, **Q**, **R** which do not pass through the same point. We have to determine the magnitude, direction and line of action of the resultant. The magnitude and direction of the resultant is the same as that for the three forces **P**, **Q**, **R** shifted parallel to themselves to act at a point, and may therefore be determined by drawing a force polygon which gives the resultant vector $\mathbf{X} = \mathbf{P} + \mathbf{Q} + \mathbf{R}$.

The additional feature here is to determine the line of action of the resultant force. For this purpose there has to be drawn in addition to the force polygon, another polygon called funicular polygon, similar to that considered in §5.2. The procedure is as follows:

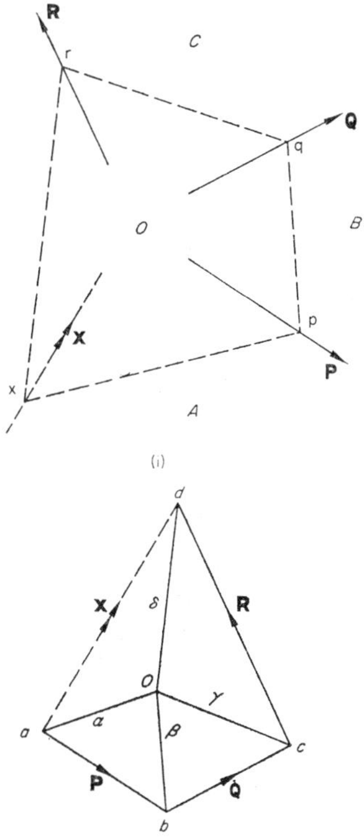

Fig. 67

The force diagram *abcd* is first drawn; and *ad* joined. The vector *ad* represents the resultant **X** in magnitude and direction. An arbitrary point *o* called the *pole* is taken and joined to each vertex of the force diagram. Let α, β, γ, δ be the lengths of *oa*, *ob*, *oc*, *od* respectively. A point *p* on the line of action of **P** is taken. A line *pq* is drawn in the space *B* parallel to *ob* to meet the line of action **Q** in *q*. Draw *qr* in space *C* parallel to *oc* meeting the line of action of **R** in *r*. Draw from *r* a line in space *D* parallel to *od* and meeting at the point *x* the line drawn from *p* in space *A* parallel to *oa*. Then *x* is a point on the line of action of the resultant. The force **X**, which is represented in the force diagram by *ad*, and which passes through the point *x* is the required resultant in magnitude, direction, and line of action of the system of forces **P**, **Q**, **R**.

In the force diagram, $\overrightarrow{ab} = \overrightarrow{ao} + \overrightarrow{ob}$, and therefore **P** at *p* is equivalent to α along *xp* and β along *qp*. Similarly **Q** at *q* is equivalent to forces β and γ, and **R** to γ and δ. In adding the components of **P**, **Q**, **R**, all the forces cancel out in pairs except the first and the last, namely α and δ acting at *x*. These two forces together are equivalent to the force **X** at *x*. Hence **X** represents in magnitude, direction and line of action the resultant of **P**, **Q**, and **R**. The polygon *pqrx* is a funicular polygon, also called a **link polygon** or a **string polygon**. It will be shown later that it has the form which would be assumed by a string loaded by the given forces. It is convenient, after the funicular polygon has been drawn, to denote the space inside it as *O*.

If the point *d* coincides with *a*, the force polygon is said to close, and the force **X** vanishes. It cannot, however, be concluded that the system is necessarily in equilibrium.

If the force polygon is closed but the funicular polygon is not closed. then α at *p* and $\delta (= \alpha)$ at *r* are equal and opposite and act along parallel lines, and hence form a couple. Thus the resultant in this case is a couple. The distance between the parallel lines is the arm of the couple, and the moment of the couple is the product of this arm and the force magnitude α.

If the force polygon as well as the funicular polygon close, then

α at p and δ at r are equal, opposite, and act in the same line and hence balance out. Then **P**, **Q**, **R** are in equilibrium.

Reciprocal Figures

The forces **P**, **Q**, **R**, whose resultant has been under discussion, all act upon one rigid body. Suppose that there is now considered a framework *pqrx* of four light rods or cords *pq*, *qr*, *rx*, *xp* which are smoothly jointed at their ends, and suppose that this framework is acted upon by the forces **P**, **Q**, **R**, $-$**X** at the vertices p, q, r, x respectively. It may then be seen that the framework will be kept in equilibrium by these forces.

The sides of the polygon may be seen to represent the forces **P**, **Q**, **R**, $-$**X** in succession. These forces being in equilibrium the force-polygon *abcd* is a closed one. The lines *oa*, *ob*, *oc*, *od* represent the tensions in the rods of the framework, in magnitude as well as in direction. The lengths of these four vectors are α, β, γ, δ which therefore give the magnitudes of the tensions in the four rods.

$\overrightarrow{ao}$ and $\overrightarrow{ob}$ are equivalent to $\overrightarrow{ab}$. Hence at the vertex p of the framework, the three forces acting, namely the force **P** and the tensions α and β, are in equilibrium. In the same way, the forces at each vertex of the framework are in equilibrium. Thus *pqrs* is the shape that will be taken up by a string when it is acted upon by the forces **P**, **Q**, **R** $-$**X**. It is for this reason that *pqrs* is called funicular, link or string polygon.

Fig. 65 may also be used to discuss another physical problem. Suppose that *abcd* represents a light framework consisting of four light rods *ab*, *bc*, *cd*, *da* smoothly jointed together, and the forces *oa*, *ob*, *oc*, *od* act at the vertices of the framework. Then *pqrx* is the force polygon and *abcd* is the funicular polygon.

Thus the two polygons *abcd* and *pqrx* have the property that one of them may be taken as the funicular polygon and then the other is the force polygon. Such figures are said to be reciprocal.

Different Poles

The pole o was chosen arbitrarily. For different positions of the pole, there will be different funicular polygons. It is of use to note the following properties:

(1) For two poles o and o' the two corresponding funiculars are such that the points of intersection of the corresponding sides of the two polygons lie on a straight line parallel to oo'. In Fig. 68(ii), let ab

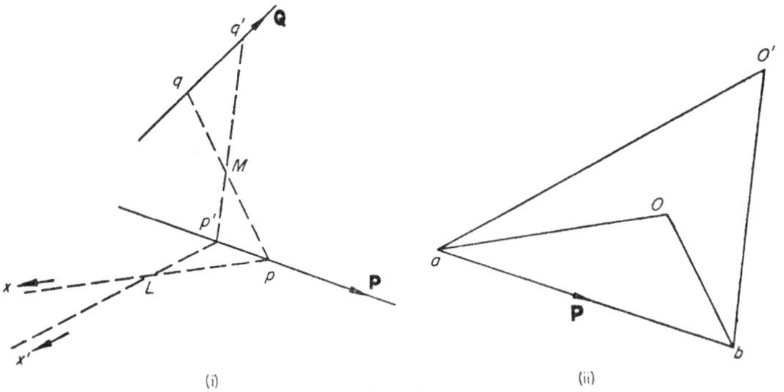

Fig. 68

be the side of the force polygon representing the force **P**. When the pole is o, the corresponding funicular taken with vertex p on the line of action of **P** has side pq parallel to bo and px parallel to oa. When the pole is o', suppose the corresponding funicular has vertex p' on the line of action of **P**. Then $p'x'$ is parallel to $o'a$ and $p'q'$ is parallel to bo'. Let px and $p'x'$ intersect in L, and pq and $p'q'$ in M.

Then

$$\mathbf{P} = \overrightarrow{ao} \text{ along } Lp + \overrightarrow{ob} \text{ along } Mp.$$

Also

$$\mathbf{P} = \overrightarrow{ao'} \text{ along } Lp' + \overrightarrow{o'b} \text{ along } Mp'.$$

Hence equating the two right-hand sides,

$$\overrightarrow{ao} \text{ acting at } L + \overrightarrow{ob} \text{ acting at } M$$
$$= \overrightarrow{ao'} \text{ acting at } L + \overrightarrow{o'b} \text{ acting at } M.$$

Rearranging,

$$\overrightarrow{o'a} + \overrightarrow{ao} \text{ at } L = \overrightarrow{o'b} + \overrightarrow{bo} \text{ at } M$$

That is,

$$\overrightarrow{o'o} \text{ at } L = \overrightarrow{o'o} \text{ at } M.$$

This is only possible if LM is parallel to $o'o$. Following the same method, it may be shown that all the points of intersection of corresponding sides of the two funiculars are on one line, which is parallel to oo'.

The point L may be chosen arbitrarily on px but once L is chosen, then as the pole moves along a line oo' the sides of the funicular polygon will all turn about their points of intersection with a line through L drawn parallel to oo'.

(2) For different positions of the pole, the locus of the point of intersection of a pair of sides of the funicular polygon is a straight line.

In Fig. 67, it was seen that the point of intersection x of the lines px and rx is on the line of action of the resultant **X**. For different positions of the pole o the locus of the vertex x is the line of action of **X**. This applies to the intersection of any pair of sides. For example, the line through q parallel to oc and the line through p parallel to oa meet at a point on the line of action of the resultant of **P** and **Q**.

In particular, it is seen that for different positions of the pole the locus of each vertex of the funicular polygon is a straight line.

The properties discussed above are useful in the solution of certain problems which require that the pole be constructed so that the funicular polygon so obtained satisfies some given requirements.

Resultant of Parallel Forces

The same method may be used to obtain graphically the resultant of a system of parallel coplanar forces. Figure 69(i) shows three parallel forces **P**, **Q**, **R**, and 69(ii) shows the force polygon *abcd*.

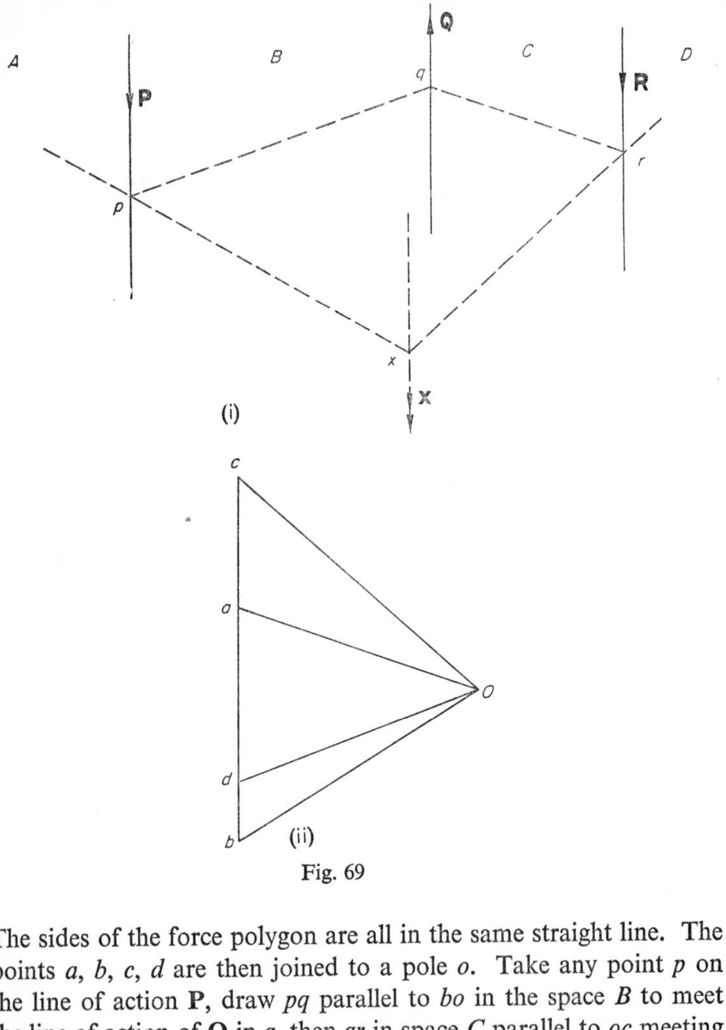

Fig. 69

The sides of the force polygon are all in the same straight line. The points *a*, *b*, *c*, *d* are then joined to a pole *o*. Take any point *p* on the line of action **P**, draw *pq* parallel to *bo* in the space *B* to meet the line of action of **Q** in *q*, then *qr* in space *C* parallel to *oc* meeting the line of action of **R** in *r*, then *px* parallel to *ao* and *rx* parallel to *od*, produced backwards where necessary, to meet at the point *x*.

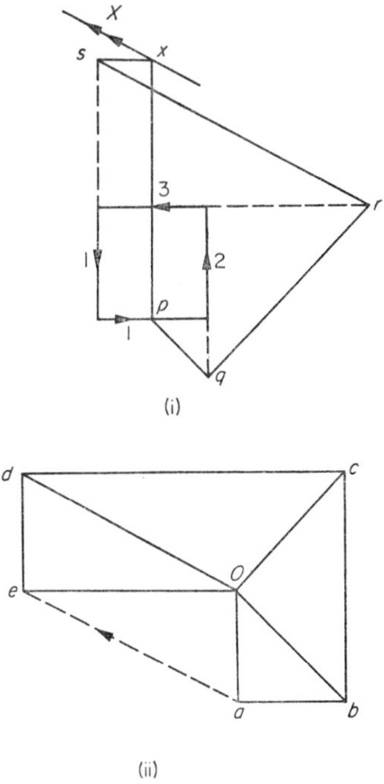

Fig. 70

If **X** is the force represented in the force diagram by *ad*, then the force **X** acting at the point *x* is the required resultant of **P**, **Q**, **R**, in magnitude, direction and line of action.

If *a* and *d* in the force polygon coincide, then the system is equivalent to a couple or is in equilibrium. In the latter case, the funicular polygon also is closed.

Example 1. Find graphically the resultant in magnitude, direction and line of action of forces 1, 2, 3, 1 cwt acting along successive sides of a square of side *a* ft.

The force polygon is *abcde*. The resultant is represented by $\overrightarrow{ae}$. Hence the resultant **X** has magnitude 2.27 cwt and makes an angle

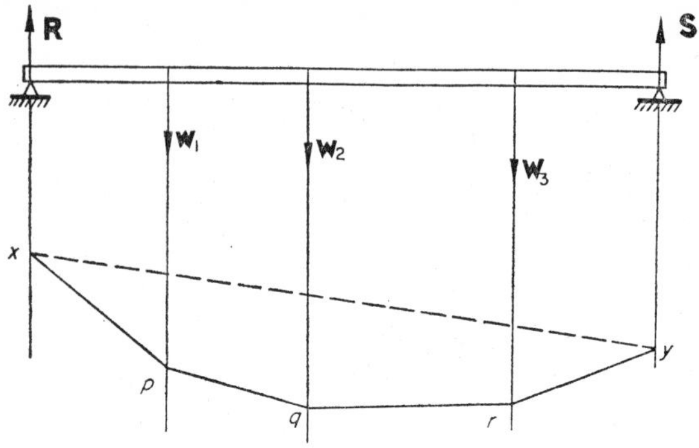

(i)

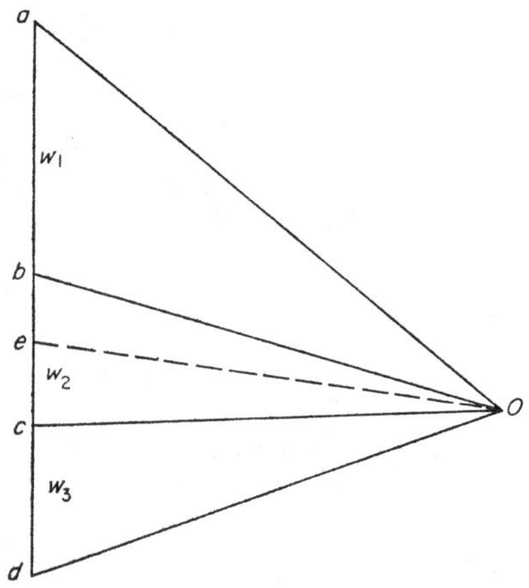

(ii)

Fig. 71

of 26° 33′ with one side of the square. Taking a pole *o*, the funicular polygon *pqrsx* is constructed. The required resultant is the force **X** through the point *x* parallel to *ae*.

It may be seen that the resultant meets one side of the square at a distance *a* from the nearest vertex, and another side at a distance 2*a* from a vertex.

Example 2. A light horizontal beam is supported freely at its ends and loaded with weights w_1, w_2, w_3 as shown in the diagram (Fig. 71(i)). Indicate how the reactions R and S at the two ends may be obtained graphically.

Draw ab, bc, cd in the same vertical line to represent w_1, w_2, w_3 respectively. We require to find the point e on this vertical line so that $abcdea$ is the closed force polygon. Then de will represent S and ea will represent R.

A pole o is taken and joined to a, b, c, d. From any point p on the line of action of w_1, px parallel to oa and pq parallel to ob are drawn to intersect the lines of actions of R and w_2 in x and q respectively. Through q, the line qr is drawn parallel to oc to meet line of action of w_3 in r. Through r the line ry is drawn parallel to od meeting line of action of S in y. xy is joined. Through o the line oe is drawn parallel to yx meeting $abcd$ at the point e. Then de represents the reaction S and ea the reaction R. (This result may be proved by the same method as for the construction in Fig. 67.)

5.4. Frameworks

Structural design is one of the most important applications of the theory of statics. In the design of a structure, such as a roof truss or a bridge, it is necessary to know the forces that would come into action in different parts of the structure when it is subject to various loads. Often the structure is made up of long straight bars connected together to form a rigid framework. When the weights of these bars are small compared to the forces they carry, the weights may be neglected and the framework treated as light.

A light bar, which is pinned or otherwise smoothly hinged at its ends to other bars, is in equilibrium under the action of forces at its two ends only. Hence these two forces are equal and opposite and act along the bar. The bar in turn exerts at the joints at its ends equal and opposite forces which may be both outward or both inward.

The force in the bar is called a stress. This may be a **tension** or **thrust**, according as the bar exerts on the joints at its ends an inward force or an outward force. A bar in a state of tension exerts an inward pull at either end and prevents the pins being pulled apart and is called a **tie**. A bar in compression exerts an outward force of thrust at either end, preventing the pins being pushed together and is called a **strut**.

The simplest rigid framework is triangular. If three given bars are joined at their ends to form a triangular frame, the shape of the triangle is fixed and cannot be deformed. Such a framework is said to be **stiff**. If four bars are joined at their ends to form a quadrilateral, the framework will not be stiff, as its shape may be changed without changing the lengths of the bar. This frame may be made stiff, however, by the addition of a bar along a diagonal of the quadrilateral. The framework so obtained is **just-stiff** or **just-rigid**. If one of the bars of a just-stiff framework is removed, then the framework ceases to be stiff. If to the quadrilateral which has been made just-stiff by the addition of a bar along a diagonal, there is added another bar along the other diagonal, the framework obtained is said to be **over-stiff**. One of the rods is then redundant. A complicated framework that is just-stiff is often built up from a number of triangle frames.

There is a relation between the number b of bars and the number j of joints of a framework that is just-stiff. For the two-dimensional case, if we have three joints A, B, C the number of bars necessary is also three, namely BC, CA, AB. The position of any other joint D is given if the bars joining it to two of the previous joints are given, such as AD, BD. Similarly for any other joint. Thus after the three joints, two extra bars are required for each joint. Hence

$$b - 3 = 2(j - 3), \text{ i.e. } b = 2j - 3.$$

In three dimensions, after the first three bars and joints, each joint requires three bars. Hence

$$b - 3 = 3(j - 3), \text{ i.e. } b = 3j - 6.$$

These are necessary conditions and not sufficient, since the beams may not be arranged to secure the rigidity of the frame.

In the following we shall be concerned only with plane just-stiff frameworks, where external forces are applied at the joints only, and act in the plane of the framework. Such a framework is called a **plane truss.** A truss is fixed in space by use of constraining supports. Often, one end of the frame is supported by a hinge and the other end upon rollers (allowing for slight movements due to temperature changes). The rollers being arranged horizontally, the reaction at this support is vertical, while the reaction at the hinge will be in whatever direction that is necessary to preserve equilibrium under the various loads.

When the external loads are known, the problem is to determine the unknown reactions at the supports and the unknown forces in the bars. The reactions consist of three unknowns, two being the components of the reaction at the hinge, and the third the vertical reaction at the roller support. The unknown forces in the b bars are the b stresses. Hence, altogether there are $b + 3$ unknowns. The conditions of equilibrium of the forces at each joint will give two independent equations, thus giving $2j$ equations for the j joints. Since $b + 3 = 2j$ for a just-stiff frame, the number of unknowns is equal to the number of equations, and hence in general the system is **statically determinate.**

In an over-stiff framework, the presence of the redundant rods makes the system **statically indeterminate.** When the equations of equilibrium are written out, there are more unknowns than equations. To solve such problems one has to go beyond rigid body statics, take into account the deformation of the rods and apply the theory of elasticity. An example of such an application will occur later in Chapter VIII.

The determination of the stresses in a just-stiff framework by the **method of joints** or by the **method of sections** will be described briefly in the rest of this Chapter.

When using the method of joints, one may either use the analytical method and solve the equations of equilibrium of the forces at each joint, or more conveniently use a graphical method. The forces at any one joint being in equilibrium, the forces at it may be represented by a closed force polygon. Whether the polygon can be constructed depends on the number of unknown quantities at the joint. There should not be more than two unknowns in all, either in magnitude or direction of the forces. A point where two bars meet is a suitable joint to start with, for the stresses in the two bars are known in direction, and if external forces at the joint are also known, then the only unknowns are the magnitudes of the stresses. Drawing the polygon then determines these magnitudes. A knowledge of the stresses thus determined can be used when considering the joints at the other ends of these bars. Separate force diagrams may be drawn for each joint, but it is advantageous to combine all these into one single stress diagram for the whole framework. The method may be illustrated by the following example:

Example. The given framework consists of seven smoothly pin-jointed rods in a vertical plane, smoothly pin-jointed to a fixed support at **A** and vertically supported at **E** so that **AE** is horizontal. The load at **B** is vertical and that at **D** is along **DC**. Find the reactions

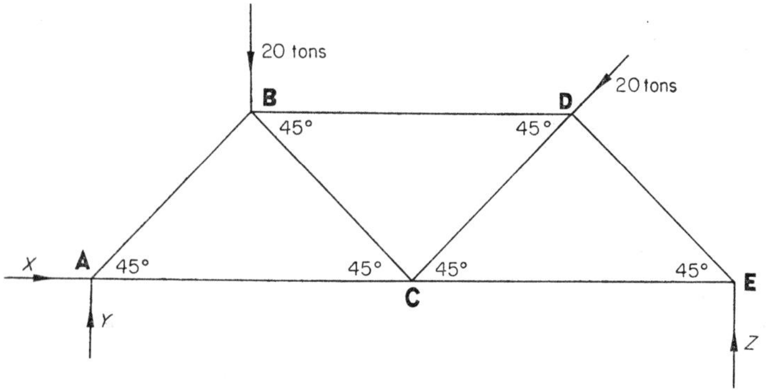

Fig. 72

at **A** and **E**, and by means of a stress diagram find the stresses in the rods, distinguishing between ties and struts. [Lond. *G* 1957.]

Let the reaction at **A** have components X, Y and the reaction at **E**, which is vertical, be Z as shown in the diagram. X, Y, Z may be determined analytically or graphically by considering the external forces on the whole framework (including the reactions at the supports). Graphically, the reaction at **A** must pass through the point

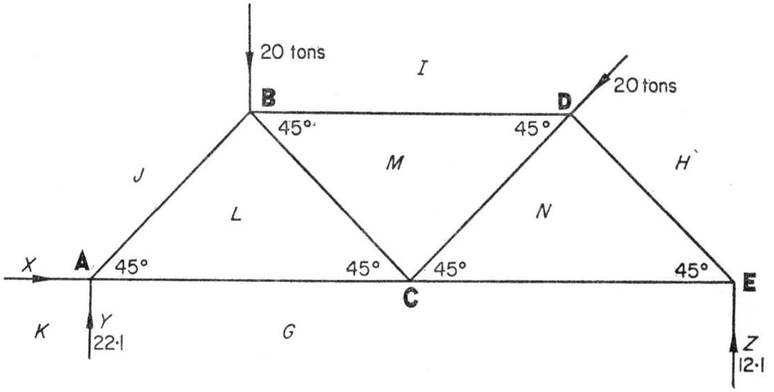

(i)

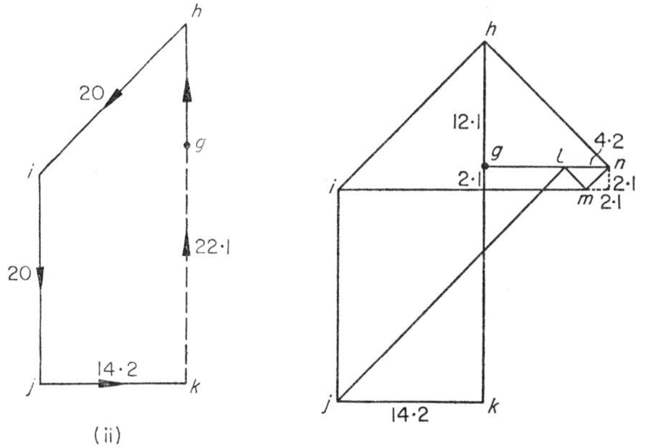

Fig. 73

where the reaction Z meets the resultant of the two given forces of 20 tons. Analytically, taking moments about **A**,

$$Z\,.\,2 = 20\,.\,\frac{1}{2} + 20\,.\,\frac{1}{\sqrt{2}} \text{ or } Z = 5(1 + \sqrt{2}) = 12{\cdot}1 \text{ tons.}$$

Resolving,

$$X = 20\,.\,\frac{1}{\sqrt{2}} = 10\sqrt{2} = 14{\cdot}2 \text{ tons}$$

$$Y = 20 + 20\,.\,\frac{1}{\sqrt{2}} - Z = 15 + 5\sqrt{2} = 22{\cdot}1 \text{ tons.}$$

Using Bow's notation, let the spaces be marked $G, H, \ldots, N$ as shown in Fig. 73(i).

The force polygon for the external forces is first drawn, these being in equilibrium by themselves. Starting from a point g, gh is drawn vertically to represent 12·1 tons, hi drawn at inclination of 45° to represent the 20 tons force at **D**, ij downwards to represent the vertical 20 tons, and jk horizontally to represent 14·2 tons. Then the diagram shows kg to be vertical and representing 22·1 tons. Figure 73(ii) gives the force diagram $ghijkg$ for the external forces.

To complete the stress diagram to include the internal forces, one has to construct the points l, m, n. First, a joint at which only two bars meet is taken, such as the joint **E**. The spaces meeting at **E** are G, H, N. Hence the triangle ghn has to be drawn, of which the vertices g and h have been already constructed. To construct n one notes that gn is parallel to **CE** which is horizontal and hn parallel to **ED** which is inclined at 45° to the horizontal. Drawing gn and hn in these directions, the point of intersection n is determined. In the triangle ghn, the sides gh, hn, ng in this order give in magnitude, direction and sense, the forces at the joint **E**. One sees that the stress in **DE** is a thrust, and in **CE** a tension.

Next one may consider the joint **C** or **D**. At **C**, however, four rods meet, and the stress in only one of them, namely in **CE**, which is represented by *gn*, is known. There being more than two unknowns, the diagram for the joint **C** cannot yet be drawn. At the joint **D**, three rods meet, the stress in one of them is known already, namely that in the bar **DE**. The force at the joint **D** due to the bar **DE**, being equal and opposite to that at **E**, is represented by *nh*. The stresses in **DC** and **DB** are not known in magnitude, but are known in direction though not in sense. Hence at the joint **D** there are only two unknowns and the force diagram for that joint may be drawn. *hi* known in magnitude and direction gives the point *i*, *im* being horizontal and *nm* inclined at 45° gives *m*. Then *hi*, *im*, *mn*, *nh* in that order represent the four forces at **D**. The stresses in **DB** and **DC** are both thrusts.

Proceeding to the joint **B**, one obtains the vertex *i* and the polygon *ijlm*. The bar **AB** is in thrust, **BC** in tension. The polygon for the vertex **A**, namely *jkgl* is already formed in the diagram. Following round the order *jkgl* the rod **AC** is seen to be in tension.

The stress diagram being thus completed, the values of the stresses are measured from the diagram. Correct to one decimal point, these are:

Tensions	*Thrust*
AC: 7·9 tons	**AB**: 31·4 tons
BC: 3·0 tons	**BD**: 24·2 tons
CE: 12·1 tons	**CD**: 3·0 tons
	DE: 17·2 tons.

Method of Sections

This method of finding stresses is used when one requires to know the stresses in certain bars only. The advantage of this method over the method of joints is that this often enables the determination of the stress in an inner bar without finding the stresses in a number of other bars.

The method consists of considering the equilibrium of a portion of the framework, the bar or bars in which the stresses have to be found being imagined to be cut so that a part of each bar comes within the

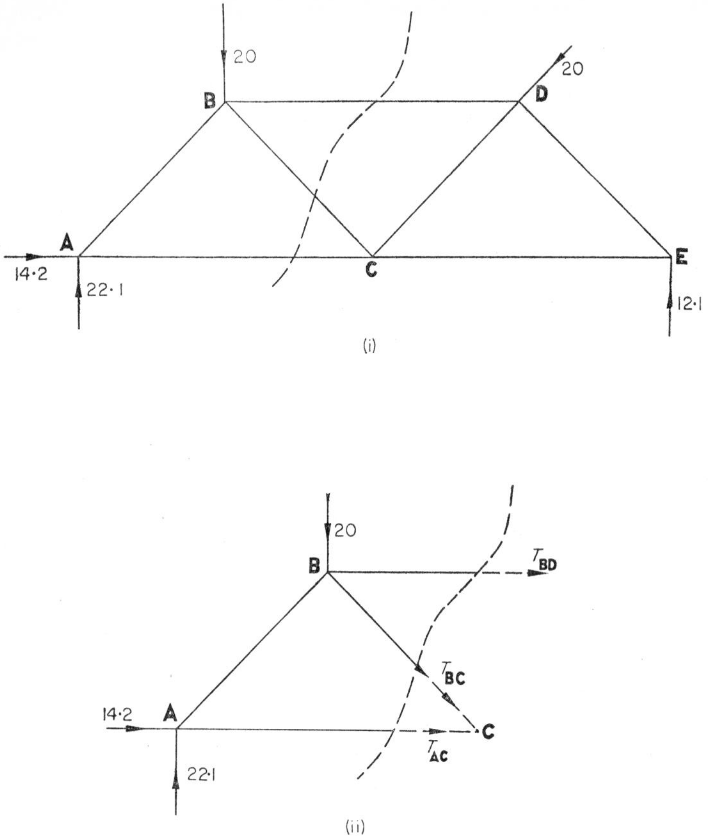

Fig. 74

portion considered. Three independent equations of equilibrium may be written for this portion, and used to determine the required stresses.

For example, suppose that it is required to find the stress in the bar **BD** of the framework of Fig. 72. Consider the left-hand portion of the framework obtained by drawing the dotted curve shown in

Fig. 74(i). The forces on this portion are shown in Fig. 74(ii), a symbol such as $T_{\mathbf{BD}}$ denoting the stress in the bar **BD**. Taking moments about **C**,

$$T_{\mathbf{BD}} \cdot \mathbf{BC} \sin 45^\circ + 22 \cdot 1 \times \mathbf{AC} - 20 \cdot \mathbf{BC} \cos 45^\circ = 0.$$

Hence

$$T_{\mathbf{BD}} = -24 \cdot 2.$$

Thus the stress in **BD** is a thrust of 24·2 tons.

Heavy Frameworks

In the frameworks considered above, the bars were all weightless, and the external forces were applied at the joints only. If the bars in a framework have weight or if other forces are applied at any intermediate points of bars, then the action on any such bar at one of its ends due to the rest of the framework will not be along the bar.

Suppose that we wish to determine the action **R** at a joint A on a bar AB due to the rest of the framework, where the rod AB may have a weight and may have other external forces applied at points on it. The weight of AB and the other external forces acting at points on it may be replaced by two forces, **P** at A and **Q** at B and statically equivalent to these. The action **R** will be unchanged by this replacement. After this replacement the framework is such that all external forces act at the joints only. If **T** is now the stress in the rod AB, the equilibrium of the joint A gives

$$\mathbf{R} + \mathbf{P} + \mathbf{T} = \mathbf{O}.$$

Hence if **T** is determined by drawing a stress diagram then $\mathbf{R} = -\mathbf{P} - \mathbf{T}$ is known.

Example. Fig. 75(i) shows a framework $ABCD$ of four equal uniform rods, each of weight W and length $2a$, hanging vertically from the vertex C and with its shape maintained by a light rod of length $2a \sin \alpha$ along the horizontal diagonal BD. Determine by a graphical method the reaction at the joint A on the rod AB. The weight W of each rod is replaced by two forces $\frac{1}{2}W$ at each end. This replacement leads to the framework shown in Fig. 75(ii). Marking the

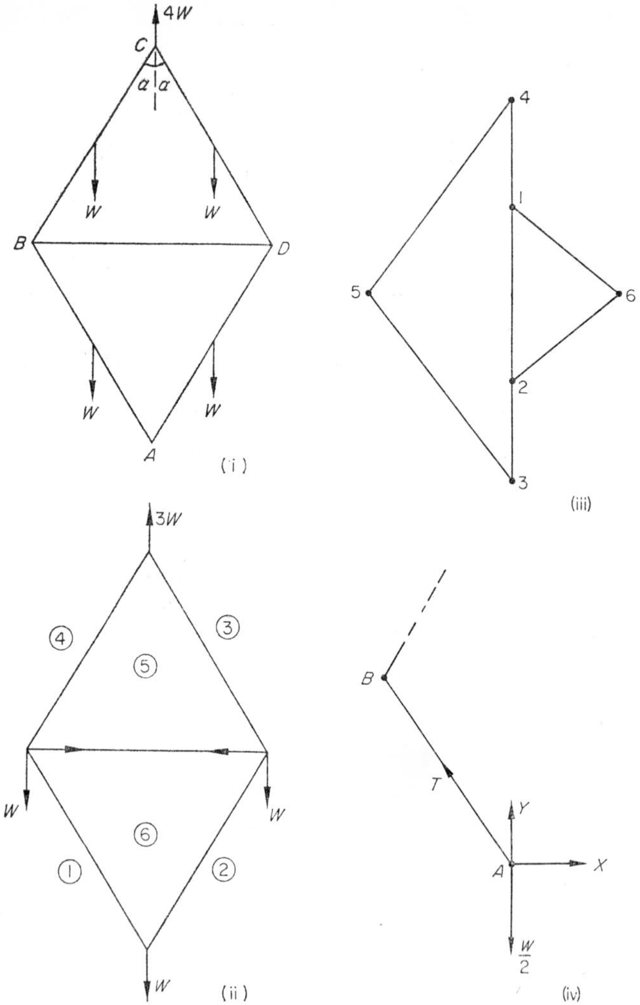

Fig. 75

spaces between forces by the symbols (1), (2), . . . , (6), (encircled on the figure) the stress diagram is drawn. This is shown in Fig. 75(iii). If **T** is the tension in the rod AB, **T** is represented in the force diagram by the side 6, 1. From the triangle whose vertices are 1, 2, 6 we obtain $T = \frac{1}{2}W \sec \alpha$, since 1, 2 represents the weight W.

Suppose the action at the joint A on the rod AB has components (X, Y). The forces at the joint are shown in Fig. 75(iv). The conditions of equilibrium at this joint give

$$X = T \sin \alpha = \tfrac{1}{2}W \tan \alpha$$

$$Y = \frac{W}{2} - T \cos \alpha = O.$$

Thus the required action is horizontal and has value $\frac{1}{2}W \tan \alpha$. (That this action is horizontal may also be seen from considerations of symmetry.)

Exercises 5

1. Three particles, each of weight W, are attached to the points, B, C, D of an endless string in the form of a parallelogram $ABCD$. The string hangs free from a fixed point at A and is prevented from collapsing by outward horizontal forces, each of magnitude P, acting on the particles B and D. Prove, by a force diagram or otherwise, that in the equilibrium position the portions AB, AD of the string are inclined to the vertical at equal angles α given by

$$2 \tan \alpha = P/W.$$

[Camb. *GCE(S)* 1952]

2. The diagram shows a system of five light rods AB, BC, AC, BD, CD freely hinged at A, B, C, D and capable of rotation in its own vertical plane about a fixed smooth horizontal axle at A. The system supports a load W at D and is maintained in equilibrium by a horizontal force T at C. Find T, the reaction at A and the stresses in AB, BC. (Fig. 76.) [Lond. *GCE(S)* 1959]

3. The figure shows a vertical framework of seven light rods smoothly jointed at A, B, C, D and E. Vertical loads W and $2W$ are applied at C and D respectively, and the framework is supported by the vertical forces R and S at B and E which are at the same horizontal level. By drawing a force diagram find the stresses in the rods AB, AC, AD and AE, distinguishing between struts and ties. (Fig. 77.)
[Lond. *G* 1956]

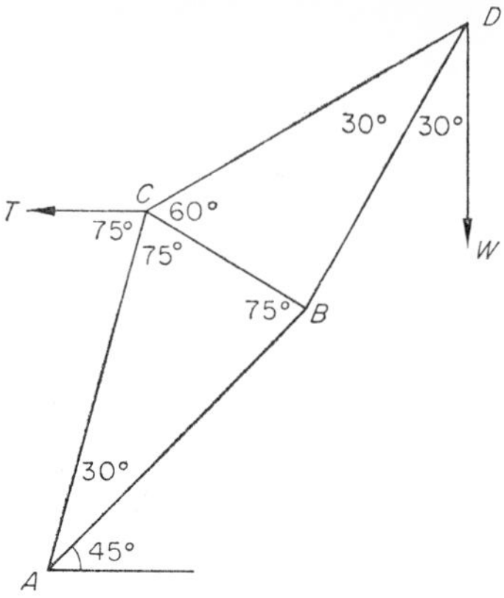

Fig. 76

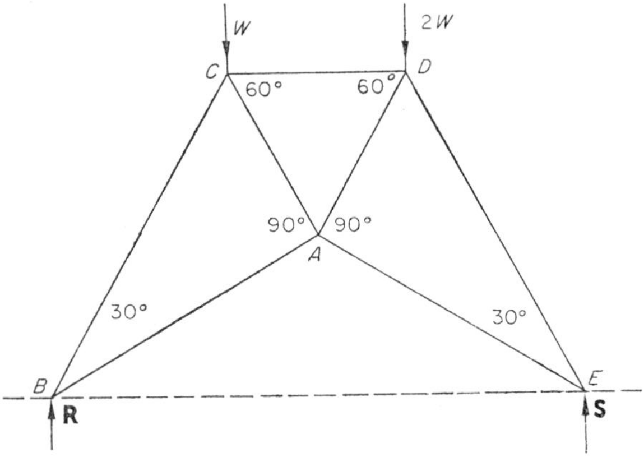

Fig. 77

4. A framework consists of nine light bars freely jointed at their ends to form a regular hexagon *ABCDEF*, with additional bars *BF*, *CF*, *CE*. It is in equilibrium under equal and opposite forces of 10 lb wt applied at the corners *A* and *D*. Determine the stresses in all the bars. [Lond. *G* 1958]

5. A framework of nine smoothly jointed light rods is in the form of a regular hexagon *ABCDEF* with additional rods *FB*, *FC*, *FD*. It is suspended by a string

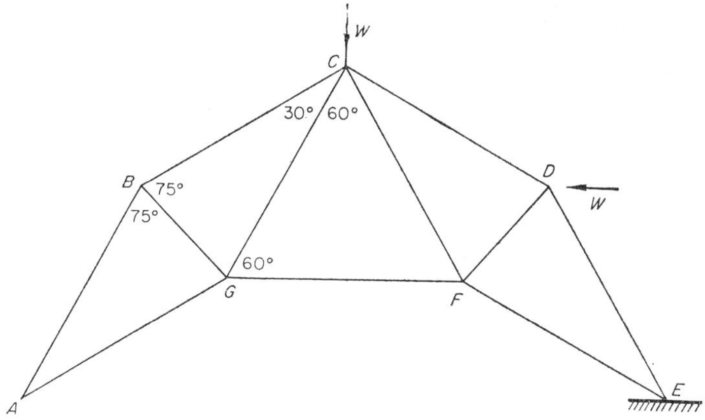

Fig. 78

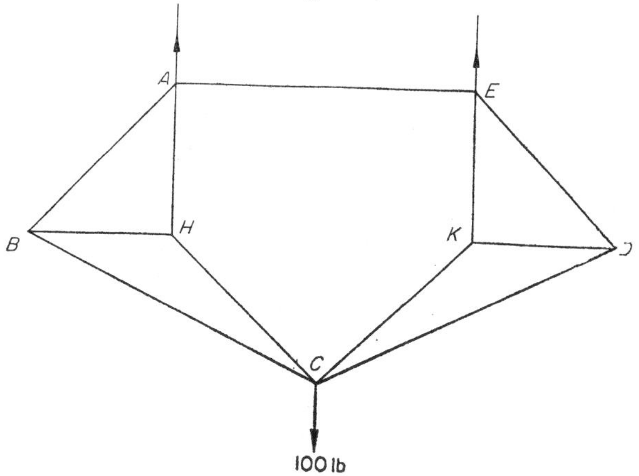

Fig. 79

attached to A and has weights each equal to W at the joints C, D and E. Find graphically the stress in each rod, distinguishing between a tie and a strut.

[Lond. *G* 1959]

6. *ABCDEFG* is a pin-jointed symmetrical frame of light bars. It is pivoted at A and is supported by a vertical reaction at E on the same level as A, and subjected to a vertical load W at C and a horizontal force W at D.

Draw a force diagram showing two stresses in all the rods of the frame and indicate which are in tension and which in compression. [Lond. *S* 1944]

7. The framework $ABCDE$ shown in the figure is composed of light, smoothly jointed rods and is such that

$$AH = HB = KD = EK = \tfrac{1}{2}AE;$$
$$AB = HC = KC = ED = \sqrt{2}AH;$$
$$BC = CD = \sqrt{5}AH.$$

It is hung up so that AE is horizontal by vertical chains at A and E, and a load of 100 lb is hung from C. Show that the stress in AE is 25 lb, and draw a stress diagram for the system. (Fig. 79.) [Ceylon *S* 1944]

8. Show that, for a system of forces in one plane, if the pole of the force polygon is made to describe a straight line while one link of the corresponding link polygon is made to pass through a fixed point, then all the other links will pass through fixed points.

$ABCDEF$ is a horizontal straight line, AB, BC, CD, DE and EF being each 2 ft. Give the construction for a string polygon to support equal weights below B, C, D and E, the ends being attached to A and to a point 2 ft vertically below F, while the middle link of the polygon is horizontal. [Lond. *S* 1945]

9. If two link polygons are drawn for two positions O, O' of the pole of the force polygon, prove that the points of intersection of the corresponding sides of the link polygon are collinear.

$(2n + 1)$ particles are connected by strings of equal lengths and the two extreme particles A, B are supported at points in the same horizontal plane. If all the particles lie on the semi-circle described on AB as diameter, show that the weights of the particles starting from the lowest are connected by the equations:

$$w_1 \cos \alpha = w_2 \cos \alpha \cos 3\alpha = w_3 \cos 3\alpha \cos 5\alpha = w_4 \cos 5\alpha \cos 7\alpha$$
$$= \ldots \text{ where } \alpha = \pi/4n.$$

[Lond. *S* 1936]

10. Show how to construct for a given system of coplanar forces the funicular polygon of which one side is given and another side passes through a given point.

A, B, C, D, E are five points in a horizontal line. A light string is attached to A and E. Four particles of weights W, $\frac{1}{3}W$, $\frac{1}{2}W$, $\frac{2}{3}W$ are attached to points P, Q, R, S of the string. P, Q, R are vertically below B, C, D respectively, QR slopes downwards at an angle $\tan^{-1}(\frac{1}{2})$ with the horizontal and $AB = a$, $BC = 2a$, $CD = 3a$, $DE = 5a$, $DR = 9a$. Find the position of S. [Lond. *S* 1935]

11. A regular pentagon consists of five equal, uniform, heavy rods AB, BC, CD, DE, EA, of the same weight, freely jointed and kept in shape by two light rods AC, AD. The framework is suspended from C. Show, by the method of sections, or otherwise, that the magnitudes of the thrusts in the two light rods are in the ratio $\sqrt{5} + 1 : 2$.

Which of the two light rods is under compression and which is under tension? [Lond. *GCE(S)* 1959]

12. A rigid body is acted on by a system of forces in a plane. Show that if the total moment of the system about each of three non-collinear points in the same plane is zero the body is in equilibrium.

The diagram shows a framework of bars freely jointed at A, B, C, D, E, F; the bars AB, BC, CD, DA form a square of side $4a$, and, relative to axes of x, y along AB, AD respectively, the coordinates of the points E, F are $(2a, a)$ and $(2a, 3a)$. The framework is in equilibrium under forces $\pm\sqrt{2}T$ applied at B and D along the diagonal BD as shown. By considering the equilibrium of the part of the framework to the left of the broken line, or otherwise, find the forces in the bars AB, CD and EF. [Camb. *NSI* 1951]

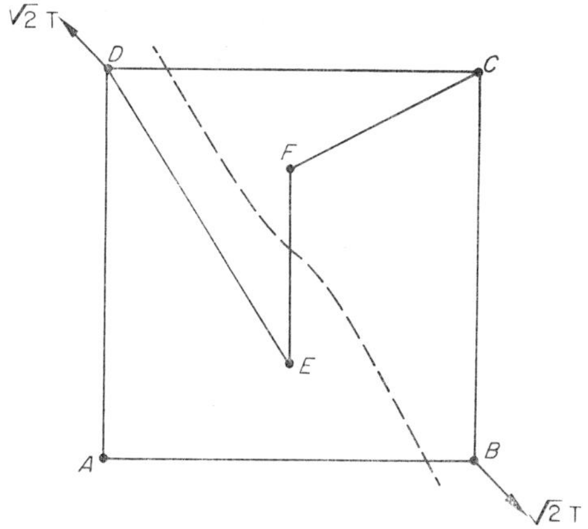

Fig. 80

13. A framework of heavy rods, freely jointed at their extremities, is kept in equilibrium by means of forces applied at the joints. Prove that the reactions at the joints can be found by regarding the rods as weightless, and applying to the ends of any rod forces statically equivalent to its weight.

A framework $A_0A_1A_2 \ldots A_{2n}$ is formed of $(2n + 1)$ equal uniform rods, each of weight W, freely jointed at A_0, A_1, A_2, $\ldots$, A_{2n}. It is suspended from the corner A_0 and maintained in the shape of a regular polygon of $(2n + 1)$ sides by means of $(n - 1)$ light rods joining A_1 to A_{2n}, A_2 to A_{2n-1}, $\ldots$, A_{n-1} to A_{n+2} respectively. Show that the stress in the rod joining A_{n-r+1} to A_{n+r} is

$$W\{(r - 1) \cot (r - 1)\,\alpha - r \cot r\alpha\},$$

where $\alpha = 2\pi/(2n + 1)$.

Find also the reaction of the joint A_{n-1} on the rod $A_{n-1}A_n$.

[Lond. *S* 1935]

14. Six equal uniform rods, each of weight W, are freely jointed to form a hexagon $ABCDEF$. The rods are suspended from A and kept in the form of a

regular hexagon by two light, rigid rods *CF*, *BE*, which can freely slide over one another, and by a light, rigid rod *CE*. Find the thrust in the rod *CE* and draw the stress diagram. [Lond. *S* 1946]

15. Five equal straight rods *AB*, *BC*, *CD*, *DE*, *EA*, each of weight *W*, are smoothly hinged together at *A*, *B*, *C*, *D*, *E*. The rods are suspended from *A*, and are kept in the form of a regular pentagon by two light strings *AC*, *AD*. Show that the tension in each string is $2W \cos 18°$.

Chapter 6

Shearing Stress and Bending Moment

6.1. Internal stresses in a beam

IN THE problems of equilibrium of a rigid body considered in previous chapters, no attention was paid to the internal forces which act between the particles of which each body is composed. In problems of structural design, however, it is important to know such internal forces, for if these forces happen to exceed the limits which the material of the body can bear, the body would break and the structure may collapse.

Let us consider the internal forces in a beam. A beam is different from the type of light bar that was used in the structures considered in the previous chapter, where each bar was subjected only to forces of tension or compression along the bar. A beam is acted upon by forces perpendicular to the length of the beam, in addition to possible forces along the beam.

Suppose *AB* is a thin straight beam in equilibrium under the action of given external forces. To find the internal forces at a section through a point *P* and perpendicular to the length of the beam, imagine that the beam is divided into two parts *AP*, *BP* by the section. In general, some of the external forces which act upon *AB* would act in the portion *AP* and the others in the portion *BP*. Those acting on *AP* alone would not be in equilibrium by themselves, but the part *AP* is in equilibrium, because it is also subject to the action of the portion *BP* across the section at *P*. This action consists of a number of forces at the section acting along the fibres connecting the two parts together. In the same way, if we consider the equilibrium of the portion *BP*, there is exerted at the section at *P* an action due to *AP*. The action on *AP* due to *BP* is equal and opposite to the action on *BP* due to *AP*.

Suppose for simplicity we consider the case where the external forces on *AB* all lie in one plane through *AB*. Then the action on *AP* at the section at *P* due to *BP* may be reduced to the following:

(i) a force parallel to the length of the beam, called the **tension** (or **thrust**) and denoted by *T*,

(ii) a force perpendicular to the length of the beam, called **shearing stress** and denoted by *S*,

(iii) a couple in the plane of the forces, called **stress couple** or **bending moment,** and denoted by *M*.

There are different conventions about the senses in which *T*, *S*, *M* are measured. Here we shall follow the convention that *T*, *S*, *M* are positive when they are in the senses shown in Fig. 81(*a*). The tension *T* tends to prevent the two parts of the beam being pulled apart. The shearing stress *S* comes into action when the beam is tending to shear under the action of forces as in Fig. 81(*b*). The

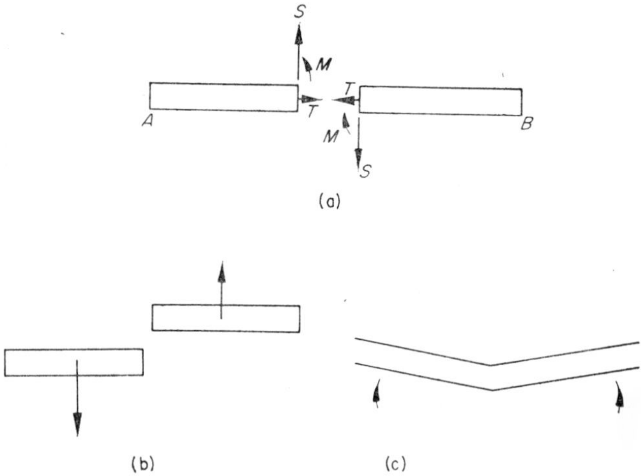

Fig. 81

bending moment arises when there is a tendency towards bending caused by couples such as those shown in Fig. 81(c) acting upon the beam.

Example 1. A light horizontal beam AB of length $a + b$ carries a load W at the point C where $AC = a$, $CB = b$, and is supported by smooth pegs at the two ends. Find the shearing stress and bending moment at all points of the beam.

Let Q and R be the reactions at A and B respectively. Considering the equilibrium of AB, taking moments about A gives

$$R = Wa/(a + b),$$

and taking moments about B, $Q = Wb/(a + b)$. Suppose P is a point of the beam at distance x from A. When P lies between A and

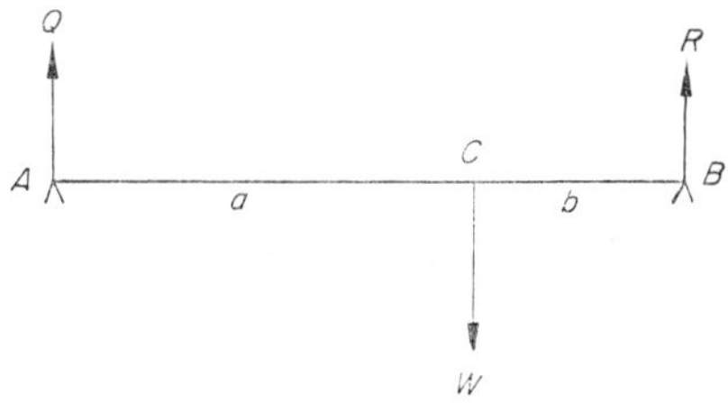

Fig. 82

C, $0 < x < a$. To obtain S and M, consider the equilibrium of the portion AP or BP. The portion AP is in equilibrium under the action of the reaction Q at A, the vertical force S and bending moment M at P. S is obtained by resolving vertically, and M by taking moments about P.

$$S = -Q = -Wb/(a + b) \qquad \text{(i)}$$

$$M = Qx = Wbx/(a + b). \qquad \text{(ii)}$$

When P lies between C and B, $a < x < a + b$, and the portion AP is acted upon by S and M at P, reaction Q at A and load W at C. Hence

$$S = W - Q = Wa/(a + b). \qquad \text{(iii)}$$

$$M = Qx - W(x - a) = aW(a + b - x)/(a + b). \qquad \text{(iv)}$$

It is seen that S has a constant value in the region AC, and a different constant value in the region CB, the discontinuity in S at C being W, which is due to the load W at C. It is also seen that M is a continuous curve the expressions (ii) and (iv) for the bending moments at C from either region being the same. Further M vanishes when $x = 0$ and when $x = a + b$, that is, at the two free ends of the beam. This property holds for a free end of any beam. If a beam is clamped at one end, however, such as in a cantilever, the bending moment at that end need not vanish.

Example 2. Find the shearing stress and bending moment at all points of a horizontal beam AB of length l supported at its ends and carrying uniform load w per unit length.

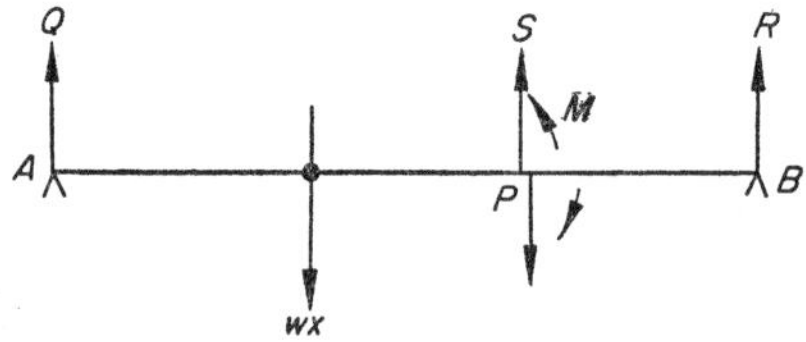

Fig. 83

The reactions Q and R are seen to be $Q = R = wl/2$. Taking $AP = x$, and considering the equilibrium of the portion AP, resolving vertically

$$S = wx - Q = w(x - l/2),$$

taking moments about P

$$M = Qx - \tfrac{1}{2}x \,.\, wx = \tfrac{1}{2}w(lx - x^2).$$

S increases uniformly from $-\ wl/2$ at one end to $wl/2$ at the other. M is zero at A and increases to its maximum value $\frac{1}{8}wl^2$ at the mid-point of the rod and decreases to zero at the end B.

Example 3. Find the shearing stress and bending moment at all points of a light horizontal cantilever AB of length l, clamped to a wall at the end A, in the two cases where it carries loads as follows:

(*a*) a load W at the free end,

(*b*) a uniformly distributed load w per unit length.

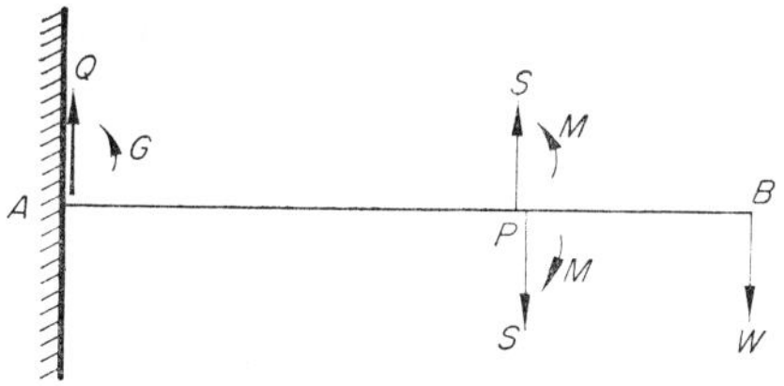

Fig. 84

(*a*) If $AP = x$, considering the equilibrium of the portion PB, resolving vertically and taking moments about P give

$$S = -W, \qquad M = -W(l - x).$$

It may be seen that at the support A, there is a vertical force $Q = W$ and couple $G = Wl$.

(*b*) When the loading is w per unit length, considering the equation of AP as before gives

$$S = -w(l - x)$$
$$M = -\tfrac{1}{2}w(l - x)^2.$$

The force Q and couple G at the support at A are

$$Q = wl, \qquad G = \tfrac{1}{2}wl^2.$$

Example 4. A light horizontal beam of length a carries a distributed load w per unit length and is supported at its ends. If w increases linearly from zero at one end, calculate the shearing stress and bending moment at any point, hence find how much of the total load is carried by each support.

Find where the beam is most likely to break.

[Camb. *PNS* 1946]

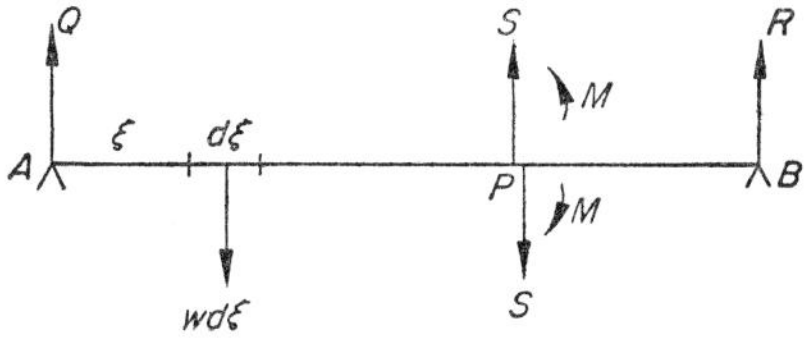

Fig. 85

Since the load is w per unit length, and w increases linearly from zero at the end A, the value of w at a point of the beam distant ξ from A is

$$w(\xi) = \lambda\xi$$

where λ is a constant. The total weight of the beam is

$$W = \int_0^a w(\xi)\, d\xi = \tfrac{1}{2}\lambda a^2.$$

Let Q and R be the reactions at A and B respectively. Let P be a point on the beam where $AP = x$, and let S and M be the shearing stress and bending moment at P. Considering the equilibrium of AP and resolving vertically

$$S = \int_0^x w(\xi)\, d\xi - Q = \tfrac{1}{2}\lambda x^2 - Q = Wx^2/a^2 - Q,$$

and taking moments about P

$$M = \int_0^x (x - \xi)\, w(\xi)\, d\xi - Qx = \frac{W}{3} \cdot \frac{x^3}{a^3} - Qx.$$

M should vanish at the free ends A and B. When $x = O$, it is seen that the expression for M vanishes. When $x = a$, $M = O$ if

$$\frac{W}{3}\, a - Qa = O, \text{ that is, } Q = \frac{W}{3}.$$

Since $Q + R = W$, $R = 2W/3$. Hence one-third the load is borne by the support at A and two-thirds by the support at B. Hence

$$S = W\left(\frac{x^2}{a^3} - \frac{1}{3}\right), \qquad M = \frac{1}{3}\, W\left(\frac{x^3}{a^3} - x\right).$$

The rod is most likely to break at the point where the bending moment is greatest. $dM/dx = O$ when $x^2 = \frac{1}{3}a^2$, that is, $x = a/\sqrt{3}$, neglecting the root $-a/\sqrt{3}$ which does not refer to a point on the beam. Thus it is found that the greatest value of the bending moment occurs when $x = a/\sqrt{3}$, and the beam is most likely to break at the point distant $a/\sqrt{3}$ from A.

6.2. Graphical representation

The shearing stress S and the bending moment M at a point P of a beam will in general vary in value as P takes different positions along the length of the beam. This variation may be conveniently exhibited by drawing the graphs of S and M as functions of x. The graphs may be straight lines or curves, and from the graphs may be seen where S or M is a maximum and where the beam is most likely

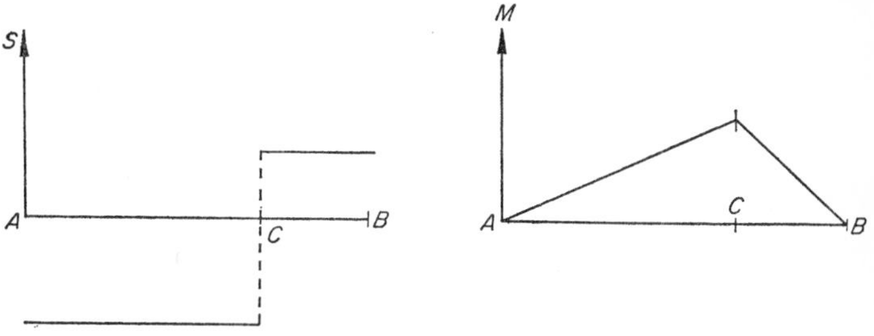

Fig. 86

to break. Thus in Example 1 of §6.1 the graphs are as in Fig. 86. Sometimes it is convenient to draw the graphs one below the other, in the same figure as the beam, as shown in Fig. 87 for the problem of Ex. 4 of §6.1.

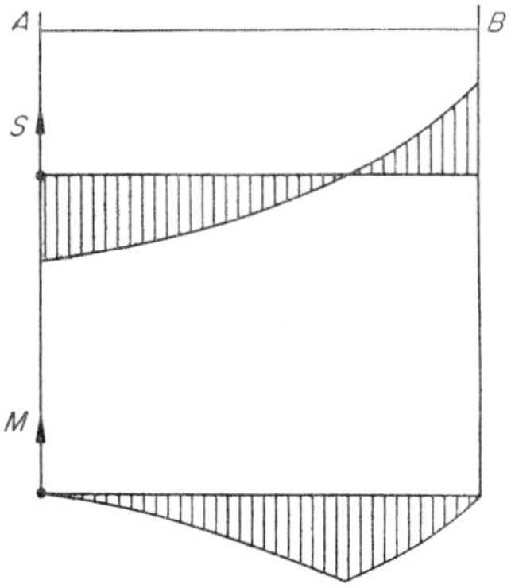

Fig. 87

6.3. Relation of shearing stress, bending moment and load

Consider a straight horizontal beam AB where the load per unit length is given by a continuous function $w(x)$, where x is the distance from one end. If we consider a small portion PQ of the beam, where $AP = x$, $PB = \delta x$, the shearing stress and bending moments are $S(x)$, $M(x)$ at P, $S + \delta S$, $M + \delta M$ at Q, and the forces are as shown in Fig. 88. Suppose that there are no supports or concentrated loads between P and Q. Then considering the equilibrium of PQ, resolving vertically

$$S + \delta S - w\delta x - S = O \text{ or } \frac{\delta S}{\delta x} = w,$$

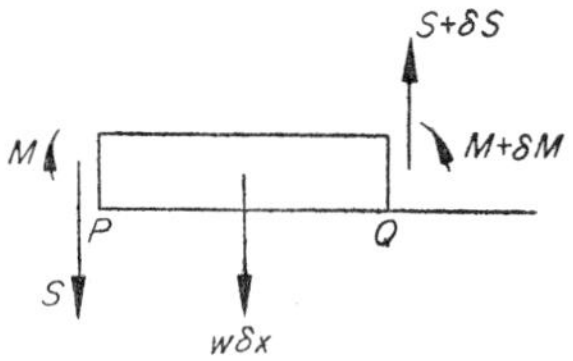

Fig. 88

taking moments about Q,

$$M + \delta M - w\delta x \,.\, \tfrac{1}{2}\delta x - M + S\delta x = O,$$

or

$$\frac{\delta M}{\delta x} = - S + \tfrac{1}{2}w\delta x.$$

In the limit as $\delta x \to O$,

$$\frac{dS}{dx} = w, \qquad \frac{dM}{dx} = - S \tag{1}$$

From these may also be derived

$$\frac{d^2M}{dx^2} = - w, \tag{2}$$

$$S = \int_{x_0}^{x} w dx + \text{const.}; \tag{3}$$

$$M = - \int_{x_0}^{x} S dx + \text{const.} \tag{4}$$

where there are no concentrated loads or supports between x_0 and x. The gradient of the shearing stress graph is the load per unit length, and is constant in the case of uniform loading. The gradient of the bending moment graph is $-S$; and thus the slope of the graphs increases when S is negative and decreases when S is positive. When S has a discontinuity, as at a point of support, there occurs a discontinuity in the slope of the bending moment graph. Maximum or minimum bending moment occurs at those points where the shearing stress vanishes.

The equation (1) may be extended to the case when the beam is not necessarily horizontal, as follows:

Suppose the axis of x is taken along the beam, and that continuously distributed forces, $p_1(x)$ and $p_2(x)$ per unit length, act along and perpendicular to the beam respectively. By following the same method as in the above it may be shown that

$$\frac{\mathrm{d}T}{\mathrm{d}x} = -p_1, \qquad \frac{\mathrm{d}S}{\mathrm{d}x} = -p_2, \qquad \frac{\mathrm{d}M}{\mathrm{d}x} = -S. \tag{5}$$

Example 1. A uniform rod of length $2a$ and weight W is smoothly pivoted to a fixed point at one end and rests inclined at an angle θ to the horizontal over a smooth peg at a distance $l(< 2a)$ from the fixed end. Find the tension, shearing stress and bending moment

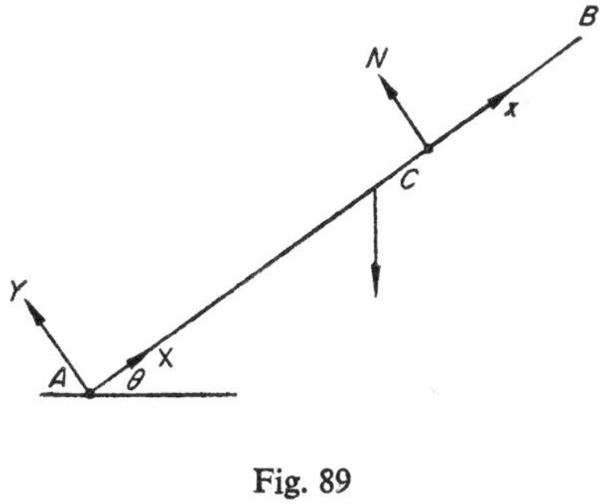

Fig. 89

at any point of the rod and prove that the bending moment is greatest at the peg when $l < a$.

[Lond. *S* 1940]

Let the reaction at the pivot have components X, Y along and perpendicular to the beam, and let N be the reaction at the peg C. Then considering the equilibrium of AB, one obtains

$$N = \frac{Wa}{l} \cos \theta, \qquad X = W \sin \theta, \qquad Y = W \cos \theta \left(1 - \frac{a}{l}\right).$$

In the notation of equation (5),

$$p_1 = -(W/2a) \sin \theta, \qquad p_2 = -(W/2a) \cos \theta,$$

and hence T, S, M satisfy the differential equations

$$\frac{dT}{dx} = (W/2a) \sin \theta, \qquad \frac{dS}{dx} = (W/2a) \cos \theta, \qquad \frac{dM}{dx} = -S.$$

Integration of these equations brings in constants of integration which are different for the parts AC and CB, owing to the discontinuities in S caused by the reaction at N.

Suppose the point P is such that $AP = x$.

(i) $O < x < l$; that is, when P lies between A and C, the constants of integration are determined from the boundary conditions at A, namely that when $x = O$, $T = -X$, $S = -Y$, $M = O$.

Hence in this range of values for x

$$\begin{aligned} T &= W \sin \theta\,(x/2a) + \text{const.} \\ &= W \sin \theta\,(x/2a - 1) \\ S &= W \cos \theta\,(x/2a) + \text{const.} \\ &= W \cos \theta \left(\frac{x}{2a} - 1 + \frac{a}{l}\right). \\ M &= W \cos \theta \left(-\frac{x^2}{4a} + x - \frac{ax}{l}\right) + \text{const.} \\ &= W \cos \theta \left(-\frac{x^2}{4a} + x - \frac{ax}{l}\right). \end{aligned}$$

(ii) $l < x < 2a$; that is when P lies between C and B, the constants of integration may be determined from the boundary conditions at C or B. At B, that is when $x = 2a$, $T = S = M = O$. Thus

$$T = W \sin \theta\, (x/2a - 1)$$
$$S = W \cos \theta\, (x/2a - 1)$$
$$M = W \cos \theta \left(-\frac{x^2}{4a} + x\right) + \text{const.} = W \cos \theta \left(-\frac{x^2}{4a} + x - a\right)$$
$$= -(W/4a) \cos \theta\, (2a - x)^2.$$

If the boundary conditions at C are to be used, these are that on passing from AC to CB, T and M are continuous at C, while S decreases by $-N$.

The result that the greatest value of M occurs at the peg when $l < a$ may be seen by comparing the expressions for M

$$M = -(W/4a) \cos \theta\, \{(2a - x)^2 - 4a^2 (1 - x/l)\}, \qquad O < x < l.$$
$$= -(W/4a) \cos \theta\, (2a - x)^2, \qquad l < x < 2a,$$

and exhibiting the results in a graph.

6.4. Graphical construction for bending moment

In §5.2 there was considered the construction of the funicular polygon. There is a relationship between the funicular polygon and the moment of a force, the construction of the polygon being equivalent to solving the moment equations.

Suppose **P** is a force acting at a point p and represented by the side ab in the force polygon (Fig. 90). A pole o is chosen and oa, ob joined. Lines pn, pq drawn through p parallel to oa and ob, are sides of the funicular polygon. To obtain the moment about a point Z of the force **P**, the line is drawn through Z parallel to **P** intersecting the sides pn, pr at points u, v respectively. The moment of **P** about Z is proportional to the intercept uv. To show this, let ok be drawn perpendicular to ab. The force **P** can be resolved into the forces $\overrightarrow{ob}$ at v and $\overrightarrow{ao}$ at u. The moment about Z of $\overrightarrow{ob}$ at v is Zv times the component of $\overrightarrow{ob}$ perpendicular to Zv and is thus $Zv \,.\, ok$. Similarly

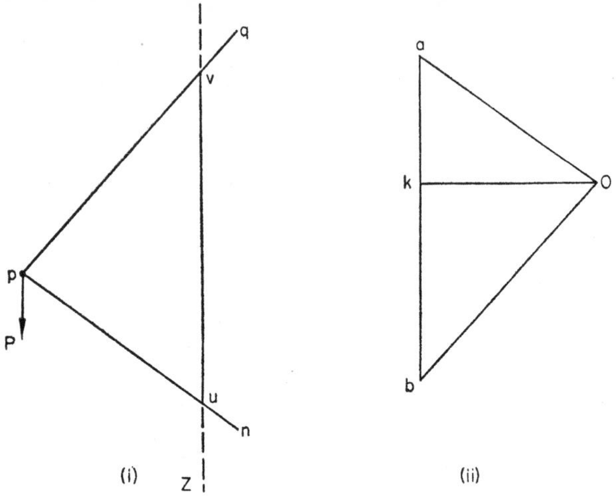

Fig. 90

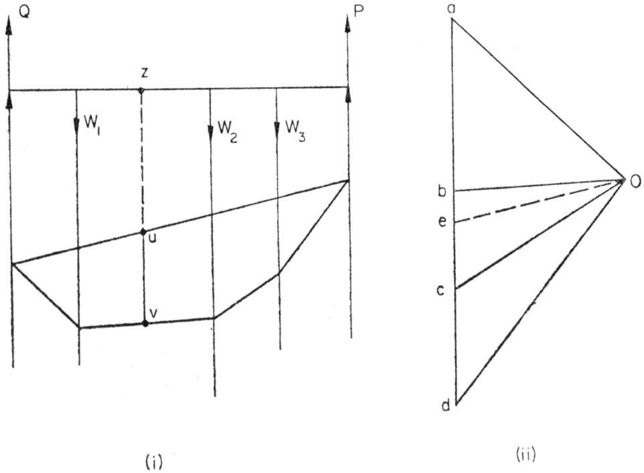

Fig. 91

the moment about Z of $\overrightarrow{ao}$ at u is $-Zu \,.\, ok$. Hence the moment of **P** about Z is $(Zv - Zu)\, ok = uv \,.\, ok$, which is proportional to uv, since ok is constant for all positions of Z.

The above method may be used to construct the bending moment at any point of a beam. The following example will illustrate the method.

Example. A light horizontal beam AB is supported at its ends and carries loads W_1, W_2, W_3 at points C, D, E. Indicate how the bending moment at any point of the beam may be constructed graphically. The force and funicular polygons are drawn (Fig. 91).

Suppose Z is the point of the beam at which the bending moment is required. Let the vertical through Z make intercept uv in the funicular polygon. Then the bending moment at Z is proportional to the intercept uv. This may be seen by considering the moments about Z of the forces on the beam to the left of Z, and applying the construction for the moment of their resultant.

The different values of the intercept for different positions of the point Z indicate how the bending moment varies along the rod.

6.5. Indeterminate systems

The preceding sections have shown how many interesting and useful results on the properties of beams may be obtained by considering the beam as a rigid body and applying to it the theory of rigid body statics. However, there are other problems of interest concerning beams where the theory of rigid body statics is not sufficient to describe adequately the physical quantities involved. For example, suppose a uniform beam is supported horizontally at three points of support A, B, C at the same horizontal level. If P, Q, R are the reactions at these supports, then when we consider the beam as a rigid body and write down equations to determine P, Q, R, then it is found that there are not enough independent equations to determine P, Q, R. However, from physical considerations one would expect that P, Q, R are well defined measurable quantities and that one should have a theory which enables the calculation of P, Q, R. It will be seen later that if we go beyond the assumptions of rigid body statics and allow for the fact that the beam will undergo bending, however slight, then the theory of elasticity could be applied, and the physical quantities calculated. Examples of these will be considered in Chapter 8.

Exercises 6

1. A uniform plank of length 12 ft and mass 180 lb rests on two supports at its ends. A man of mass 150 lb stands on the plank at a point 4 ft from one end. Draw diagrams showing the bending moment and shearing stress at any point of the plank, stating your units and sign conventions. [Camb. *NST* 1945]

2. A uniform heavy rod $ABCDE$ of wt W and length l is suspended in a horizontal position by vertical strings attached to the rods at B and D, and a wt W is hung from C, $AB = l/6$, $AC = l/3$, $AD = 2l/3$. Find the tensions in the strings at B and D.

   Prove that there are two points of the rod (other than the ends) at which the bending moment vanishes, and find the distances of these points from the end A. [Camb. *MT* 1948]

3. A bridge is of length l and weight w per unit length. A train of length $l'(< l)$ and weight w' per unit length crosses the bridge. Sketch the curves of shearing stress and bending moment when the engine is at a distance a from the nearer end of the bridge. Find also the maximum bending moment during the crossing. [*CCS*(*L*) 1960]

4. A uniform beam of length $2l$ and wt W is supported in a horizontal position by support at one end A and a point B, distant $a\,(< l)$ from the other end. Obtain expressions for the bending moment at any point of the beam.

   Show that the position of the support B which ensures that the greatest bending moment is as low as possible is determined by $a = (2 - \sqrt{2})\,l$. [Oxf. *I* 1955]

5. A uniform rod, of length $2a$ and weight W, rests horizontally on a prop placed under one end A of the rod and another prop placed under a point B at a distance $b\,(> a)$ from A. Draw the shearing stress and bendng moment diagram for the rod and show that the greatest bending moment is at the point B if $a\sqrt{2} > b$. [Lond. *S* 1945]

6. A uniform rod AB, of length $2a$ and weight $2wa$, rests on two pegs at its ends A and B, the peg being in the same horizontal plane. Another uniform rod CD, of length a and weight wa, rests along AB with C and D at distances y and

$a + y$ respectively from A, y being less than a. Draw the shearing stress and bending moment diagrams for the rod AB and prove that the greatest bending moment is

$$7\frac{w}{64}(7a^2 - 4ay - 4y^2).$$

[Lond. *S* 1946]

7. A uniform beam, of length $2a$ and weight w per unit length, rests on two pegs at the same horizontal level and distance $2\lambda a$ apart, $0 < \lambda < 1$. Obtain the shearing stress and bending moment at all points of the beam.

If $\lambda > \frac{1}{2}$, show that the tendency to break will be greatest at a peg or at the mid-point of the beam according as $\lambda \gtrless 2/(2 + \sqrt{2})$, and that if $\lambda < \frac{1}{2}$, the tendency to break will be greatest at a peg.

Discuss the case $\lambda = 2/(2 + \sqrt{2})$.

Sketch the bending moment curve. [*CCS*(*L*) 1957]

8. A uniform bridge, of weight 1 ton and length 20 ft, is supported at its ends which are at the same level. A trolley on 2 axles, 4 ft apart, uniformly loaded with 1 ton total weight is crossing the bridge. Find the bending moment at any section of the bridge when the back axle of the trolley has advanced x ft on to the bridge and prove that the greatest bending moment is found at a section between the axles when x is between 7 and 9.

Sketch the curves of bending moment for the cases $x = 1$ and $x = 8$.

[Lond. *S* 1934]

9. The end B of a rod AB of length a is attached rigidly to the mid-point of a second rod CD of length b so that the two rods are at right angles. Both rods may be assumed rigid and their weights neglected. The rod CD is pivoted freely about a fixed point at C, and the end D rests against a stop vertically below C. A load W is attached to A. Find the bending moment and shearing force at any point of CD, and exhibit your results in a diagram. [Camb. *PNS* 1948]

10. A man of weight W can just walk across a certain uniform horizontal plank, of weight kW and length $2a$ and supported at its ends, without breaking it. Show that when the plank, still horizontal, is clamped at one end and is free at the other, the man may move along it with safety a distance

$$\tfrac{1}{2}a(1 - 3k/2).$$

11. A uniform rod AB, of length $2a$ and weight W, has a load W attached to it at a point C distant b from A, and is clamped at A so that it is in equilibrium in a horizontal position. Draw diagrams to show the variation in shearing stress and bending moment for the rod.

If the rod is just about to break under the action of the bending moment when the load is at C, show that when a length $4a - 2\sqrt{(2a^2 + ab)}$, is cut off the rod from the free end, the load can be moved to its furthest position from A without breaking the rod. [Lond. *S* 1935]

12. A non-uniform rod is supported at its ends. If the bending moment at any point is proportional to the line density at that point, show that the line density at a distance x from an end is of the form $k \sin \pi x/l$.

Find also the shearing stress and bending moment in the rod when it is supported at its points of trisection. [*CCS*(*L*) 1961]

13. A uniform rod rests in a vertical plane with one end on a rough horizontal floor and the other against a smooth vertical wall. Find the bending moment at a point of the rod, and discuss how it varies with the inclination of the rod, the coefficient of friction at the lower end being μ. [*CCS*(*L*) 1958]

Chapter 7

Work, Energy and Stability

7.1. Work

A FORCE is said to do work when its point of application undergoes a displacement in the direction of the force. Thus when a crane lifts a weight, or a horse pulls a carriage, or steam pressure moves the piston of an engine, work is done.

Quantitatively work is defined in the following way: when the point of application of a force undergoes a small displacement, the work done by the force is the product of the magnitude of the force and of the component of the displacement in the direction of the force. In Fig. 92, the point of application of the force **F** is displaced from A to A'. The point M is the projection of the point A' on the line of action of **F**. The work done by the force **F** in the displacement of its point of application from A to A' being denoted by δW,

$$\delta W = F \,.\, AM = F \,.\, AA' \cos\phi = \mathbf{F} \,.\, \delta\mathbf{s} \qquad (1)$$

where $\delta\mathbf{s}$ is the vector AA', and ϕ is the angle between the force

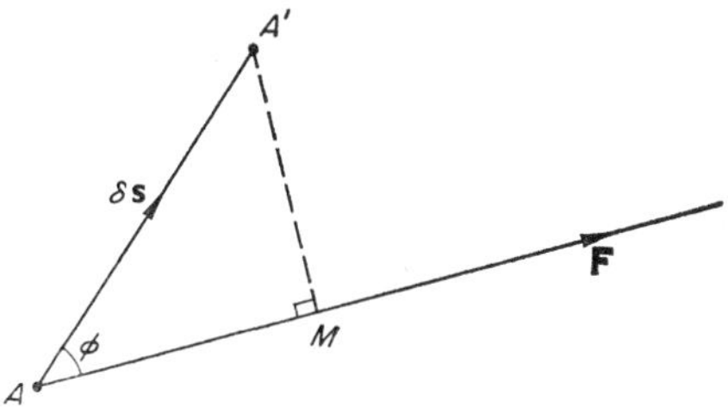

Fig. 92

vector and the displacement vector. The work done is thus the scalar product of the force and displacement vectors. If the angle ϕ is acute, the work done is positive, if ϕ is obtuse the work is negative, and if ϕ is a right angle the work is zero.

In terms of Cartesian components, if the force **F** has components (X, Y, Z) and the displacement $\delta\mathbf{s}$ has components $(\delta x, \delta y, \delta z)$,

$$\delta W = X\delta x + Y\delta y + Z\delta z. \tag{2}$$

Work is a scalar quantity and has the dimensions $[ML^2T^{-2}]$ where M, L, T denote the dimensions of mass, length and time, respectively. The unit of work in the C.G.S. system is the erg, which is the work done by a force of one dyne in a displacement along it of one cm. In the F.P.S. system, work is expressed in foot-pounds or foot-poundals, according as the force is in pounds weight or poundals.

Rate of working (or $\mathrm{d}W/\mathrm{d}t$) is called the power and has the dimensions $[ML^2T^{-3}]$. The units are erg per sec, foot-pounds per sec or foot-poundals per sec. A unit often used for practical purposes is the horse-power, one horse-power having the value of 550 ft-lb per sec. This quantity was estimated by James Watt as the power of a horse, but has turned out to be on the high side.

In a finite displacement of the point of application of a force from a point A to a point B by means of a succession of small displacements, the work done is

$$\sum \delta W \tag{3}$$

where summation is carried out over all the displacements.

If the point of application moves along a smooth curve from A to B, and the force is a function of position, the work done may be written

$$\int_A^B \mathbf{F} \cdot \mathrm{d}\mathbf{s} = \int_A^B (X\,\mathrm{d}x + Y\,\mathrm{d}y + Z\,\mathrm{d}z), \tag{4}$$

where integration is carried out along the path of the point of application. This integral is an example of a curvilinear integral or more briefly a line-integral. In general, the value of this integral depends upon the positions of the points A and B as well as on the particular path from A to B. The method of calculation of the work done by certain commonly occurring forces is indicated below:

(i) *Work Done by the Tension in an Elastic String*

When an elastic string of natural length l and modulus of elasticity λ is extended through a length x, the tension in the string is, by Hooke's Law,

$$T = \frac{\lambda}{l} x. \tag{5}$$

To extend the string further by a small distance δx it is necessary to overcome the tension T. Hence the work done in stretching from a position of extension x to one of extension $x + \delta x$ is $T\delta x$. The work done in stretching from a position of extension a to one of extension b is

$$W = \int_a^b T\,\mathrm{d}x = \tfrac{1}{2}\frac{\lambda}{l}\int_a^b x\,\mathrm{d}x = \tfrac{1}{2}\frac{\lambda}{l}(b^2 - a^2). \tag{6}$$

This may also be written in the form

$$\begin{aligned} W &= \tfrac{1}{2}(\lambda/l)(b + a)(b - a) \\ &= \tfrac{1}{2}(T_a + T_b) \times \text{extension} \\ &= (\text{mean of the initial and final tensions}) \times \text{extension}. \end{aligned} \tag{7}$$

(ii) *Work Done by the Weight of a Body*

Suppose a particle of mass m is moved from a point A to a point B along a curve, as shown in Fig. 93. Taking Cartesian axes of co-ordinates such that the z-axis is vertically upwards, the weight of the particle is a force $\mathbf{F}$ where

$$X = O, \qquad Y = O, \qquad Z = -mg. \tag{8}$$

The work done by the weight in the displacement from A to B is

$$\int_A^B -mg\,\mathrm{d}z = [-mgz]_A^B = \Delta\{-mgz\} = -mg(z_B - z_A). \tag{9}$$

The symbol Δ stands for the excess of the final over the initial value. It may be noted that the work done in this case does not depend on the path but only on the initial and final positions. The Work done = − (weight) × (displacement in height).

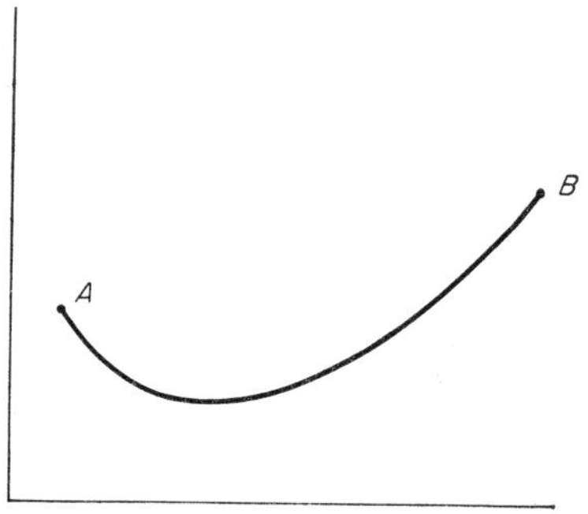

Fig. 93

For a system of particles $m_1, m_2, \ldots m_p$, if $z_1, z_2, \ldots z_p$ are their respective z-coordinates, the centre of mass of the particles has z-coordinates $\bar{z}$ given by

$$M\bar{z} = \sum m_i z_i \tag{10}$$

where $M = \sum m_i$ is the total mass. The work done in a displacement is

$$\Delta\{-\sum_{i=1}^{p} m_i g z_i\} = \Delta\{-Mg\bar{z}\} = -Mgh, \tag{11}$$

where h is the upward displacement of the centre of mass. The work done is thus the same as if the whole mass of the system is concentrated at the centre of mass. This result would also apply to a rigid body, since the rigid body may be looked upon as an agglomeration of particles. In a displacement of a rigid body of mass M the work done by its weight is

$$-Mgh \tag{12}$$

where h is the upward displacement of the centre of mass.

(iii) *Work Done by a Couple G*

Suppose that the arm of the couple is AB of length l, the forces of the couple are $(\mathbf{F}, -\mathbf{F})$, and the moment of the couple is $G = lF$.

In a displacement in which the arm of the couple moves in a plane perpendicular to the forces, there is no work done by the forces of the couple.

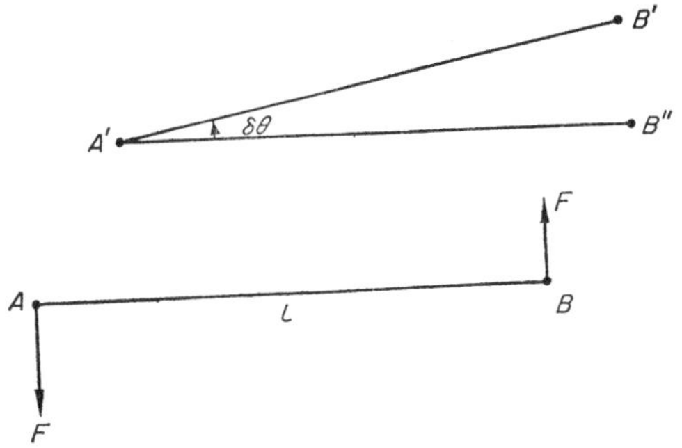

Fig. 94

For displacements of the arm of the couple in the plane of the forces, the work that may be done is evaluated as follows: Let us consider a small displacement in the plane of the couple, where A moves to A' and B to B' with the length of the arm unchanged. It is convenient to consider the displacement as made up of two parts, first a displacement of translation in which AB moves parallel to itself to $A'B''$, and then a rotation about A' bringing B'' to B'. There is no work done by the couple in the first displacement, since the work done by $\mathbf{F}$ at B is equal and opposite to that by $-\mathbf{F}$ at B. In the rotation from $A'B''$ to $A'B'$ there is no work done by the force at A', but work is done by the force at B''. The displacement of B'' is approximately $A'B''. \delta\theta = l\delta\theta$, where $\delta\theta$ is the angle $B'AB''$, that is the angle turned by the arm of the couple. Hence the work done by the couple G in the displacement in which the arm of the couple is rotated in the plane of the couple through an angle $\delta\theta$ is

$$G\delta\theta. \tag{13}$$

In a finite displacement in which the arm of the couple is rotated in the plane of the couple, through a finite angle α, with the moment of the couple remaining unchanged, the work done is

$$\int_0^\alpha G\,d\theta = G\alpha. \tag{14}$$

In a general infinitesimal displacement, if the rotatory part of the displacement consists of a rotation through an angle $\delta\theta$ about an axis along which unit vector is $\mathbf{e}$, the work done by the couple $\mathbf{G}$ is

$$\mathbf{G} \,.\, \mathbf{e}\,\delta\theta.$$

Example 1. A cylindrical cork of radius a and length l is pulled out slowly from the neck of a bottle. The resistance at any stage is C times the surface area of contact between the neck and the unextracted portion of the cork at that time, where C is a constant. Show that the work done in extracting the cork out from the position where it is just fully inside is $\pi a l^2 C$.

When a portion of the cork of length x is outside the neck, the surface area of the cork which is in contact with the bottle is $2\pi a(l-x)$, and therefore the resistance is $C \,.\, 2\pi a(l-x)$. The pull exerted has to overcome this resistance, and hence the work done in pulling a distance δx is

$$C2\pi a(l-x)\,\delta x.$$

Hence the work done in pulling out the cork from its initial position is

$$\int_0^l C2\pi a(l-x)\,dx = \pi a l^2 C.$$

Example 2. Gas is contained in a cylindrical vessel such that the length of the portion containing gas may be varied. A volume Ω of gas at pressure P occupies a length h of the cylinder. If due to expansion of gas, under Boyle's law with the temperature remaining constant, the length of the portion occupied by gas increases to h_1, show that the work done in the expansion is

$$P\,\Omega \log \frac{h_1}{h}.$$

Suppose the cross-section of the cylinder is A. Then $Ah = \Omega$. If p is the pressure when the length occupied by gas is x,

$$px = \text{constant} = Ph.$$

The force due to the pressure is Ap, and the work done by the pressure when the length changes from x to $x + \delta x$ is

$$Ap\delta x = \Omega P\delta x/x.$$

Thus the required work is

$$\Omega P \int_{h}^{h_1} \frac{\mathrm{d}x}{x} = \Omega P \log \frac{h_1}{h}.$$

7.2. Virtual work

There are different ways of expressing the conditions of equilibrium of the forces acting upon a body which is at rest. In early days, from the time of Archimedes, the principle of the lever was used to compound a system of forces and to investigate the conditions of equilibrium. About the sixteenth century there were developed, notably by Stevinus and Varignon, the methods that were described in the previous chapters of this book.

The principle of virtual work provides an alternative approach to the foundations of mechanics, and was used by John Bernoulli early in the eighteenth century, and by Lagrange in his famous treatise *Mécanique analytique* (1788).

Though theoretically all the methods are equivalent, in practice a particular method may be more suitable than others for the solution of certain types of problems. The method of virtual work sometimes enables certain results to be obtained more simply than by the other methods. Also this formalism has proved to be useful for further developments in mechanics.

The displacements that were discussed in §6.1 in the definition and computation of work, were actual displacements. But statics deal with bodies at rest, and one is therefore not concerned here with motion but with equilibrium. There is therefore no actual displacement of the statical system considered.

However, it has been found useful to introduce the concept of a virtual displacement. Suppose that a particle is in equilibrium under the action of a system of forces $\mathbf{F}_1, \mathbf{F}_2, \ldots, \mathbf{F}_p$. To effect an actual displacement of the particle from its position of equilibrium, some external force has to be used. We may, however, imagine the particle to undergo an imaginary or hypothetical displacement $\delta\mathbf{s}$ without the forces acting on the particle undergoing any change, and without considering the external forces that are necessary in the case of an actual displacement. Such an imaginary displacement is described as *virtual* to distinguish it from an actual displacement. The work that would be done by a force in a virtual displacement is called virtual work. This is the work that would be done by the force if the virtual displacement could be effected.

If the resultant of $\mathbf{F}_1, \mathbf{F}_2, \ldots \mathbf{F}_p$ is $\mathbf{R}$, then

$$\mathbf{R} = \mathbf{F}_1 + \mathbf{F}_2 + \ldots + \mathbf{F}_p$$

and $\mathbf{R} \,.\, \delta\mathbf{s} = \mathbf{F}_1 \,.\, \delta\mathbf{s} + \mathbf{F}_2 \,.\, \delta\mathbf{s} + \ldots + \mathbf{F}_p \,.\, \delta\mathbf{s}$. If the particle is in equilibrium, $\mathbf{R} = \mathbf{O}$, and therefore $\mathbf{R} \,.\, \delta\mathbf{s} = O$. Hence

$$\mathbf{F}_1 \,.\, \delta\mathbf{s} + \mathbf{F}_2 \,.\, \delta\mathbf{s} + \ldots + \mathbf{F}_p \,.\, \delta\mathbf{s} = O.$$

That is, the sum of the virtual works of the forces is zero.

Thus we have the result that if a system of forces acting on a particle keep it in equilibrium, the algebraic sum of the virtual works done by these forces in an infinitesimal virtual displacement of the particle is zero.

Conversely, if the forces acting on a particle are such that the algebraic sum of the virtual works done by them in every arbitrary infinitesimal virtual displacement of the particle is zero, then the forces are in equilibrium. For if,

$$\mathbf{F}_1 \,.\, \delta\mathbf{s} + \mathbf{F}_2 \,.\, \delta\mathbf{s} + \ldots + \mathbf{F}_p \,.\, \delta\mathbf{s} = O,$$

then $\mathbf{R} \,.\, \delta\mathbf{s} = O$, that is, either $\mathbf{R} = \mathbf{O}$ or $\delta\mathbf{s} = \mathbf{O}$ or $\mathbf{R}$ and $\delta\mathbf{s}$ are perpendicular. Hence if the result is true for every $\delta\mathbf{s}$, the only possibility is $\mathbf{R} = \mathbf{O}$.

The two statements may be combined into the following: A system of forces acting upon a particle is in equilibrium if and only if zero virtual work is done by them in every arbitrary infinitesimal virtual displacement of the particle.

The result is known as the **Principle of Virtual Work** for a single particle.

Example. A particle of weight W is in equilibrium on a rough inclined plane of angle α. Use the principle of virtual work to determine the normal and frictional components of the reaction of the plane.

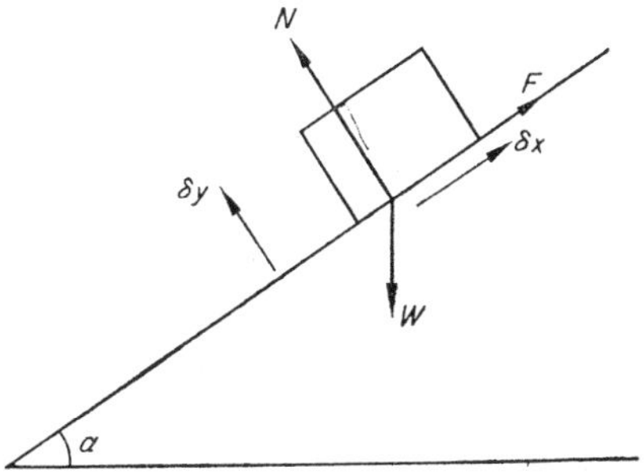

Fig. 95

Let N and F be the normal and frictional components. Suppose that the particle is given a virtual displacement δx in the plane along the upward line of greatest slope. The equation of virtual work is

$$F\delta x - W \sin \alpha \delta x = 0,$$

no work being done by the normal reaction which is perpendicular to the displacement. Hence

$$F = W \sin \alpha.$$

Consider now a virtual displacement δy of the particle normal to the plane. The equation of Virtual Work gives

$$N\delta y - W \cos \alpha \delta y = 0$$

or

$$N = W \cos \alpha.$$

These equations may also have been obtained more simply by resolving parallel and perpendicular to the plane. The method of virtual work offers no particular advantage in this case.

One may note here a difference between a virtual and an actual displacement. If an actual displacement δx up the plane is given, the frictional force will act downwards, but in the virtual displacement, the friction F is assumed to continue to act upwards. Again, if an actual displacement δy of the particle perpendicular to the plane, contact between the particle and the plane is lost and the reaction vanishes. But in the virtual displacement δy the reaction N is assumed to continue to act unchanged.

General Principle of Virtual Work

For a system of particles in equilibrium it is generally convenient to distinguish between the external forces (applied forces) and the internal forces (or forces of constraint). If the system is given a virtual displacement the net virtual work done by the force on each particle is zero, and hence the sum of the virtual works of all the forces (internal and external) acting upon all the particles is also zero. This is the general principle of virtual work.

Some forces do not contribute to virtual work in certain types of displacements. For example, if the virtual displacements are of the first order of smallness and are taken to be consistent with the geometrical constraints in the system considered, the virtual work done by certain internal forces are found to be of the second or higher order of smallness.

In the equation of virtual work, where only the first-order terms are considered, the second-order contributions from such internal forces will therefore not be included. Hence when writing the equation of virtual work, such forces may be left out of consideration. Only the external applied forces need be taken into account when calculating virtual work.

Let us now consider a system of two particles P and Q which are rigidly connected together and are in equilibrium. The internal forces between the two particles consist of two equal and opposite forces acting along the line joining the two particles. Let these be **T** and −**T** as shown in the diagram. Suppose the system is given a small

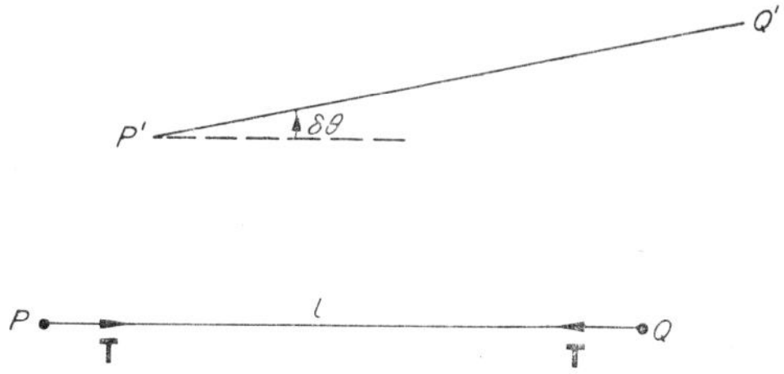

Fig. 96

displacement, in which the distance between the particles is kept fixed, with P moving to P' and Q moving to Q' so that

$$P'Q' = PQ = l,$$

and $P'Q'$ making an angle $\delta\theta$ with PQ. The virtual work done by **T** at P is $\mathbf{T} \cdot \overrightarrow{PP'}$ and by −**T** at Q is $-\mathbf{T} \cdot \overrightarrow{QQ'}$. Hence the total work done is

$$\mathbf{T} \cdot (\overrightarrow{PP'} - \overrightarrow{QQ'}) = \mathbf{T} \cdot [(\overrightarrow{PQ} + \overrightarrow{QP'}) - (\overrightarrow{QP'} + \overrightarrow{P'Q'})]$$

using the triangle rule. This may be written

$$\mathbf{T} \cdot (\overrightarrow{PQ} - \overrightarrow{P'Q'}) = Tl\,(1 - \cos\delta\theta) = \tfrac{1}{2}Tl\,(\delta\theta)^2$$

approximately, and is of the second order in $\delta\theta$. Hence the work done by the internal forces may be omitted when writing the equation of virtual work.

This result would also apply to the tension in an inextensible string or to the tension or thrust in a light inextensible rod joining two particles.

The above result concerning the omission of internal forces in the equation of virtual work for a system of two particles may be extended also to a system consisting of a number of particles, and therefore also to a rigid body, since a rigid body may be regarded as an agglomeration of rigidly connected particles.

We may thus state the principle of virtual work in the form that a system of forces acting upon a system of particles or rigid bodies is in equilibrium if and only if the algebraic sum of the work done by the external forces acting on the system, in any arbitrary infinitesimal virtual displacement, consistent with the geometrical conditions of the system, is zero.

The following alternative proof of the principle of virtual work for a coplanar force system acting on a plane lamina is of interest.

Suppose we consider a small displacement of a lamina in its plane. It is convenient to analyse the displacement as consisting of two steps, one a translation of the lamina as a whole, and the other a

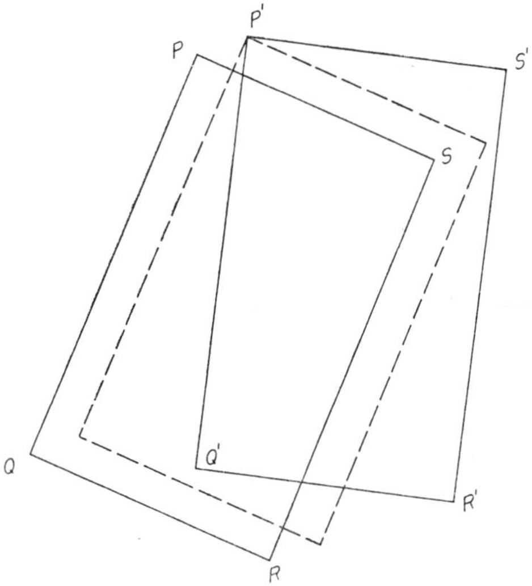

Fig. 97

rotation. If a rectangle $PQRS$, marked out on the lamina in its initial position, becomes $P'Q'R'S'$ in the new position, the displacement may be looked upon as made up of a translation of every point of the lamina equal and parallel to $\overrightarrow{PP'}$, and then a rotation of the lamina about the point P' through an angle $\delta\theta$ so that the side PQ in the initial position now becomes $P'Q'$.

Now suppose that a system of forces

$$(X_1, Y_1), (X_2, Y_2), \ldots, (X_p, Y_p)$$

act at points $P_1(x_1, y_1)$, $P_2(x_2, y_2)$, ..., $P_p(x_p, y_p)$ respectively, of a plane lamina. Consider a small displacement of the lamina in which a point $A(a, b)$ of the body has a translation with components

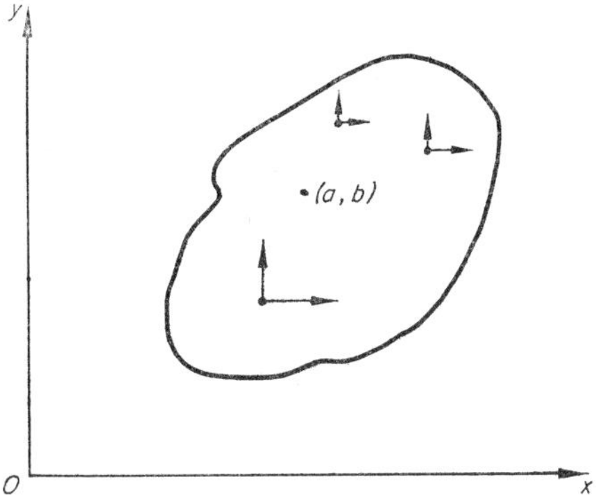

Fig. 98

$(\delta a, \delta b)$, and the lamina is thereafter rotated in its plane through an angle $\delta\theta$ in the anticlockwise sense. The point (x_r, y_r) will then have a displacement whose components parallel to the axes are

$$\delta a - (y_r - b)\,\delta\theta, \qquad \delta b + (x_r - a)\,\delta\theta.$$

The virtual work done by the force (X_r, Y_r) is thus

$$X_r\{\delta a - (y_r - b)\,\delta\theta\} + Y_r\{\delta b + (x_r - a)\,\delta\theta\}.$$

Summing for all the forces $r = 1, 2, \ldots p$, the total virtual work may be written

$$\begin{aligned}\delta W &= \delta a \sum X_r + \delta b \sum Y_r + \delta\theta \sum \{(x_r - a)\, Y_r - (y_r - b)\, X_r\} \\ &= X\delta a + Y\delta b + G\delta\theta,\end{aligned}$$

where X, Y, G are the force and couple components of the system of forces acting on the lamina when reduced to act at the point $A(a, b)$. If the system of forces acting on the body is in equilibrium, then $X = Y = G = O$, and hence $\delta W = O$. Conversely if $\delta W = O$ for arbitrary δa, δb and $\delta\theta$ then $X = Y = G = O$ and the system is in equilibrium. Thus we obtain the principle of virtual work for a plane lamina that is acted upon by a system of forces in the plane.

7.3. Forces which may be omitted from the equation of virtual work

It is convenient to list some of the forces which, when the system is given a small virtual displacement, do no work or whose work is of the second or higher order of smallness, and may be left out of consideration when writing the equation of virtual work.

(1) *The tension of an inextensible string*, or the tension or thrust in an inextensible rod may be omitted if in the virtual displacement the length remains unchanged. (This has already been discussed in the previous section.)

(2) *The reaction at a fixed point or a fixed axis of rotation* may be omitted from the equation of virtual work, since the displacement of the point of application is zero.

(3) If a body is in contact with a smooth fixed surface and is given a small sliding displacement on the surface, the reaction on the body due to the surface may be omitted from the equation of virtual work since the force and the displacement are perpendicular to one another. (This would not apply if the surface is rough, since in that case the frictional component will do work.)

(4) If a body is given a small rolling displacement on a fixed surface, the work done by the reaction of the surface may be omitted, even when the surface is a rough one. In Fig. 99, the points of contact of the fixed body before and after rotation are P and Q. The corresponding points of the moving body are P' and Q', where Q' coincides with Q at the end of the displacement. The displacement being one of rolling

$$PQ = P'Q' = \delta s,$$

and the angle rotated by the moving body is approximately

$$\delta\theta = \frac{\delta s}{\rho} + \frac{\delta s'}{\rho'}$$

where ρ and ρ' are the radii of curvature of the two curves at the point of contact. The point where the reaction acts initially is P,

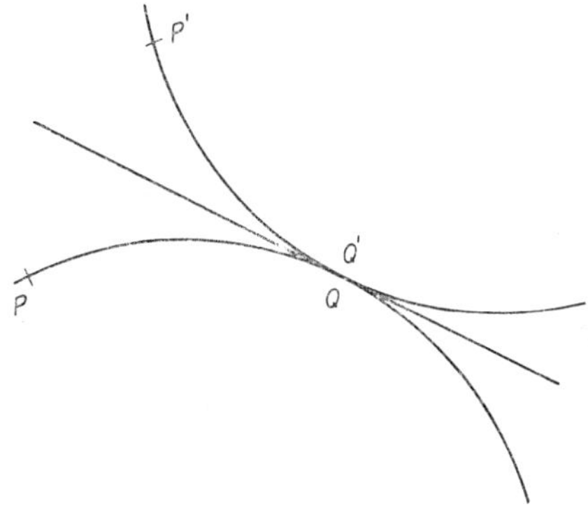

Fig. 99

which on displacement moves to P'. Hence the work done is proportional to PP' which is approximately $PQ \, . \, \delta\theta$. This expression is of the order of $(\delta\theta)^2$, and thus the reaction may be omitted from the equation of virtual work.

(5) The mutual reactions between two bodies which are in contact may be omitted from the equation of virtual work for displacements in which contact is preserved unchanged. Action and reaction being equal and opposite, and the points of application being the same displacement, the work done by one force is equal but opposite in sign to the work done by the other. Hence the total contributions from both forces cancel out.

A particular case of this result is the mutual reactions at a joint between two bodies, in a displacement in which the joint is not broken.

7.4. Applications

In applying the principle of virtual work the displacement has to be selected so that a particular result one seeks may be obtained as directly as possible. Often the problem is to determine certain unknown forces or to obtain some geometrical property of the equilibrium position. If one is not interested in determining a particular force, **F** say, it is convenient to choose a virtual displacement such that the point of application either does not move or moves perpendicular to **F**, and hence there is no contribution made by **F** in the equation of virtual work.

The displacement is generally taken to be consistent with the geometrical conditions of the system. Then the internal forces may be left out of the equation of virtual work. Sometimes, however, it would be of use to choose a displacement which does violate some geometrical condition. Then internal forces would contribute to the virtual work, and the principle of virtual work may be used to determine such internal forces. For example, an inextensible string may be given a virtual displacement in which the length of the string is changed. In the equation of virtual work the contribution from the tension in the string has then to be included. Or again, at a joint connecting two bodies, if in the virtual displacement the joint is imagined to be broken with the points at the joint of the two bodies undergoing different displacements, there should be included in the equation of virtual work the contributions from the reactions at the joint.

The following examples serve to illustrate some of the applications of the principle of virtual work.

Example 1. Two equal uniform rods OA, OB, each of weight W and length $2l$, are freely jointed at O. The rods rest in a vertical plane in contact with a smooth fixed horizontal cylinder of radius b, so that they make equal and opposite angles θ with the downward vertical. Equilibrium is maintained by a light rod joining A to B, AB below the lowest generator of the cylinder. By the method of virtual work, or otherwise, show that the tension in the rod is

$$\frac{1}{2} W \left(\frac{b}{l} \operatorname{cosec}^2 \theta - \tan \theta\right).$$

[Lond. *G* 1958]

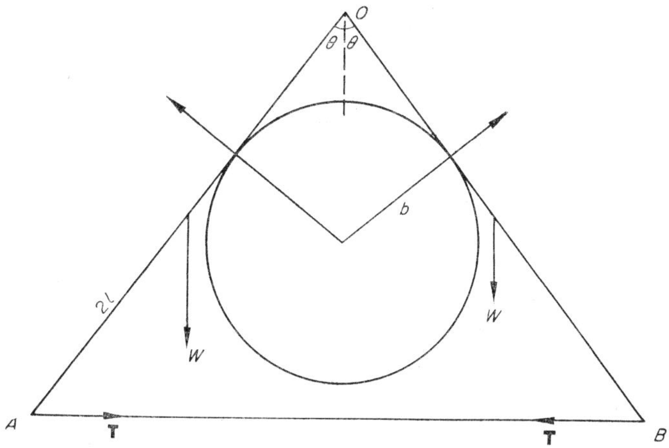

Fig. 100

Let T be the tension in the rod AB. Consider a symmetrical vertical displacement in which the angle θ changes to $\theta + \delta\theta$, the point O moves vertically downwards, the lengths OA, OB are unchanged, and the rods retain contact with the cylinder. No work is done by the reactions on the rods due to the cylinder or by the reactions at the joint O. The height of the mid-point of each rod above the centre of the cylinder is $b \operatorname{cosec} \theta - l \cos \theta$, and hence the virtual work done by each weight is $-W\delta(b \operatorname{cosec} \theta - l \cos \theta)$. The length of AB is $4l \sin \theta$ and the virtual work done by the tension in AB is $-T\delta(4l \sin \theta)$. Hence the equation of virtual work is

$$-2W\delta(b \operatorname{cosec} \theta - l \cos \theta) - T\delta(4l \sin \theta) = O,$$

that is

$$-2W(-b \operatorname{cosec} \theta \cot \theta\delta\theta + l \sin \theta\delta\theta) - T \,.\, 4l \cos \theta\delta\theta = O.$$

Hence

$$T = \frac{1}{2} W \left(\frac{b}{l} \operatorname{cosec}^2 \theta - \tan \theta\right).$$

Example 2. A regular octahedron $OABCDE$ is formed of twelve uniform rods each of weight W. It is suspended from O; the square $ABCD$ is horizontal and OE is vertical. Show, by means of the principle of virtual work (or otherwise), that the thrust in each horizontal rod is $3W/\sqrt{2}$, and that the tension in the rods AE, BE, CE, DE is $W/\sqrt{2}$.

[Oxf. *I* 1958]

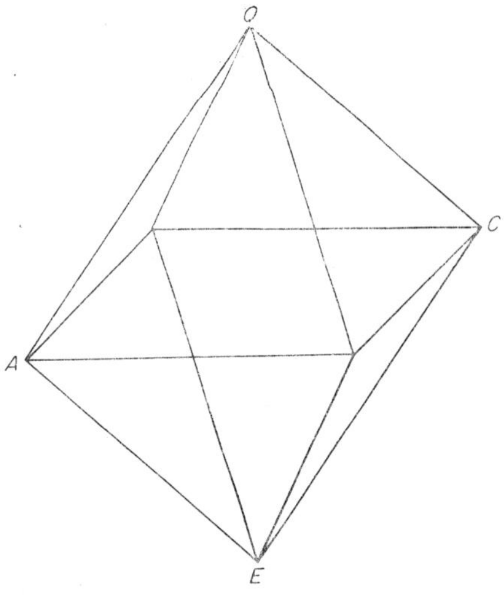

Fig. 101

If the inclined rods make angle θ with the vertical, in the equilibrium position $\theta = 45°$. Let P be the thrust in each horizontal rod and T the tension in each of the lower inclined rods. Consider a symmetrical virtual displacement in which the point O is fixed, E moves vertically upwards, the lengths of the inclined rods are unchanged, and the rods make angle $\theta + \delta\theta$. The horizontal rods change in length by $\delta(2a\sqrt{2} \sin \theta)$. The equation of virtual work gives

$$4W\delta\,(a \cos \theta) + 4W\delta\,(2a \cos \theta) + \\ + 4W\delta\,(3a \cos \theta) + 4P\delta\,(2\sqrt{2}a \sin \theta) = O,$$

that is,

$$-\,24Wa \sin \theta\delta\theta + 8\sqrt{2}Pa \cos \theta\delta\theta = O$$

$$P = \frac{3W}{\sqrt{2}} \tan \theta = \frac{3W}{\sqrt{2}},$$

where $\theta = \pi/4$ is substituted after the differentiation.

Consider now a displacement in which the points O, A, B, C, D are unchanged in position. The depth of E below the level of $ABCD$ being c, which in the equilibrium position is $a\sqrt{2}$, suppose E is moved vertically downwards through distance δz. The length of the lower rods before displacement is $\sqrt{(2a^2 + z^2)}$, and hence increase in length due to virtual displacement is $\delta\{\sqrt{(2a^2 + z^2)}\}$. Hence the equation of virtual work gives

$$-\,4T\delta\{\sqrt{(2a^2 + z^2)}\} + 4W\delta(\tfrac{1}{2}z) = O$$

that is

$$-\,4T\frac{z\delta z}{\sqrt{(2a^2 + z^2)}} + 4W \,.\, \tfrac{1}{2}\delta z = O,$$

or

$$T = \frac{1}{2}\,W \,.\, \frac{2a}{a\sqrt{2}} = \frac{W}{\sqrt{2}},$$

where after differentiation the value $z = a\sqrt{2}$ has been substituted.

Example 3. Four rods AB, BC, CD, DE, each of length a and weight W, are freely jointed together at B, C and D to form a chain. The ends A, E of the chain are freely attached to supports at the same level at a distance $14a/5$ apart, and B, D are joined by a light string of length $8a/5$. Use the principle of virtual work to determine the tension in the string.

What weight suspended from C will cause the tension just to vanish? [Camb. *MT* 1948]

Let θ, ϕ be the inclinations of AB, BC to the horizontal, and T the tension in the string BD. In the equilibrium position, the values of θ, ϕ satisfy the relations

$$2a \cos \theta + \cos \phi = 14a/5$$

$$2a \cos \phi = 8a/5.$$

Hence

$$\cos \phi = 4/5, \qquad \cos \theta = 3/5.$$

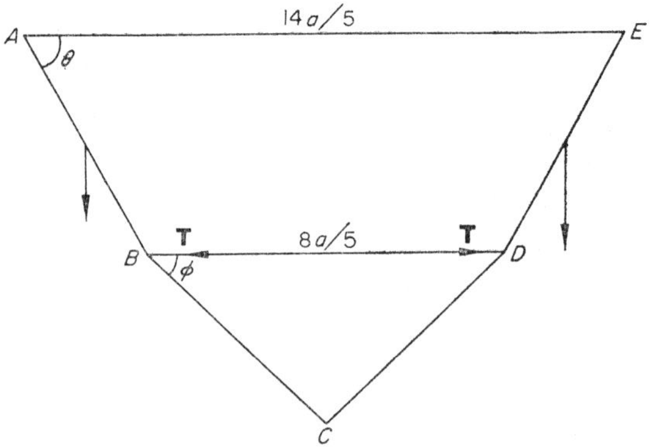

Fig. 102

Suppose the system is given a symmetrical virtual displacement in which θ changes to $\theta + \delta\theta$, ϕ to $\phi + \delta\phi$, the points A and E are unchanged, the lengths of the rods are unchanged, the vertex C moves vertically and the length BD changes. The equation of virtual work gives

$$2W\delta(\tfrac{1}{2}a \sin \theta) + 2W\delta(a \sin \theta + \tfrac{1}{2}a \sin \phi) - T\delta\,(2a \cos \phi) = O$$

that is,

$$3W \cos \theta\delta\theta + W \cos \phi\delta\phi + 2T \sin \phi\delta\phi = O.$$

The variations $\delta\theta$, $\delta\phi$ are not independent of each other. θ, ϕ are still connected by the relation

$$2a \cos \theta + 2a \cos \phi = 14a/5.$$

Hence $\delta\theta$, $\delta\phi$ are connected by the equation that is obtained from this by considering the differentials of each side, that is,

$$\delta(2a \cos\theta) + \delta(2a \cos\phi) = O.$$

Hence

$$-\sin\theta\delta\theta - \sin\phi\delta\phi = O,$$

or

$$\frac{\delta\phi}{\delta\theta} = -\frac{\sin\theta}{\sin\phi}.$$

Substituting,

$$3W\cos\theta - (W\cos\phi + 2T\sin\phi)\sin\theta/\sin\phi = O.$$

Hence

$$T = W\left(\frac{3}{2}\cot\theta - \frac{1}{2}\cot\phi\right) = \frac{11}{24}W,$$

on substituting the equilibrium values of θ and ϕ.

Now suppose that a weight w suspended from the point C is such that the tension in BD vanishes. The equation of virtual work now gives for the same virtual displacement

$$2W\delta(\tfrac{1}{2}a\sin\theta) + 2W\delta(a\sin\theta + \tfrac{1}{2}a\sin\phi) + \\ + w\delta(a\sin\theta + a\sin\phi) = O,$$

that is

$$(3W + w)\cos\theta\delta\theta + (W + w)\cos\phi\delta\phi = O.$$

Substituting for $\delta\phi/\delta\theta$

$$-(3W + w)\cos\theta\sin\phi + (W + w)\cos\phi\sin\theta = O$$

or

$$(3W + w)/(W + w) = \tan\theta\cos\phi = 16/9$$

giving

$$w = 11/7\ W.$$

Example 4. Two uniform rods AB, BC of weights W, w and lengths $2a$, $2b$ respectively are freely jointed at B and hang vertically from A If θ and ϕ are the inclinations of AB and BC to the vertical when a horizontal force X is applied at C, show by using the principle of virtual work that

$$\tan \phi = 2X/w, \qquad \tan \theta = 2X/(W + 2w).$$

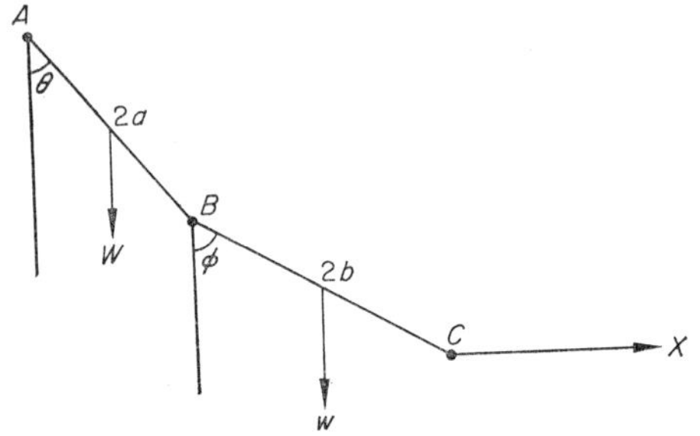

Fig. 103

The midpoints of the rods are at depths $a \cos \theta$, $2a \cos \theta + b \cos \phi$ below the level of A; and C is at a horizontal distance

$$2a \sin \theta + 2b \sin \phi$$

from the vertical through A. Hence considering a virtual displacement in which θ changes to $\theta + \delta\theta$, and ϕ to $\phi + \delta\phi$, the equation of virtual work gives

$$X\delta\,(2a \sin \theta + 2b \sin \phi) + W\delta\,(a \cos \theta) + \\ + w\delta\,(2a \cos \theta + b \cos \phi) = O,$$

that is,

$$(2X \cos \theta - W \sin \theta - 2w \sin \theta)\, a\delta\theta + \\ + (2X \cos \phi - w \sin \phi)\, b\delta\phi = O.$$

Now $\delta\theta$, $\delta\phi$ are independent quantities (unlike in the previous example where they were related), and hence the coefficients of $\delta\theta$ and $\delta\phi$ in the equation of virtual work vanish separately. Hence

$$2X \cos \theta - W \sin \theta - 2w \sin \theta = O$$
$$2X \cos \phi - w \sin \phi = O,$$

giving

$$\tan \phi = 2X/w, \qquad \tan \theta = 2X/(W + 2w).$$

Example 5. A freely jointed framework consists of four light rods AB, BC, CD and DA, forming a plane quadrilateral, and a light rod PR joining the midpoints P, R of AB and CD respectively. If a string having tension T joins the midpoints Q, S of BC and DA, prove that the thrust created in PR is of amount $T \cdot PR/QS$.

[Camb. *PM* 1947]

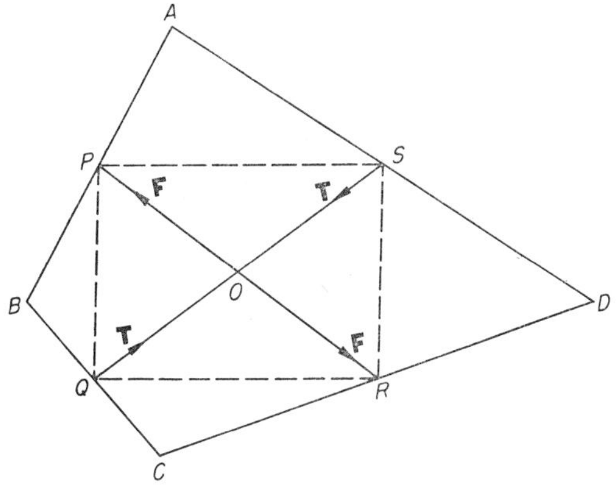

Fig. 104

Consider a virtual displacement in which the sides of the quadrilateral $ABCD$ are unchanged in length, but the angles of the quadrilateral vary. If F is the thrust in the rod PR, the equation of virtual work gives

$$F\delta(PR) - T\delta(QS) = O. \qquad \text{(i)}$$

To find the relationship between $\delta(PR)$ and $\delta(QS)$, we use the geometrical properties of the system. When PQ, QR, RS, SP are joined, we see that the figure $PQRS$ is a parallelogram, because PS and QR are parallel, being both parallel to BD, and PQ and SR are parallel, being both parallel to AC. Hence the diagonals PR and QS bisect each other, at the point O say. Since OQ is a median of the triangle BOC,

$$OB^2 + OC^2 = \tfrac{1}{2}BC^2 + \tfrac{1}{2}QS^2.$$

From the triangle COD,

$$OC^2 + OD^2 = \tfrac{1}{2}CD^2 + \tfrac{1}{2}PR^2.$$

Subtracting

$$OB^2 - OD^2 = \tfrac{1}{2}(BC^2 - CD^2) + \tfrac{1}{2}(QS^2 - PR^2).$$

Similarly

$$OB^2 - OD^2 = \tfrac{1}{2}(BA^2 - AD^2) + \tfrac{1}{2}(PR^2 - QS^2).$$

Subtracting these, one obtains

$$QS^2 - PR^2 = \tfrac{1}{2}(BA^2 - AD^2 - BC^2 + CD^2) = \text{const.}$$

for the virtual displacement considered. Taking differential elements,

$$QS\delta\,(QS) - PR\delta\,(PR) = O. \qquad \text{(ii)}$$

Hence

$$\frac{F}{T} = \frac{\delta\,(QS)}{\delta\,(PR)} = \frac{PR}{QS}.$$

7.5. Potential energy

When a particle is situated at a point P in a field of force, it has a certain capacity to do work in virtue of its position, work being done when the particle is moved from the position P to a chosen standard position, P_0 say. Let $\mathbf{F}(\mathbf{r})$, with components (X, Y, Z), be the force on the particle when its position vector is $\mathbf{r}$. The work done in moving from P to P_0 is given by the line integral

$$\int_{\mathbf{r}}^{\mathbf{r}_0} \mathbf{F} \,.\, \mathbf{ds}$$

the integral being taken along the path of the particle from P to P_0.

Given P and P_0, the value of such an integral would generally depend on the particular path from P to P_0. There are, however, special cases of interest where the integral is found to be independent of the path. For example, if $X = 4x$, $Y = 2y$, $Z = O$, the integral is

$$\int_{\mathbf{r}}^{\mathbf{r}_0} 4x\mathrm{d}x + 2y\mathrm{d}y = [2x^2 + y^2]_{\mathbf{r}}^{\mathbf{r}_0} = 2x_0^2 + y_0^2 - 2x^2 - y^2,$$

which depends on the coordinates of P and P_0 and not on the path joining them. But if we take the case $X = 4y$, $Y = 2x$, $Z = O$, then the integral is

$$\int_{\mathbf{r}}^{\mathbf{r}_0} (4y\, dx + 2x\, dy)$$

which has different values for different paths, as may be verified by considering two separate paths along the sides of a rectangular solid formed by planes parallel to the axial planes through P and P_0.

When **F** is such that the integral is independent of the path, then **F** is to be a conservative field of force. A particle moving in such a field is said to have a *potential energy*, the value of which in the position P and relative to the standard position P_0 is given by the potential energy function

$$V(P) = V(\mathbf{r}) = \int_{\mathbf{r}}^{\mathbf{r}_0} \mathbf{F} \,.\, d\mathbf{s}.$$

This may also be written

$$V(\mathbf{r}) = -\int_{\mathbf{r}_0}^{\mathbf{r}} \mathbf{F} \,.\, d\mathbf{s} = -\int_{P_0}^{P} (X\, dx + Y\, dy + Z\, dz).$$

Different choices of the standard position P_0 would change the potential energy function by a constant, but does not affect the value of the difference between the potential energy functions at two points. By definition, the point P_0 has the property $V(P_0) = O$. Often the standard position is taken at ∞. Then

$$V(P) = -\int_{\infty}^{P} \mathbf{F} \,.\, d\mathbf{s}.$$

If P' is a point $\mathbf{r} + \delta\mathbf{r}$ in the neighbourhood of P,

$$V(P') - V(P) = V(\mathbf{r} + \delta\mathbf{r}) - V(\mathbf{r}) = -\int_{P}^{P'} \mathbf{F} \,.\, d\mathbf{s} = -\mathbf{F} \,.\, \delta\mathbf{s}.$$

Thus

$$\delta V = -\mathbf{F} \,.\, \delta\mathbf{s} = -(X\delta x + Y\delta y + Z\delta z).$$

Hence $X\,dx + Y\,dy + Z\,dz$ is a perfect differential $-dV$. Also

$$X = -\frac{\partial V}{\partial x}, \qquad Y = -\frac{\partial V}{\partial y}, \qquad Z = -\frac{\partial V}{\partial z}$$

or

$$\mathbf{F} = -\operatorname{grad} V$$

in vector notation.

As an example, if one considers a particle of mass m in the gravitational field of the earth, then taking ground level as standard level of potential energy, and origin O is a point at ground level, then $X = 0$, $Y = 0$, $Z = -mg$ and the potential energy of the particle when it occupies the position $P(x, y, z)$ is

$$V = -\int_0^P (-mg\,dz) = mgz,$$

The potential energy of a system of n particles m_1 at P_1, m_2 at P_2, ... is $\sum_{i=1}^{n} m_i g z_i = Mg\bar{z}$ where $M = \sum m_i$, and $\bar{z}$ is the height of the centre of mass above ground level.

Potential Energy of an Elastic String

Suppose the unstretched state is taken as the standard configuration of zero potential energy. Taking x-axis along the string, the force at the free end when the extension is x is given by

$$X = -T = -\frac{\lambda x}{l}, \qquad Y = 0, \qquad Z = 0,$$

where λ is the modulus of elasticity and l the unstretched length of the string

$$V(x) = -\int_0^x \left(-\frac{\lambda x}{l}\right) dx = \frac{1}{2}\frac{\lambda x^2}{l}$$

$$= \tfrac{1}{2}\,\text{modulus} \times (\text{extension})^2/(\text{natural length}).$$

Conditions of Equilibrium of a Conservative System

The principle of virtual work gives the condition of equilibrium of a system as equivalent to $\delta W = O$. But from the above it is seen that for a conservative system $\delta W = -\delta V$, and hence the condition of equilibrium may be expressed in the form $\delta V = O$. That is, the potential energy function V is stationary at positions of equilibrium for small displacements.

For a single particle whose coordinates are x, y, z and which is acted upon by conservative forces, the potential energy is a function of x, y, z and the equilibrium conditions may be written

$$\frac{\partial V}{\partial x} = \frac{\partial V}{\partial y} = \frac{\partial V}{\partial z} = O.$$

For a particle or a system of particles or bodies under the influence of their weights, other forces not contributing to energy loss or to potential energy of the system, $V = Mg\bar{z}$, and the condition of equilibrium is that $\bar{z}$, which is the height of the centre of mass of the system above some fixed horizontal level, is stationary in the equilibrium position. This property may be used to determine the possible position of equilibrium of a system.

Example 1. Three uniform rods, OA, OB, and OC are each of length l and of weight W; they are smoothly jointed together at O and are placed symmetrically over a smooth fixed sphere of radius a, the joint O being vertically above the centre and the rods resting on its surface in equilibrium. Show that

$$l \sin^3 \alpha = 2a \cos \alpha,$$

where α is the angle each rod makes with the downward vertical, and deduce that the rods will be at right angles if (and only if) $l = 3a/\sqrt{2}$. [Oxf. *I* 1956]

The system is symmetrically placed, and the height of centre of mass of the system above the level of the centre of the sphere is

$$\bar{z} = a \operatorname{cosec} \alpha - \frac{l}{2} \cos \alpha.$$

For equilibrium, $\bar{z}$ is stationary for varying values of α. Hence the value of α in the position of equilibrium is given by $d\bar{z}/d\alpha = O$.

$$\frac{d\bar{z}}{d\alpha} = -a \operatorname{cosec} \alpha \cot \alpha + \frac{l}{2} \sin \alpha = O.$$

Hence

$$l \sin^3 \alpha = 2a \cos \alpha.$$

If the rods are at right angles to each other, then referred to OA, OB, OC as axes, the direction cosines of the downward vertical through O are ($\cos \alpha$, $\cos \alpha$, $\cos \alpha$) and hence the sum of their squares is unity, that is, $3 \cos^2 \alpha = 1$, or $\cos \alpha = 1/\sqrt{3}$, and $\sin \alpha = \sqrt{(2/3)}$. Therefore

$$l = 2a \cdot \frac{1}{\sqrt{3}} \cdot \sqrt{\left(\frac{3}{2}\right)^3} = 3a/\sqrt{2}.$$

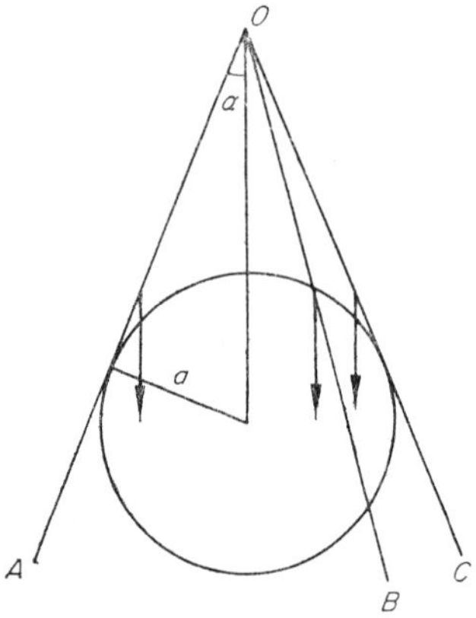

Fig. 105

Example 2. Five equal, uniform rods are freely jointed together at their ends to form a closed chain *ABCDEA*, and the system hangs freely from *A*. Prove that, if *AB* and *BC* are inclined to the vertical at angles θ and ϕ respectively, then

$$\tan \phi = 2 \tan \theta.$$

Prove that $\sin \theta$ is the root between O and $\frac{1}{4}$ of the equation

$$(1 - 2x)^2 = \frac{16x^2}{1 + 3x^2},$$

and show that the equation has one, and only one, root in this range. [Camb. *MT*]

Let each rod be of length l. The angles θ and ϕ are not independent but are connected by the relation

$$AB \sin\theta + BC \sin\phi = \tfrac{1}{2} CD \text{ or } \sin\theta + \sin\phi = \tfrac{1}{2}. \qquad \text{(i)}$$

One of the angles may be treated as an independent variable. Suppose that θ is so treated, then the variation of ϕ with θ is given by

$$\cos\theta + \cos\phi \frac{d\phi}{d\theta} = 0 \text{ or } \frac{d\phi}{d\theta} = -\cos\theta \sec\phi. \qquad \text{(ii)}$$

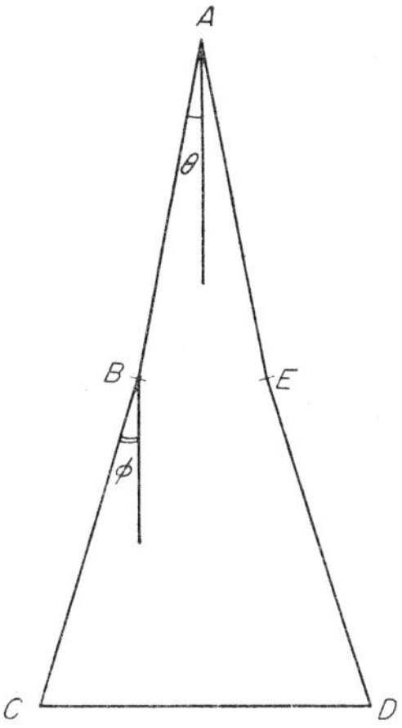

Fig. 106

The potential energy function is

$$\left.\begin{aligned} V(\theta) &= -2 \,.\, mg\frac{l}{2}\cos\theta - 2mg\left(l\cos\theta + \frac{l}{2}\cos\phi\right) - \\ &\qquad - mg\,(l\cos\theta + l\cos\phi) \\ &= -2mgl\,(2\cos\theta + \cos\phi). \end{aligned}\right\} \qquad \text{(iii)}$$

$$\begin{aligned} \frac{dV}{d\theta} &= -2mgl\left(-2\sin\theta - \sin\phi\frac{d\phi}{d\theta}\right) \\ &= -2mgl\,(-2\sin\theta + \tan\phi\cos\theta) = O \end{aligned}$$

gives

$$\tan \phi = 2 \tan \theta. \tag{iv}$$

Squaring

$$\tan^2 \phi = 4 \tan^2 \theta,$$

from which

$$\sin^2 \phi = \frac{4 \tan^2 \theta}{1 + 4 \tan^2 \theta} = \frac{4 \sin^2 \theta}{\cos^2 \theta + 4 \sin^2 \theta} = \frac{4 \sin^2 \theta}{1 + 3 \sin^2 \theta}.$$

Putting $\sin \theta = x$ and $\sin \phi = \frac{1}{2} - x$, this becomes

$$(\tfrac{1}{2} - x)^2 = \frac{4x^2}{1 + 3x^2} \text{ or } (1 - 2x)^2 = \frac{16x^2}{1 + 3x^2}. \tag{v}$$

Since $\phi > \theta$, and $\sin \theta + \sin \phi = \frac{1}{2}$, it follows that $\sin \theta < \frac{1}{4}$. Thus $\sin \theta$ is the value of x between 0 and $\frac{1}{4}$ and satisfying the equation (v).

To show that the equation has one and only one root in this range, suppose that one draws the two curves

$$y = (1 - 2x)^2, \qquad y = 16x^2/(1 + 3x^2)$$

for positive values of x. The first curve starts when $x = O$ at the point $y = 1$ and decreases steadily as x increases, while the second curve starts at the origin and increases steadily as x increases. Hence there is one and only one point of intersection of the two curves for positive values of x, that is, the equation has one and only one positive root. This root lies between 0 and $\frac{1}{4}$.

Example 3. A particle moves under a force of attraction μ/r^2 towards a centre of force O, where r is the distance from O and μ is a constant. Find the potential energy of the particle.

The force on the particle is

$$\mathbf{F} = - \mu\mathbf{r}/r^3$$

where $\mathbf{r}$ is the position vector of the particle. Taking infinity as standard configuration of zero potential energy, the potential energy at P is

$$V(P) = - \int_\infty^P (- \mu\mathbf{r}/r^3) \,.\, d\mathbf{s} = \int_\infty^P \mu\mathbf{r} \,.\, d\mathbf{r}/r^3,$$

since $\mathbf{ds} = \mathbf{dr}$. Also since $\mathbf{r}^2 = r^2$, by differentiation $\mathbf{r} \cdot \mathbf{dr} = r\mathrm{d}r$, and hence

$$V(P) = \int_{\infty}^{P} \mu \frac{\mathrm{d}r}{r^2} = \left[-\frac{\mu}{r}\right]_{\infty}^{P} = -\frac{\mu}{OP}.$$

The integral is independent of the path, and the force is conservative.

7.6. Generalized coordinates

To describe the position of a particle in space, there are used three coordinates, which may be Cartesian coordinates (x, y, z) or spherical polar coordinates (γ, θ, ϕ) or more general curvilinear coordinates (u_1, u_2, u_3). To describe a pair of particles there are required six coordinates, and for a system of p particles $3p$ coordinates are required. If, however, the particles have some geometrical relationship between them, as for example when two particles are connected by a rod of given length, the number of independent variables is reduced. Thus a rigid body though it may be thought of being composed out of a large number of particles has only six independent variables.

If a system is such that its configuration is specified by a set of k independent variables $q_1, q_2, \ldots, q_k$, then k is said to be the number of **degrees of freedom** of the system, and the variables $q_1, \ldots q_k$ are called *generalized coordinates* of the system. If such a system is acted upon by conservative forces, there is then a potential energy function which may be expressed in terms of the k variables as $V(q_1, \ldots, q_k)$. $-\mathrm{d}V$ is then expressible as a sum of linear terms in the differentials $\mathrm{d}q_1, \ldots, \mathrm{d}q_k$ in the form

$$-\mathrm{d}V = Q_1\,\mathrm{d}q_1 + \ldots\ Q_i\,\mathrm{d}q_i + \ldots + Q_k\,\mathrm{d}q_k,$$

where the coefficient of $\mathrm{d}q_i$ is Q_i, $i = 1, \ldots, k$. Since $\mathrm{d}q_1, \ldots \mathrm{d}q_k$ are independent, it follows that

$$Q_i = -\frac{\partial V}{\partial q_i}, \qquad i = 1, \ldots, k.$$

By analogy with

$$-\mathrm{d}V = X\,\mathrm{d}x + Y\,\mathrm{d}y + Z\,\mathrm{d}z,$$

the expressions $Q_1, Q_2, \ldots, Q_k$ are called generalized components of forces, Q_i being the '*force tending to increase* q_i'. If q_i denotes an angle θ, then the corresponding coefficient Q_i is the couple tending to increase θ. If q_i is a length, then Q_i is a force in the usual sense.

The conditions of equilibrium of the system, namely that the potential energy function is stationary, is now equivalent to the k equations,

$$\frac{\partial V}{\partial q_1} = \frac{\partial V}{\partial q_2} = \ldots = \frac{\partial V}{\partial q_k} = O.$$

As an example let us consider a particle P of mass m, joined by an inextensible string of length l to a fixed point O. The particle moves on a sphere, and its position may be specified by two polar angles θ and ϕ, the point $\theta = O$ being vertically above the centre of sphere. θ, ϕ may be taken as the generalized coordinates of the particle. The forces acting on the particle are its weight and the tension of the string. The potential energy is $mgl \cos \theta$. The generalized forces Q_θ, Q_ϕ are given by

$$Q_\theta \, d\theta + Q_\phi \, d\phi = - dV = - d(mgl \cos \theta) = mgl \sin \theta \, d\theta$$

so that

$$Q_\theta = mgl \sin \theta, \qquad Q_\phi = O.$$

7.7. Stability of equilibrium

The positions of equilibrium of a system may be classified as **stable, unstable** or **neutral,** in the senses indicated below. Suppose that a body in equilibrium is given a slight displacement and released. If after every such displacement the forces acting upon the body in the displaced position tend to restore the body to the original equilibrium position, then the body is said to be in stable equilibrium. If, however, the forces in the displaced position tend to move the body further away from the equilibrium position, then the body is in unstable equilibrium. The case when the forces tend to restore for some displacements and move further away for others is also described as unstable, the term stability being used only when restoring forces come into action in every displacement. If after every displacement the forces in the displaced position are still in equilibrium, then the body is said to be in neutral equilibrium.

Take the case of a uniform rod that is free to turn about a fixed point O of it. There are two possible positions of equilibrium, in both of which the rod is vertical. In one, the centre of gravity G of the rod is vertically above O, and in the other G is vertically below O. The position with G above O is unstable, because a small disturbance would cause the rod to turn right away from this position and swing downwards. The position with G below O is stable since after every small displacement the rod will tend to swing back to its original position. In the case where O and G coincide, that is, when the rod is pivoted at its midpoint, equilibrium is neutral. A lead pencil stood vertically upon a table or a stone resting on a mountain peak are examples of unstable systems.

It was seen above that for a conservative system the potential energy function provides a good way of determining the positions of equilibrium by using the property that the function V is stationary at positions of equilibrium. The function V may be further used to investigate whether positions of equilibrium are stable or not.

It may be shown that a position of equilibrium is stable if, and only if, the potential energy is a minimum at this position.

Let E_o denote the position of equilibrium and E the neighbouring displaced position from which the system is released. We make use of the principle of conservation of energy in the form

$$T + V = \text{constant.}$$

When the system is released from rest at E, $T(E) = O$, and since E is not a position of equilibrium, the system will commence to move and T will begin to increase. The motion will be in that sense which makes $T + V$ remain a constant and therefore in the sense in which V decreases. Now if V is a minimum at E_o, then $V(E) > V(E_o)$, and hence the direction in which V decreases is towards E_o, and therefore the motion is towards the position of equilibrium. Hence the equilibrium is stable in this case. If, however, V is a maximum at E_o, then

$V(E) < V(E_0)$, and the direction in which V decreases is away from E_0, and therefore the motion is away from the equilibrium position.

Hence equilibrium is stable if V is a minimum at the position of equilibrium and is unstable if V is a maximum.

For a system of one degree of freedom, if the variable used is q and the potential energy function $V(q)$, then if $q = q_0$ is a position of stable equilibrium

$$\left(\frac{dV}{dq}\right)_{q_0} = 0$$

and dV/dq changes sign from negative to positive as q increases through q_0, or

$$\left(\frac{d^2V}{dq^2}\right)_{q_0} > 0.$$

$q = q_0$ is a position of unstable equilibrium if $\left(\frac{dV}{dq}\right)_{q=q_0} = 0,$

and dV/dq changes sign from positive to negative as q increases through q_0 or

$$\left(\frac{d^2V}{dq^2}\right)_{q=q_0} < 0.$$

The rule may be summed up in the following table:

$\frac{dV}{dq}$	$\frac{d^2V}{dq^2}$	V	Equilibrium classification
0	$+$	minimum	stable
0	$-$	maximum	unstable

Example 1. A uniform rod AB of weight W and length $2a$ can turn freely about a fixed hinge at one end A and has a smooth light ring fixed to the other end B. A light inextensible string has one end attached to a fixed point C at the same level as A and distant $2a$

from it, passes through the ring at B and carries at its other end a load $W/10$ hanging vertically. In the position of equilibrium in which B is below AC find the angle CAB and prove that this position is stable. [Lond. G 1936]

Suppose the angle CAB is θ, and the length of the string CD is l. Then $BC = 4a \sin \frac{1}{2}\theta$, $BD = l - 4a \sin \frac{1}{2}\theta$. The potential energy, taking AC as level of zero potential energy, is

$$V = -Wa \sin \theta - \frac{W}{10}(2a \sin \theta + l - 4a \sin \tfrac{1}{2}\theta).$$

$$\frac{dV}{d\theta} = Wa\left[-\cos\theta - \frac{1}{5}\cos\theta + \frac{1}{5}\cos\frac{1}{2}\theta\right] = O$$

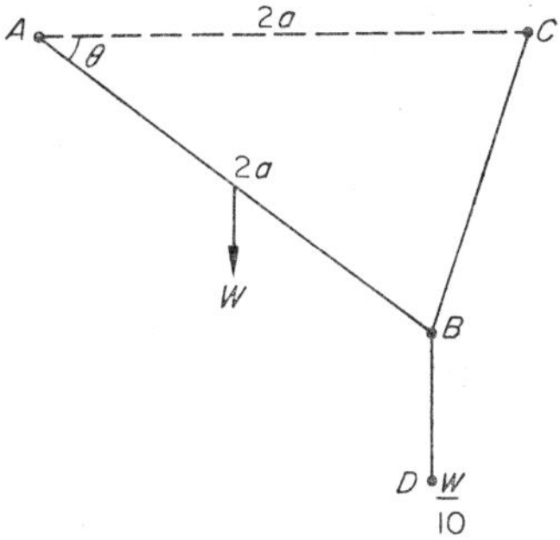

Fig. 107

when

$$6 \cos\theta = \cos\tfrac{1}{2}\theta$$

or

$$12 \cos^2 \tfrac{1}{2}\theta - \cos\tfrac{1}{2}\theta - 6 = O,$$

that is

$$(4 \cos\tfrac{1}{2}\theta - 3)(3 \cos\tfrac{1}{2}\theta + 2) = O.$$

Since $\theta < \pi$, the permissible value of $\cos\frac{1}{2}\theta$ is positive. Hence the angle θ in the position of equilibrium satisfies $\cos\theta/2 = \frac{3}{4}$ from which $\cos\theta = 2 \cdot \frac{9}{16} - 1 = \frac{1}{8}$.

To discuss the stability of this position, we proceed to evaluate $d^2V/d\theta^2$.

$$\frac{d^2V}{d\theta^2} = Wa\left(\frac{6}{5}\sin\theta - \frac{1}{10}\sin\tfrac{1}{2}\theta\right)$$

$$= Wa\sin\tfrac{1}{2}\theta\left(\frac{12}{5}\cos\tfrac{1}{2}\theta - \frac{1}{10}\right)$$

$$= Wa\sin\tfrac{1}{2}\theta\left(\frac{12}{5}\cdot\frac{3}{4} - \frac{1}{10}\right) > 0$$

Hence the equilibrium position is stable.

Example 2. A uniform square lamina of side $2a$ rests in a vertical plane with two of its sides in contact with horizontal smooth pegs distant b apart, and in the same horizontal line.

Show that, if $a/\sqrt{2} < b < a$, a non-symmetrical position of equilibrium is possible in which

$$b(\sin\theta + \cos\theta) = a,$$

where θ is the inclination of a side of the square to the horizontal.

Investigate the stability of this position.

[Lond. *G* 1956]

Let θ be the inclination to the horizontal of those sides of the square which have the least inclination, that is, $O < \theta \leqslant \pi/4$. If z denotes the height of the centre of gravity of the body above the level of the pegs

$$z = a\sqrt{2}\sin\left(\theta + \frac{\pi}{4}\right) - b\cos\theta\sin\theta$$

$$= a(\sin\theta + \cos\theta) - b\cos\theta\sin\theta.$$

$$\frac{dz}{d\theta} = a(\cos\theta - \sin\theta) - b(\cos^2\theta - \sin^2\theta)$$

$$= (\cos\theta - \sin\theta)[a - b(\cos\theta + \sin\theta)].$$

Hence the positions of equilibrium are given by

$$\cos\theta - \sin\theta = O \qquad \text{(i)}$$

$$b(\sin\theta + \cos\theta) = a. \qquad \text{(ii)}$$

The solution of (i) corresponds to the symmetrical position for which $\theta = \pi/4$. A non-symmetrical position $\theta = \alpha$, $O < \alpha < \pi/4$ is possible when the equation (ii) has a real solution $\theta = \alpha$. Equation (ii) may be written

$$\sin\left(\alpha + \frac{\pi}{4}\right) = \left(\frac{a}{b\sqrt{2}}\right).$$

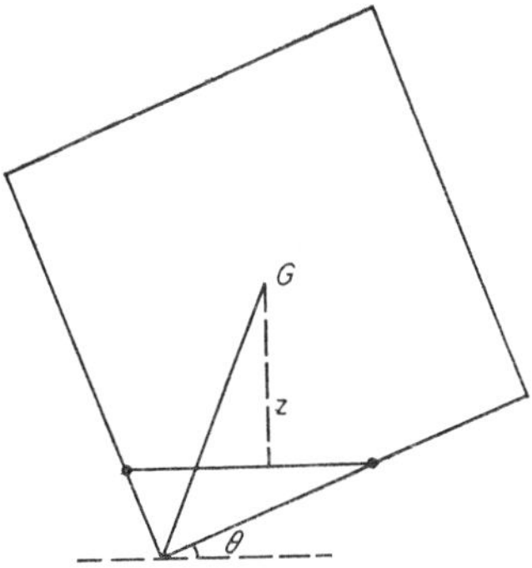

Fig. 108

In the range

$$\frac{\pi}{4} < \alpha + \frac{\pi}{4} < \frac{\pi}{2},$$

$$\sin\frac{\pi}{4} < \sin\left(\alpha + \frac{\pi}{4}\right) < \sin\frac{\pi}{2},$$

that is

$$\frac{1}{\sqrt{2}} < \frac{a}{b\sqrt{2}} < 1$$

or

$$\frac{a}{\sqrt{2}} < b < a.$$

Hence under the conditions stated, a non-symmetrical position of equilibrium $\theta = \alpha (O < \alpha < \pi/4)$ exists.

To consider stability,

$$\frac{d^2z}{d\theta^2} = (\cos\theta - \sin\theta)\, b(\sin\theta - \cos\theta) -$$
$$- (\sin\theta + \cos\theta)[a - b(\cos\theta + \sin\theta)].$$

Hence

$$\left(\frac{d^2z}{d\theta^2}\right)_{\theta=\alpha} = -\, b(\sin\alpha - \cos\alpha)^2 < O.$$

Therefore this position of equilibrium is unstable.

Example 3. A uniform rod AB, of length a and weight W, is smoothly hinged to fixed point at the end A, while B is connected to a fixed point C, which is at a distance $3a$ vertically above A, by a light elastic string. The natural length of the string is a, and the tension needed to double the length is kW. Prove that the potential energy of the system when the string CB has length $na(2 \leqslant n \leqslant 4)$ is

$$\frac{aW}{12}(6k-1)\left(n - \frac{6k}{6k-1}\right)^2 + \text{constant}.$$

Hence show that, if $k < 2/9$, the position with B vertically above $A(n = 2)$ is unstable, and the position with B vertically below $A(n = 4)$ is stable. Show also that, if $k > \frac{1}{3}$, the position $n = 2$ is stable, and the position $n = 4$ is unstable.

Examine the positions of equilibrium if $2/9 \leqslant k \leqslant 1/3$. Show in a diagram the values of n in the positions of equilibrium for all positive values of k, indicating which positions are stable and which are unstable. [Camb. *MT* 1957]

The modulus of the string is kW. Potential energy is due to the weight of the rod as well as the elasticity of the string. If θ is the inclination of the rod AB to the upward vertical, length of BC being na,

$$n^2 = 10 - 6\cos\theta, \qquad \text{(i)}$$

and the potential energy of the system is

$$
\begin{aligned}
V &= \frac{1}{2} Wa \cos \theta + \frac{1}{2}\frac{kW}{a} \{a\sqrt{(10 - 6 \cos \theta)} - a\}^2 \\
&= \tfrac{1}{2} Wa (10 - n^2)/6 + \tfrac{1}{2} kW (n - 1)^2 a \\
&= \frac{Wa}{12} [(6k - 1) n^2 - 12 kn + 10] \\
&= \frac{Wa}{12} (6k - 1)\left[\left(n - \frac{6k}{6k-1}\right)^2 + 10 - \left(\frac{6k}{6k-1}\right)^2\right] \\
&= \frac{Wa}{12} (6k - 1)\left(n - \frac{6k}{6k-1}\right)^2 + \text{const.}
\end{aligned} \tag{ii}
$$

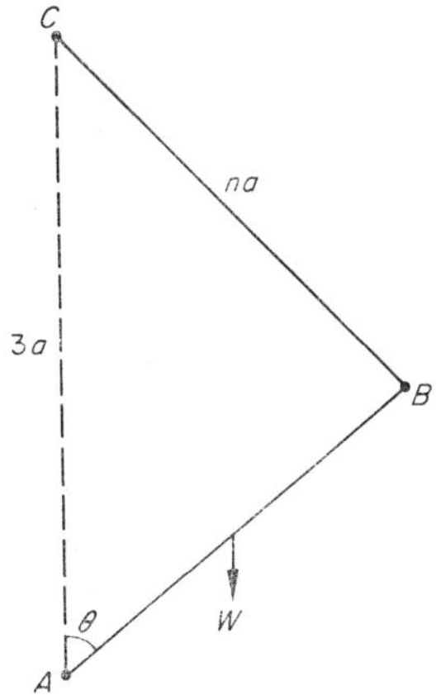

Fig. 109

By writing the last term as a constant, the particular level chosen as standard position for measurement of potential energy is left unspecified, and is often a convenience in the calculation.

$$
\begin{aligned}
\frac{dV}{d\theta} &= \frac{Wa}{12} (6k - 1)\, 2\left(n - \frac{6k}{6k-1}\right) \frac{dn}{d\theta} \\
&= \frac{Wa}{2} \left[6k - 1 - \frac{6k}{n}\right] \sin \theta,
\end{aligned} \tag{iii}
$$

using

$$\frac{dn}{d\theta} = \frac{3 \sin \theta}{n}. \tag{iv}$$

Possible positions of equilibrium are given by $dV/d\theta = O$, that is

$$\sin \theta = O \text{ or } n = \frac{6k}{6k - 1}.$$

Hence $\theta = O$ and $\theta = \pi$ are both positions of equilibrium, $\theta = O$ giving the position with B vertically above A and $n = 2$, and $\theta = \pi$ the position with B vertically below A and $n = 4$.

A third position $\theta = \alpha$ would exist if the equation $n = 6k/(6k-1)$ leads to a real value for θ between O and π. Such a position will certainly not exist if $k < 1/6$, for then the term in square brackets in the expression (iii) for $dV/d\theta$ would be negative and cannot vanish. From $n = \sqrt{(10 - 6 \cos \theta)}$, $|\cos \theta| < 1$, the condition for the existence of the inclined position $\theta = \alpha$ is

$$\sqrt{(10 - 6)} < 6k/(6k - 1) < \sqrt{(10 + 6)}$$

or

$$2(6k - 1) < 6k < 4(6k - 1)$$

from which one obtains

$$2/9 < k < 1/3.$$

Hence when $2/9 < k < 1/3$, there is a third position of equilibrium $\theta = \alpha$, $O < \alpha < \pi$.

To investigate stability, one may use the sign of $d^2V/d\theta^2$. (For convenience, in writing, dashes are used to indicate differentiation.) From (iii)

$$V''(\theta) = \frac{aW}{2}\left[\left(6k - 1 - \frac{6k}{n}\right) \cos \theta + \frac{18k}{n^3} \sin^2 \theta\right]$$

$$V''(O) = \frac{aW}{2} (3k - 1)$$

$$V''(\pi) = -\frac{aW}{2}\left(\frac{9k}{2} - 1\right)$$

$$V''(\alpha) = \frac{aW}{2} . 18k \left(\frac{6k - 1}{6k}\right)^3 \sin^2 \alpha.$$

When $k < 2/9$, there are only two positions of equilibrium, namely $\theta = O$, $(n = 2)$ and $\theta = \pi$, $(n = 4)$. $V''(O)$ is negative and $V''(\pi)$ positive. Hence V is a maximum at $\theta = O$, and a minimum at $\theta = \pi$, that is, the position $\theta = O$ is unstable and position $\theta = \pi$ stable.

When $k > 1/3$, then also there are only two positions of equilibrium, namely $\theta = O$ and $\theta = \pi$. $V''(O)$ is positive, $V''(\pi)$ is negative, and hence the position $\theta = O$ is stable while the position $\theta = \pi$ is unstable. When $2/9 < k < 1/3$, $V''(O) < O$, $V''(\pi) < O$, $V''(\alpha) > O$. Hence the inclined position is stable, and the remaining two positions are unstable.

There still remain for consideration the cases when $k = 2/9$ and $k = 1/3$. When $k = 2/9$

$$V'(\theta) = \frac{aW}{6}(1 - 4/n)\sin\theta$$

$$V''(\theta) = \frac{aW}{6}\left[\left(1 - \frac{4}{n}\right)\cos\theta + \frac{4}{n^3}\sin^2\theta\right].$$

$\theta = O$ and $\theta = \pi$ are the only solutions of $V'(\theta) = O$. Further

$$V''(O) = -\frac{aW}{6}, \qquad V''(\pi) = O.$$

The position $\theta = O$ is unstable. For the position $\theta = \pi$, this test is inconclusive. To consider whether V is a maximum or minimum one may consider higher derivatives.

$$V'''(\theta) = \frac{aW}{6}\left[-\left(1 - \frac{4}{n}\right)\sin\theta + \frac{20}{n^3}\sin\theta\cos\theta - \frac{36}{n^5}\sin^3\theta\right]$$

$$V''''(\pi) = \frac{aW}{6}\left[\left(1 - \frac{4}{n}\right) + \frac{20}{n^3}\right] = \frac{5aW}{96},$$

using $n = 4$ when $\theta = \pi$.

Hence V is a minimum at $\theta = \pi$, and this position is stable.

When

$$k = \tfrac{1}{3},$$

$$V'(\theta) = \frac{aW}{2}\left(1 - \frac{2}{n}\right)\sin\theta.$$

$$V''(\theta) = \frac{aW}{2}\left[\left(1 - \frac{2}{n}\right)\cos\theta + \frac{6}{n^3}\sin^2\theta\right].$$

$$V''(O) = O, \qquad V''(\pi) = \frac{aW}{2}(-\tfrac{1}{2}) < 0.$$

Hence the position $\theta = \pi$ is unstable. The method, however, is inconclusive for $\theta = O$. As before

$$V'''(\theta) = \frac{aW}{2}\left[-\left(1 - \frac{2}{n}\right)\sin\theta + \frac{18}{n^3}\sin\theta\cos\theta - \frac{54}{n^5}\sin^3\theta\right]$$

$$V''''(O) = \frac{aW}{2}\left[-\left(1 - \frac{2}{n}\right) + \frac{18}{n^3}\right] = \frac{9}{256}\,aW > 0,$$

using $n = 2$ when $\theta = O$.

Hence V is a minimum at $\theta = O$, and the position is stable.

The results may be summarized in the following table:

k	$0<k\leqslant\frac{2}{9}$	$\frac{2}{9}<k<\frac{1}{3}$	$k\geqslant\frac{1}{3}$
Number of positions of equilibrium	2	3	2
n	$n=2$; unstable $n=4$: stable	$n=2$: unstable $n=6k/(6k-1)$, $2<n<4$: stable $n=4$: unstable	$n=2$: stable $n=4$: unstable

It may be noted that maxima and minima of a function of a single variable occur alternately, and hence stable and unstable positions also occur alternately.

This example shows that the rule for determining stability from the sign of the second derivative becomes cumbersome when the second derivative vanishes. A convenient alternative method of determining whether a stationary value $q = q_0$ is a maximum, minimum or a point of inflexion is to consider the sign of $\mathrm{d}V/\mathrm{d}q$ as q increases from a value just less than q_0 to a value just greater than q_0. If there is a change of sign from negative to positive, V is a minimum, if from positive to negative V is a maximum, and if there is no change in sign then V has a point of inflexion at $q = q_0$.

Thus in the above example, to investigate whether $\theta = O$ is a maximum, minimum or a point of inflexion, one considers the sign of $\mathrm{d}V/\mathrm{d}\theta$ as θ goes from $-\epsilon$ to $+\epsilon$, where ϵ is a small positive quantity. If $k \neq \frac{1}{3}$,

$$V'(-\epsilon) = -\tfrac{1}{2}\, Wa\,(3k - 1)\,\epsilon$$
$$V'(\epsilon) = \tfrac{1}{2}\, Wa\,(3k - 1)\,\epsilon$$

approximately, where $n = 2$ is substituted. V is a maximum at $\theta = O$ if $k < \frac{1}{3}$ and minimum if $k > \frac{1}{3}$.

If $k = \frac{1}{3}$,

$$\begin{aligned} V'(-\epsilon) &= -\tfrac{1}{2}\, Wa\,[1 - 2/\sqrt{(10 - 6\cos\epsilon)}]\,\epsilon \\ &= -\tfrac{1}{2}\, Wa\,.\,\tfrac{3}{8}\,\epsilon^3 \\ V'(\epsilon) &= \tfrac{1}{2}\, Wa\,.\,\tfrac{3}{8}\,\epsilon^3 \end{aligned}$$

Hence V is a minimum in this case.

Thus the position $\theta = O$ is stable if $k \geqslant \frac{1}{3}$ and unstable if $k < \frac{1}{3}$. Similarly the other positions also may be investigated conveniently by this method.

If a particular stationary value $q = q_0$ corresponds to a point of inflexion, the tangent at $q = q_0$ is parallel to the q-axis since $V'(q_0) = O$, the position would be stable for displacements on one side and unstable for other displacements, and hence by definition the system is unstable.

7.8. Rocking cylinders and spheres

Some interesting problems of stability arise in connection with rocking cylinders and spheres. The following example illustrates some features of these problems.

Suppose a circular cylinder of radius r is uniform along its length, but not necessarily uniform over its cross-section, and rests upon a fixed circular cylinder of radius R, the axes of the cylinders being horizontal and parallel, and in the same vertical plane. If the surfaces are rough enough to prevent slipping, it is of interest to investigate the stability of equilibrium for small rolling displacements of the upper cylinder, the axes remaining parallel and horizontal. Suppose height of the centre of gravity of the body above the line of contact is h.

Figure 110 shows the central cross-section of the cylinders before and after displacement. Suppose O is the position of the centre of the upper cylinder, G its centre of gravity and I the point of contact after displacement, and let the suffix zero denote the corresponding quantities in the equilibrium position. Let θ and ϕ be the angles shown. Then θ and ϕ are related by the rolling condition

$$II_0 = IJ, \text{ that is, } R\theta = r\phi. \qquad \text{(i)}$$

The equilibrium is stable or not according as G lies to the left or right of the vertical through I, that is, according as

$$OI \sin \theta \lesseqgtr OG \sin (\theta + \phi),$$

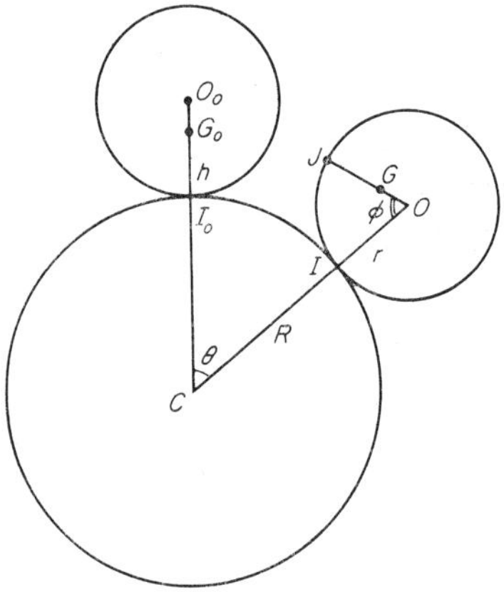

Fig. 110

i.e.

$$r \sin \theta \lesseqgtr (r - h) \sin (\theta + \phi). \tag{ii}$$

Substituting for ϕ in terms of θ from (i) and expanding the sine functions,

$$\left.\begin{aligned} &r\left(\theta - \frac{1}{3!}\theta^3 + \ldots\right) \\ &\qquad \lesseqgtr (r-h)\left\{\frac{R+r}{r}\theta - \frac{1}{3!}\left(\frac{R+r}{r}\theta\right)^3 + \ldots\right\} \end{aligned}\right\}. \tag{iii}$$

θ being small, taking only first order terms in θ, the inequality is

$$r \lesseqgtr (r-h) \, . \, \frac{R+r}{r}$$

from which is obtained

$$\frac{1}{h} \lesseqgtr \frac{1}{R} + \frac{1}{r}. \tag{iv}$$

Hence it is seen that given R and r, the centre of gravity G has to be below a certain height for stability.

If $1/h = 1/R + 1/r$, that is, $h = Rr/(R + r)$, equilibrium is neutral to the first order. To investigate the stability further, the next higher order terms in inequality (iii) should be considered, giving

$$r\left(-\frac{1}{3!}\theta^3\right) \lesseqgtr \left(r - \frac{Rr}{R+r}\right)\left[-\frac{1}{3!}\left(\frac{R+r}{r}\theta\right)^3\right]$$

or

$$r^2 \lesseqgtr (R+r)^2.$$

Since only the lower inequality holds, the equilibrium is unstable in this case.

These results could also have been obtained by taking the height of the centre of gravity of the upper cylinder above a fixed level as

$$z = (R + r) \cos \theta - (r - h) \cos (R\theta/r)$$

and investigating if z is a minimum or not at the position $\theta = O$.

These considerations could also be used if the two bodies are spherical instead of cylindrical. The condition for stability for small rolling displacements of a sphere of radius r resting on a fixed sphere of radius R with the line of centres vertical and the centre of gravity of the upper sphere at a height h above the point of contact is

$$\frac{1}{h} > \frac{1}{R} + \frac{1}{r}.$$

Coming back to the case of two cylinders, if the lower surface is concave (instead of convex) at the point of contact (Fig. 111),

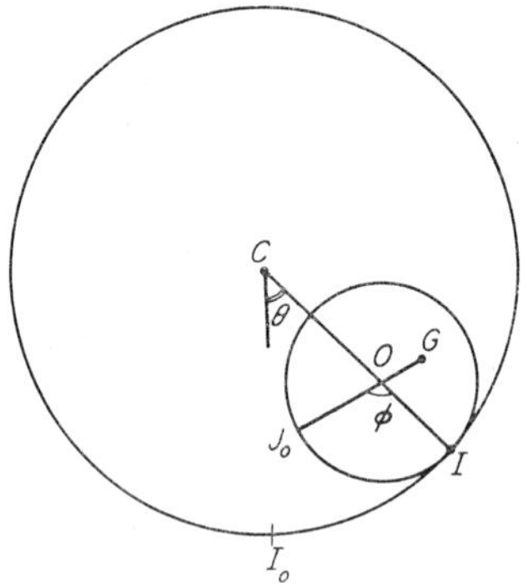

Fig. 111

$R\theta = r\phi$, and equilibrium is stable or not according as G is to the left or right of the vertical through I. Measuring horizontally from O, this condition is

$$r \sin \theta \gtrless (h - r) \sin (\phi - \theta)$$

i.e.

$$r\left(\theta - \frac{1}{3!}\,\theta^3 + \ldots\right)$$
$$\gtrless (h - r)\left\{\frac{R - r}{r}\,\theta - \frac{1}{3!}\left(\frac{R - r}{r}\right)^3 \theta^3 + \ldots\right\}.$$

Hence, taking first order terms only, equilibrium is stable or not according as

$$r \gtrless (h - r)(R - r)/r,$$

or

$$\frac{1}{h} \gtrless \frac{1}{r} - \frac{1}{R}.$$

In the critical case when $1/h = (1/r) - (1/R)$, considering higher powers, condition is

$$-r \gtrless -\left(\frac{Rr}{R-r} - r\right)\left(\frac{R-r}{r}\right)^3,$$

i.e.

$$r^2 \gtrless (R-r)^2 \text{ or } R \gtrless 2r.$$

When $R = 2r$, then $h = 2r$, $\phi = (R\theta/r) = 2\theta$, and G is vertically above I. Thus the inner cylinder will be in equilibrium after the displacement also, and equilibrium in this case is neutral.

Bodies of Variable Curvature

The above methods may also be extended to consider stability when the cylinders are not necessarily circular, and also where the common tangent plane at the position of equilibrium is not necessarily horizontal but inclined at an angle α, say, to the horizontal. The conclusion in these cases is that equilibrium is stable or not according as

$$\frac{\cos\alpha}{h} \gtrless \frac{1}{\rho} + \frac{1}{\rho'}$$

where ρ and ρ' are the radii of curvature at the point of contact of the curves formed by the central cross-section of the two cylinders.

The figure shows the cylinders before and after the upper cylinder rolls over the fixed lower cylinder. Let I be the point of contact after displacement, where $I_oI = J_oI = \delta s$. Let G be the new position of centre of gravity, $GI = r$, $\widehat{J_oGI} = \theta$, i the angle between IG and the vertical, $\pi/2 - \phi$ the angle between IG and the common normal at I, and ψ the angle between GJ_o and the tangent at I. If the suffix zero denotes the values in the equilibrium position, $r_o = h$, $\theta_o = O$,

$i_o = O$, $\phi_o = \pi/2 - \alpha$, $\psi_o = \pi/2 - \alpha$. Since ψ is the angle between the tangent and the line GJ_0 which is fixed in the upper cylinder, and $\psi = \theta + \phi$, the curvature of the upper cylinder at the point of contact is

$$\frac{1}{\rho} = \frac{d\psi}{ds} = \frac{d\theta}{ds} + \frac{d\phi}{ds}.$$

Also

$$\sin\phi = r\frac{d\theta}{ds}.$$

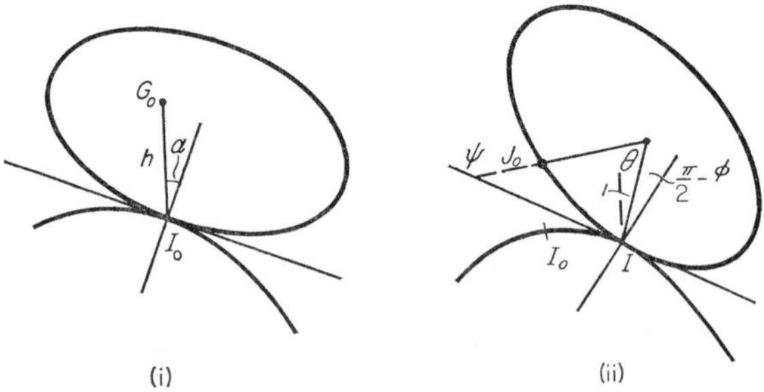

Fig. 112

Again, since the angle between the tangent and the horizontal is $\pi/2 - \phi + i$, the curvature of the lower cylinder at the point of contact is

$$\frac{1}{\rho'} = \frac{d}{ds}\left(\frac{\pi}{2} - \phi + i\right) = \frac{di}{ds} - \frac{d\phi}{ds}.$$

Hence

$$\frac{1}{\rho} + \frac{1}{\rho'} = \frac{d\theta}{ds} + \frac{di}{ds} = \frac{\sin\phi}{r} + \frac{di}{ds}.$$

That is,

$$\frac{di}{ds} = \frac{1}{\rho} + \frac{1}{\rho'} - \frac{\sin\phi}{r}.$$

Now

$$i = i_0 + \delta s\left(\frac{di}{ds}\right)_o + \frac{1}{2!}(\delta s)^2\left(\frac{d^2 i}{ds^2}\right)_o + \dots.$$

The condition for stability is that when $\delta s > 0$, G is to the left of I, that is, $i < 0$. To the first order, this condition is

$$\left(\frac{di}{ds}\right)_0 = \frac{1}{\rho_0} + \frac{1}{\rho_0'} - \frac{\sin\left(\frac{\pi}{2} - \alpha\right)}{r} < O.$$

Hence

$$\frac{\cos\alpha}{r} > \frac{1}{\rho_0} + \frac{1}{\rho_0'}.$$

When

$$\frac{\cos\alpha}{r} = \frac{1}{\rho_0} + \frac{1}{\rho_0'},$$

equilibrium is neutral to first order, and one has to investigate the sign of $(d^2i/ds^2)_0$, and still higher derivatives if this vanishes.

The above results may also be used to consider the stability of a body resting on a plane, or a body with a plane face resting on a fixed cylinder, by taking the radius of curvature of the plane face as infinite.

Example 1. A body consisting of a cone and a hemisphere on the same base rests on a rough horizontal plane with the hemisphere in

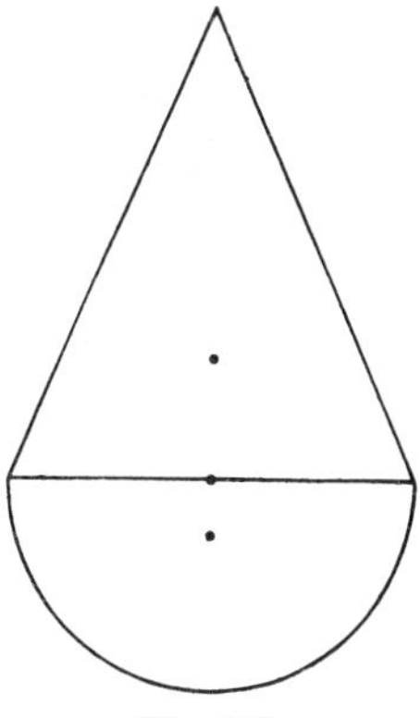

Fig. 113

contact with the plane. If H is the height of the cone, and a the radius of the base, show that for stability $H < a\sqrt{3}$.

The height of the centre of gravity G above the plane is

$$h = \frac{\frac{2}{3}\pi a^3\rho \cdot \frac{5}{8}a + \frac{1}{3}\pi a^2 H\rho\left(\frac{H}{4} + a\right)}{\frac{2}{3}\pi a^3\rho + \frac{1}{3}\pi a^2 H\rho} = \frac{5a^2 + 4aH + H^2}{4(2a + H)}.$$

Also, in the previous notation, R is infinite and $r = a$.

Hence the condition for stability

$$\frac{1}{h} > \frac{1}{r} + \frac{1}{R}$$

gives

$$\frac{4(2a + H)}{5a^2 + 4aH + H^2} > \frac{1}{a} + \frac{1}{\infty},$$

i.e.

$$H^2 < 3a^2.$$

Hence the result.

Example 2. Show that the centre of gravity of a uniform right cylinder whose cross section is the limacon $r = a + b\cos\theta$, where $a > b > O$, is at a distance $b(4a^2 + b^2)/(4a^2 + 2b^2)$ from the line through the origin parallel to a generating line of the cylinder.

If the cylinder rests on a horizontal plane with the axis of its cross section vertical, the origin being at a distance $a + b$ from the point

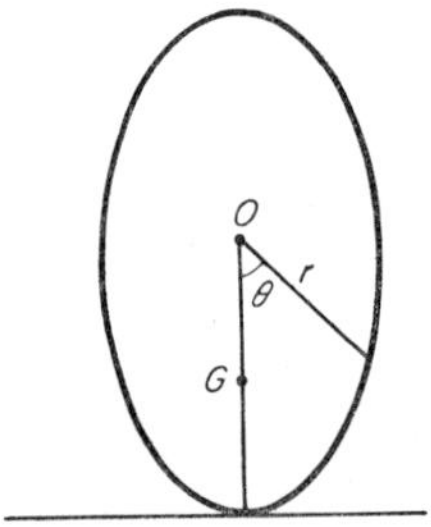

Fig. 114

of contact with the plane, show that the equilibrium is stable for all values of a and b.

[Lond. *S*]

$$OG = \frac{\int \frac{1}{2} r^2 \, d\theta \, . \, \frac{2}{3} r \cos \theta}{\int \frac{1}{2} r^2 d\theta}$$

$$= \frac{2}{3} \frac{\int_0^\pi \cos \theta (a + b \cos \theta)^3 \, d\theta}{\int_0^\pi (a + b \cos \theta)^2 \, d\theta} = \frac{\frac{2}{3} [3a^2 b\pi/2 + 3b^3\pi/8]}{\frac{1}{2} [a^2\pi + b^2\pi/2]}$$

$$= b(4a^2 + b^2)/(4a^2 + 2b^2).$$

To determine the radius of curvature, one method is to find the (p, r) equation of the curve and to use $\rho = r \, dr/dp$.

From $\log r = \log (a + b \cos \theta)$

$$\cot \phi = \frac{1}{r} \frac{dr}{d\theta} = \frac{b \sin \theta}{a + b \cos \theta}, \qquad \sin \phi = \frac{a + b \cos \theta}{\sqrt{(a^2 + b^2 + 2ab \cos \theta)}}.$$

Hence

$$p = r \sin \phi = \frac{r^2}{\sqrt{[a^2 + b^2 + 2a (r - a)]}} = \frac{r^2}{\sqrt{[b^2 + 2ar - a^2]}}.$$

When $\theta = O$, $r = a + b$ and

$$\left(\frac{dp}{dr}\right) = \frac{2(a + b)}{a + b} - \frac{a(a + b)^2}{(a + b)^3} = \frac{a + 2b}{a + b}.$$

Hence

$$\rho = \left(\frac{r \, dr}{dp}\right)_{a+b} = \frac{(a + b)^2}{a + 2b}.$$

The condition for stability is obtained by substituting this value for ρ, and

$$h = a + b - b(4a^2 + b^2)/(4a^2 + 2b^2), \qquad \rho' = \infty$$

in

$$1/h > 1/\rho + 1/\rho', \text{ or } \rho > h,$$

that is

$$\frac{(a+b)^2}{a+2b} > \frac{4a^3+2ab^2+b^3}{4a^2+2b^2}$$

which works out to $4a > b$.

This condition is satisfied for all values of a and b since it is given that $a > b > 0$. Hence the equilibrium is stable for all values of a and b.

Exercises 7

1. Two equal uniform rods AB, BC, each of weight W, are smoothly hinged at B, and AB is freely hinged to a fixed point A. A light inextensible string connects A and C, and the system hangs in equilibrium with $\angle ABC = 2\theta$. Find the tangent of the angle that AB makes with the downward vertical and prove that the tension of the string is

$$\frac{3W \sin \theta}{2(1+3\sin^2\theta)^{1/2}}$$

[Lond. *G* 1959]

2. Two equal smooth uniform circular cylinders almost touch along a generator and lie on a smooth horizontal plane; a third equal cylinder is in contact with both cylinders along generators and equilibrium is maintained by a taut string round the cylinders and in a plane perpendicular to their axes. Show that the tension in the string is $W/2\sqrt{3}$ where W is the weight of one of the cylinders. [Oxf. *I* 1960]

3. A plane framework consisting of seven equal uniform rods, each of weight W, freely jointed together, is kept in the shape of two squares $ABCD$, $CDEF$ by two light struts DB, EC which are parallel, and freely jointed at their ends. The framework hangs freely under gravity from A. Show that the thrusts in the struts DB, EC are $W\sqrt{10}$, $W\sqrt{(8/5)}$ respectively. [Oxf. *I* 1959]

4. A uniform rod AB of weight w is smoothly jointed at the end A to a smooth vertical wall and at the other end B to a point on the surface of a uniform sphere, of weight W, which rests against the wall. Show by using the principle of virtual work that when the system is in equilibrium, the angles θ and ϕ made with the vertical by the rod and the radius of the sphere to the joint B respectively satisfy the quatione

$$\tan\phi/\tan\theta = 1 + w/2W.$$

[Cey. *G* 1944]

5. Four uniform rods AB, BC, CD, DA, each of weight W and length l are smoothly jointed at A, B, C and D, and rest in a vertical plane with A vertically above C and BC, DC in contact with two smooth horizontal pegs, which are at

the same horizontal level and distant $2b$ apart. A weight $4nW$ is attached to C, and equilibrium is maintained by a light rod joining A to C. If the angle between CB and CD is 2θ, show by the method of virtual work that the tension in the rod is

$$2W\left\{(n+1)\frac{b}{l}\operatorname{cosec}^2\theta - 1\right\}.$$

[Lond. *G* 1957]

6. Six equal rods, each of length $2a$ and weight W, are freely jointed at their ends to form a hexagon $ABCDEF$, not necessarily regular. The joints B and F, and the joint C and E are jointed by light struts, and the framework is freely suspended from A, the struts BF, CE being horizontal and inside the hexagon. If AB, BC, CD make acute angles θ, ϕ, ψ with the vertical, and CE is not greater than BF, prove that the thrusts in BF, CE are respectively

$$\tfrac{1}{2}W(5\tan\theta + 3\tan\phi), \qquad \tfrac{1}{2}W(\tan\psi - 3\tan\phi).$$

Find the reaction at the joint D. [Lond. *S* 1946]

7. A weight W is hung from the vertex O of a tripod standing on the ground. The legs of the tripods are uniform rods, each of length l and weight w, freely jointed together at O, and the feet A, B, C form an equilateral triangle ABC whose sides are of length a. Use the principle of virtual work to prove that, for equilibrium to be possible, the coefficient of friction μ at the ground must be at least μ_o, where

$$\mu_o = \frac{a}{\sqrt{(3l^2 - a^2)}}\,\frac{2W + 3w}{2(W + 3w)}.$$

Prove that, if μ is less than μ_o, and if equilibrium is maintained by strings BC, CA, AB joining the feet, the tension in each string must be at least

$$(\mu_o - \mu)(W + 3w)/(3\sqrt{3})$$

[Camb. *MT* 1956]

8. A framework of smoothly jointed rods in the form of a closed plane polygon is subject to an inward normal pressure of uniform intensity p per unit length. Show that, if the area of the polygon increases by δA in a virtual displacement, then the virtual work done by the pressure is $-p\delta A$.

A framework of smoothly jointed rods has the form of a regular hexagon $ABCDEF$ together with the radii AO, BO, CO, EO, FO (omitting DO), O being the geometrical centre of the hexagon. Verify by the method of virtual work that when this framework is subjected to a uniform inward pressure the stress in each radial rod is zero. [Lond. *S* 1939]

9. A heavy uniform pyramid of equilateral triangular base rests vertex downwards with its base horizontal and its edges supported by the smooth sides of an equilateral triangular aperture in a horizontal plate, the sides of the triangular aperture being the same as that of the base. Prove that the horizontal torque that is necessary to prevent the pyramid falling down into the aperture is

$$\frac{\sqrt{3}}{2}\,\frac{Wh}{a^2}\,x\sqrt{(a^2 + 3x^2)}$$

where W is the weight of the pyramid, h is its height, $2a$ the length of a side of the base and x the distance of the points of contact of its edges on the sides of the aperture from the midpoints of these sides. [Lond. *S* 1936]

10. A uniform circular disc of radius a is suspended in the loop of an endless light elastic string of natural length $2a$ which hangs over a small smooth fixed peg, so that the vertical plane of the disc is that of the loop. If the modulus of the string is equal to the weight of the disc, show that there is a position of stable equilibrium in which the straight parts of the string make an angle θ with the vertical given by the equation

$$\sec\theta = 2\left\{\cot\theta + \theta + \frac{\pi}{2} - 1\right\}.$$

[Lond. *G* 1934]

11. Three uniform rigid bars AB, BC, CD of weights P, Q, R respectively are smoothly jointed together at their common ends whilst the ends A and D are freely jointed to two fixed points at the same level. If in the position of equilibrium the bars are inclined to the vertical at angles θ, ϕ, ψ respectively, prove that

$$\frac{(P+Q)\sin\theta}{\sin(\phi-\theta)} = \frac{(Q+R)\sin\psi}{\sin(\phi+\psi)}$$

[Lond. *S* 1934]

12. Four equal uniform rods, each of length $2a$, are rigidly fixed together to form a square framework. This is hung over two smooth pegs on the same horizontal line at a distance d apart. Prove that there is an unsymmetrical position of equilibrium if $a/\sqrt{2} < d < a$, explaining carefully why d must lie between these limits.

Prove that this position is stable, and (with the same restriction on d) the position of equilibrium in which each rod makes an angle $\pi/6$ with the horizontal is unstable. [Oxf. *GCE*(*S*) 1956]

13. A smooth hemispherical bowl of radius a is fixed with its rim horizontal and its vertex downwards. A uniform rod of length $2l$ has one end on the inner surface of the bowl and one point on the rim of the bowl. Prove that there is a position of equilibrium if $l \leqslant 2a$.

Determine whether this position is stable or unstable.

[Oxf. *GCE*(*S*) 1959]

14. Three uniform rods OA, OB, OC, each of length $2l$ and weight W, are smoothly jointed together at O, and pass respectively through three small smooth rings fixed at the corners of an equilateral triangle, whose sides are of length a and whose plane is horizontal. A weight w is attached at O. Prove that two symmetrical positions of equilibrium are possible if

$$\frac{w}{3W} < \frac{l\sqrt{3}}{a} - 1,$$

in one of which O lies above the plane of the triangle while in the other O lies below this plane. Investigate the stability of these positions of equilibrium.

[Oxf. *GCE*(*S*) 1960]

15. The ends of a uniform heavy rod are constrained to move, without friction, on a parabola, which is fixed in a vertical plane with its axis vertical and vertex downwards. The length of the rod is $2b$, and the latus rectum of the parabola is $4a$. Prove that, when the rod is inclined at an angle θ to the horizontal, the height of the centre of gravity above the directrix of the parabola is

$$\frac{1}{4a}\left(b^2 \cos^2 \theta + \frac{4a^2}{\cos^2 \theta}\right).$$

Hence prove that, if $b < 2a$, there is only one position of equilibrium, and it is stable. If $b > 2a$, find the positions of equilibrium, and discuss their stability. [Camb. *MT* 1958]

16. A uniform lamina in the shape of a rhombus consisting of two equilateral triangles of side a rests in a vertical plane with two adjacent sides on two smooth pegs in a horizontal line, distance $a\sqrt{3}/4$ apart. Prove that in equilibrium either a diagonal or a side is vertical, and find which of these is a position of stable equilibrium. [Oxf. *I* 1957]

17. Three equal uniform rods AB, BC, CD, each of length $2a$, are freely jointed at B and C. The ends A and D are constrained to slide on a smooth wire in the form of a circle centre O and radius b with its plane vertical. If the rods are in equilibrium with the centre rod horizontal and the radii OA, OD in the circle inclined upwards at an angle of 60° with the horizontal, show that

$$b = a\{2 + 4(\sqrt{3/7})\}.$$

Show that this position of equilibrium is unstable. [Lond. *S* 1936]

18. A rigid body, whose position is defined by the value of a simple coordinate q, is acted on by reactions at smooth surfaces, and by a field of force in which it has potential energy $V(q)$. State and prove a set of conditions on V sufficient to ensure that the body is in stable equilibrium at $q = q_0$.

A uniform lamina in the shape of an isosceles triangle ABC rests in equilibrium with its equal sides AB and AC in contact with two smooth pegs at the same level and distance c apart. Prove that the height of the centre of gravity G above the level of the pegs is

$$\tfrac{2}{3}\, a \cos \tfrac{1}{2} A \sin \theta + \tfrac{1}{2} c \cos 2\theta \operatorname{cosec} A - \tfrac{1}{2} c \cot A,$$

where θ is the inclination of AG to the horizontal and $a = AB$. Show also that there are three equilibrium positions if $c > \frac{1}{3} a \cos \frac{1}{2} A \sin A$.

Discuss the stability of the symmetrical position when the above condition is satisfied. [Lond. *G* II 1960]

19. A uniform thin rod of length $2a$ and weight W is freely hinged at one end to a fixed support so that it is constrained to remain in a vertical plane. The other end is joined by a light elastic string of modulus λ and unstretched length $l (l < 4a)$ to a fixed hook situated vertically above the hinge at a distance $2a$. Show that a position of equilibrium exists with the rod inclined to the vertical if

$$\lambda(4a - l) > Wl,$$

and that this position is stable. [Camb. *MT* 1959]

20. Four equal smooth spheres, of radius a, rest on a horizontal table; initially each is in contact with two others and their centres are at the vertices of a square. They are kept in position by an endless elastic band of length $2a(\pi + 4)$, in the plane of their centres and the band is unstretched when the spheres are in contact. A fifth uniform heavy sphere, of radius r, is then placed above them. Prove that, if in a position of equilibrium the line joining the centre of the upper sphere to the centre of one of the lower spheres is inclined at an angle θ to the vertical, the equilibrium is stable for symmetrical displacements if

$$\sin^3 \theta < a\sqrt{2}/(a + r).$$

[Lond. *S* 1935]

21. A uniform rod AB, of weight W and length l, is free to turn about a smooth hinge at A and is supported at B by an elastic string whose natural length is a and modulus of elasticity W/n. The other end of the string is fastened to a fixed point at a distance c vertically above A where $c > l + a$. Show that if

$$1 - \frac{a}{a + l} > \frac{na}{2c} > 1 - \frac{a}{c - l}$$

there is an oblique position of equilibrium and that it is stable.

Discuss the stability of the vertical positions of equilibrium when the oblique position does not exist. [Lond. *S* 1934]

22. A uniform rod of weight W and length $2l$ has light rings attached to its ends, one of which slides on a smooth horizontal wire OA and the other on a smooth vertical wire OB, where B is below O. A light elastic string of modulus λ and natural length l has one end attached to the centre of the rod and the other to a fixed point C vertically above O where $OC = l$. Show that the potential energy of the system is

$$l(\lambda - W)\cos 2\theta - 2\lambda l \cos \theta + \text{const.},$$

where θ is the angle made by the string with the downward vertical.

Hence show that if $\lambda > 2W$ there are two possible positions of equilibrium and investigate the stability of these positions. [Lond. *G* 1957]

23. A uniform rod AB of length $2a$ and weight W can rotate in a vertical plane about a hinge at the end A, which is fixed. A string attached to B passes over a smooth pulley at a height $2a$ vertically above A, and carries at its end a weight λW ($\lambda \neq 1$). When the rod makes an angle θ with the upward vertical, prove that the potential energy of the system is

$$4\lambda Wa \,|\sin \tfrac{1}{2}\theta\,| + Wa\cos\theta + \text{constant}.$$

If $\lambda < 1$, prove that oblique positions of equilibrium exist and that they are unstable.

Prove also that $\theta = \pi$ is always an equilibrium position, and that it is stable if $\lambda < 1$. [Lond. *G* 1958]

24. A uniform elliptic disc of axes $2a$, $2b$ rests in a vertical plane in contact with two smooth parallel rails which are fixed in a horizontal plane at a distance

$2c$ apart. Show that, if $a > c\sqrt{2} > b$, there is a position of unstable equilibrium in which the points of contact of the disc with the rails are at the ends of conjugate diameters of the ellipse. [Lond. *S* 1947]

25. Three thin uniform rods, each of length $2a$ and of weight W, are freely jointed together at their common middle point O. Three of the ends of the rods are placed on a smooth horizontal table and are at the vertices of an equilateral triangle. A uniform smooth circular hoop, of radius $r(< a)$ and weight w, is placed over the rods and is in a horizontal plane below O. A uniform smooth sphere, of radius r and weight w, is placed in contact with the rods and with its centre above O. Prove that the system is in equilibrium when the rods are inclined to the vertical at angle θ, where

$$(2W + w)\,a(2\sin\theta + \sin 2\theta) = 2wr.$$

Prove that there is a root θ of this equation which is less than $\pi/3$ and that for this value of θ the equilibrium is stable. [Lond. *S* 1947]

26. A uniform rod AB of weight W and length $2a$ is smoothly hinged at A; the end B is fastened to a light elastic string, of natural length $l_0(< 4a)$ and modulus W, the other end of which is attached to a fixed point C a vertical distance $2a$ above A. Prove that when AB makes an angle θ with the downward vertical, and the string is stretched, the potential energy is

$$\frac{1}{2}\frac{W}{l_0}\left(4a\cos\frac{1}{2}\theta - l_0\right)^2 - aW\cos\theta + \text{constant}.$$

Prove that if $l_0 < 2a$, there are three positions of equilibrium with the string stretched, two stable and one unstable; while if $l_0 > 2a$ there is only one position of equilibrium with the string stretched and this is stable. [Oxf. *I* 1955]

27. A uniform hemisphere, of weight W and radius a, rests in equilibrium with its base upwards on top of a fixed sphere of radius $2a$. Show that the greatest weight which can be placed at the centre of the plane face without disturbing stability for small rolling displacement is $\frac{1}{8}W$.

28. A light sphere of radius r, having a heavy particle attached to a point of its surface, rests inside a fixed hollow sphere of radius R, so that the common radius of the two spheres is inclined at an angle α to the vertical. The contact between the two surfaces is everywhere rough enough to prevent any slipping. Show that the equilibrium is stable for all values of $\alpha(\,|\,\alpha\,| < \pi/2)$ if the heavy particle is situated at the point of contact; and that if it is situated vertically above the point of contact, the equilibrium is stable, neutral or unstable according as $r > R/2$, $r = R/2$ or $r < R/2$. [Lond. *S* 1940]

29. A uniform solid hemisphere of radius a rests with its vertex at the highest point of a perfectly rough fixed sphere of radius b. By considering the potential energy of the system, prove that equilibrium is stable or unstable according as $3b \gtrless 5a$.

Investigate the stability when $3b = 5a$. [Lond. *G* 1959]

30. A uniform solid figure is formed by rotating about the x-axis the segment cut from the parabola $y^2 = 4ax$ by the line $x = b$. Prove that its centre of mass is at a distance $\frac{2}{3} b$ from the vertex.

The figure is placed with its curved surface touching a horizontal plane. Prove that, if $b > 3a$, there is an unsymmetrical position of equilibrium, which is stable, and that the symmetrical position is unstable.

Prove that, if $b < 3a$, the only position of equilibrium is the symmetrical one, and that it is stable. [Oxf. *GCE*(*S*) 1958]

31. An inverted top is formed from the lower half of an oblate spheroid, obtained by rotating an ellipse about its minor axes which is vertical and of length b, by fixing to its flat surface a right circular cone of height h and radius a. Show that the top can stand with its axis vertical and the surface of the spheroid resting on a horizontal plane in stable equilibrium if

$$(1 - e^2)\, h^2 - 4b\, e^2 h < b^2(3 + 5\, e^2),$$

where e is the eccentricity of the ellipse.

32. G is the centre of mass and PGQ the axis of a uniform solid of revolution S. If P is in contact with a perfectly rough horizontal plane show that the position of equilibrium is stable or unstable according as h is less than or greater than ρ, where $h = PG$ and ρ is the radius of curvature of the meridian section of S at P.

Show that the centre of mass of a uniform body B obtained by rotating the region $x \geqslant 0$ of the ellipse $x^2/a^2 + y^2/b^2 = 1$, about Ox is at a distance $3a/8$ from the plane face and that the radius of curvature at the vertex is b^2/a.

A uniform hemispherical body of radius b and weight $4W$ is attached symmetrically to B with plane faces in contact. If $a = 2b$ and the weight of B is W, show that this composite body can rest with its axis vertical on a rough horizontal table in stable or unstable equilibrium according as B is above or below the hemisphere. [Lond. *G* 1955]

33. A rigid cylinder, whose centre of mass is G, rests in equilibrium on a rough horizontal plane with G at a height h above the plane and P_0 is the point of contact in the cross-section through G. The cylinder is given a small rolling displacement so that the point of contact in the cross-section through G is the point P where $P_0P = s$, and z is the height of G above the plane. If κ is the curvature of the cross-section at P, and accents denote differentiation with respect to s, show that

$$z'' - \frac{1}{\kappa}\kappa' z' + \kappa^2 z = \kappa.$$

Hence, or otherwise, show that equilibrium is stable or unstable according as $h \lessgtr 1/\kappa_0$, where κ_0 is the curvature at P_0. If $h = 1/\kappa_0$, show that for stability $(\kappa')_0 = O$, $(\kappa'')_0 < O$.

If the arc of contact is a catenary with P_0 at the vertex, investigate stability when $h = 1/\kappa_0$. [C.C.S. (*H*) 1952]

Chapter 8

Strings and Chains

8.1. Flexibility

PREVIOUS chapters have been concerned mainly with the statics of particles and of rigid bodies. Though based on concepts such as "a body of no size" and "a perfectly rigid body", which are not exactly realizable in practice, this theory of statics has been eminently successful in describing the properties of many actual physical systems. There are, however, certain physical systems for the description of which we need to modify these assumptions. One example of such a system that has been considered so far is that of elastic strings or springs which may be stretched in the direction of their lengths. In this chapter, we consider the equilibrium of strings, ropes and chains which are not rigid bodies but are flexible.

In a thin wire or a string, the actions across any normal section will in general reduce to a force and a couple. If, however, the string or wire is such that there is no resistance to bending it at any point, then it is said to be perfectly flexible. A perfectly flexible string of thin section may be taken as occupying a geometrical curved line. The action across any normal section of it will consist of a single force acting along the tangent to the string.

A thin chain whose links are very small and smooth may also be treated in the same way as a perfectly flexible string. In the rest of this chapter, a chain or a string, unless otherwise stated, will be taken as perfectly flexible.

8.2. The common catenary

When a uniform string or chain is suspended from its ends and hangs freely under the action of gravity, the curve which it assumes is called the common catenary. Its equation may be found as follows:

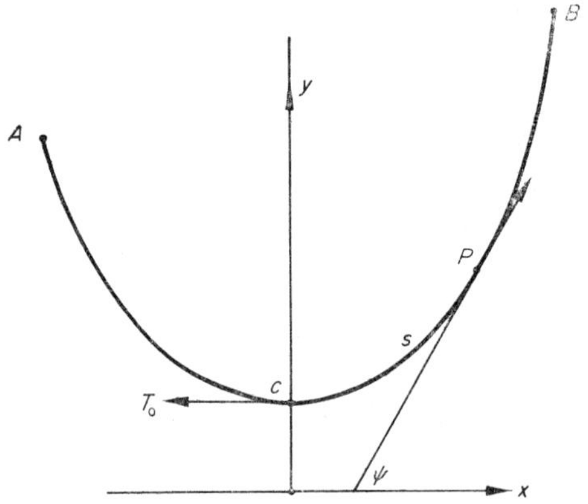

FIG. 115

Let C be the lowest point of the curve, P any point on the string and $CP = s$, and A, B the points of suspension. The tension at P will be along the tangent to the curve at P. Let ψ be the inclination of the tangent at P to the horizontal. Let the tension at C, which is a horizontal force, be T_0. If w is the weight per unit length, the weight of CP is ws. The portion CP is in equilibrium under the action of the following forces:

(i) Tension T along the tangent at P.
(ii) Tension T_0 at C along the horizontal.
(iii) Weight ws acting vertically downwards.

Hence resolving horizontally and vertically

$$T \cos \psi = T_0 \tag{1}$$

$$T \sin \psi = ws. \tag{2}$$

Dividing (2) by (1),

$$\tan \psi = \frac{ws}{T_0}, \text{ or } s = \frac{T_0}{w} \tan \psi.$$

If we write $T_0/w = c$, this relation may be written

$$s = c \tan \psi. \tag{3}$$

This is the intrinsic equation of the catenary. The constant c is called the parameter of the catenary.

It is useful to obtain also the Cartesian equation of the catenary. For this purpose the following well known elementary properties of curves may be used:

$$\frac{dx}{ds} = \cos \psi, \qquad \frac{dy}{ds} = \sin \psi, \qquad \frac{dy}{dx} = \tan \psi,$$

where the x-axis is horizontal and y-axis vertical. From $dy = ds \sin \psi$, one obtains

$$dy = c \sec^2 \psi \sin \psi \, d\psi = c \sec \psi \tan \psi \, d\psi.$$

Integrating with respect to ψ

$$y = c \sec \psi + D$$

where D is a constant of integration. If we choose the location of the axis of x such that at the lowest point of the string, namely the point C, y has the value c, that is, $y = c$ when $\psi = O$, then $D = O$. Hence by taking the axis of x at a depth c below the lowest point of the chain

$$y = c \sec \psi. \tag{4}$$

Again

$$dx = ds \cos \psi = c \sec \psi \, d\psi.$$

Integrating

$$x = c \log_e (\sec \psi + \tan \psi) + E$$

where E is a constant of integration. If the location of the axis of y is taken so that at the lowest point $x = O$, that is $x = O$ when $\psi = O$, then $E = O$. Hence by taking the axis of y to be the vertical through the lowest point of the chain,

$$x = c \log (\sec \psi + \tan \psi). \tag{5}$$

Equations (4) and (5) express x and y in terms of the angle ψ. We may obtain the relationship between x and y by eliminating ψ. From equation (5),

$$\sec \psi + \tan \psi = e^{x/c}. \tag{6}$$

From the identity $\sec^2 \psi - \tan^2 \psi = 1$ by dividing by the terms in (6), there is obtained

$$\sec \psi - \tan \psi = e^{-x/c}. \tag{7}$$

From (6) and (7) we have

$$\sec \psi = \tfrac{1}{2}(e^{x/c} + e^{-x/c}) = \cosh x/c \tag{8}$$

and

$$\tan \psi = \tfrac{1}{2}(e^{x/c} - e^{-x/c}) = \sinh x/c. \tag{9}$$

Thus by substituting in (4), the Cartesian equation of the catenary is obtained,

$$y = c \cosh (x/c). \tag{10}$$

Other useful relations are

$$s = c \tan \psi = c \sinh x/c.$$

Also

$$y^2 = c^2 \sec^2 \psi = c^2 (1 + \tan^2 \psi) = c^2 + s^2.$$

The curve (10) is symmetrical about the y-axis. The y-axis is called the axis of the catenary, the x-axis the directrix and the lowest point C the vertex.

The tension T at the point P is from (1)

$$T = T_0 \sec \psi = wc \sec \psi = wy. \tag{13}$$

Thus the tension at any point is proportional to the height above the directrix of that point.

The above relations may be collected together in the following table:

$s = c \tan \psi$ $y = c \sec \psi$ $x = c \log (\sec \psi + \tan \psi)$	$y = c \cosh x/c$ $s = c \sinh x/c$
$y^2 = c^2 + s^2$ $T = wy$	

If ρ is the radius of curvature at the point P,

$$\rho = \frac{ds}{d\psi} = c \sec^2 \psi.$$

The radius of curvature at the lowest point is c. When the string is rather tight and therefore somewhat flat near the vertex then the parameter c is large. If the string is loose, and much curved near its vertex, then the parameter c is small. Some of the geometrical properties may be shown in a diagram (Fig. 116). T, N, M are points

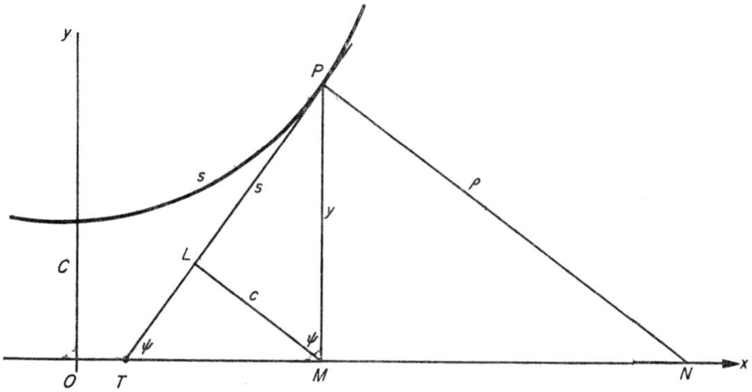

Fig. 116

where the tangent at P, the normal at P, and the ordinate at P, respectively meet the directrix. ML is the perpendicular from M on TP. Then it may be seen that $ML = c$, $PL = s$, $PN = \rho$.

In the neighbourhood of the lowest point, the curve is approximately a parabola. In $y = c \cosh (x/c)$, where x is small $\cosh (x/c)$ may be expanded as a series in powers of x/c, giving

$$y = c \left[1 + \frac{1}{2!}\left(\frac{x}{c}\right)^2 + \frac{1}{4!}\left(\frac{x}{c}\right)^4 + \dots \right],$$

so that for small x, neglecting $(x/c)^4$ and higher powers, the form of the curve is approximately

$$x^2 = 2c(y - c).$$

Example 1. B is the midpoint of a uniform chain ABC, of length $2l$ and weight w per unit length, which is in equilibrium with BC resting on a line of greatest slope of a smooth plane inclined at $\pi/4$ to the horizontal. The upper end A is attached to a point above the plane. Show that the tension at A is $wl\sqrt{(5/2)}$ and find the horizontal and vertical distances of C from A.

[Lond. *G* II 1961]

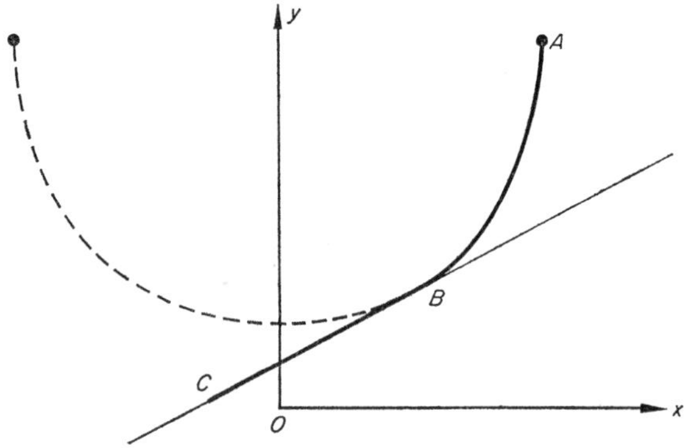

Fig. 117

The dotted lines in the figure show the continuation of the catenary of which the portion AB is a part. The axes of x and y are taken along the directrix and axis of this catenary. Let x_A, y_A denote coordinates of A, with similar notation for B and C. The tangent at B to this catenary makes angle $\pi/4$ with the horizontal. Applying $T = wy$ to the point B of the catenary,

$$T_B = wy_B.$$

But considering the portion BC, and resolving along the plane

$$T_B = wl \sin \pi/4 = wl/\sqrt{2}$$

and therefore

$$y_B = l/\sqrt{2}.$$

Hence it is seen that the point C is on the directrix. Further applying $y = c \sec \psi$ to the point B,

$$l/\sqrt{2} = c \sec(\pi/4), \text{ or } c = \tfrac{1}{2} l.$$

Also $s_B = c \tan \pi/4 = c$. Applying $s = c \tan \psi$ to the point A,

$$s_A = l + c = c \tan \psi_A \text{ or } \tan \psi_A = 3.$$

The required tension at A is

$$wy_A = wc \sec \psi_A = \frac{wl}{2} \cdot \sqrt{10} = wl\sqrt{(5/2)}.$$

Again

$$y_A - y_B = c(\sec \psi_A - \sec \psi_B) = \tfrac{1}{2} l(\sqrt{10} - \sqrt{2})$$
$$x_A - x_B = c \log [(\sec \psi_A + \tan \psi_A)/(\sec \psi_B + \tan \psi_B)]$$
$$= \tfrac{1}{2} l \log [(\sqrt{10} + 3)/(\sqrt{2} + 1)].$$

Hence

$$y_A - y_C = \frac{l}{\sqrt{2}} + y_A - y_B = \tfrac{1}{2} l\sqrt{10}$$

$$x_A - x_C = \frac{l}{\sqrt{2}} + x_A - x_B$$
$$= \tfrac{1}{2} l[\sqrt{2} + \log \{(\sqrt{10} + 5)(\sqrt{2} - 1)\}].$$

Example 2. A chain AB of length $2l$ has its ends A, B attached to light rough rings which can slide on a fixed horizontal rod. The coefficient of friction between the rings and the rod is $\sqrt{2}/4$. Show that when equilibrium is limiting at both ends the depth of the mid-point C of AB below the rod is $\frac{1}{2} l\sqrt{2}$.

If a particle of the same weight as the chain is suspended from C and the chain takes up a new symmetrical position of limiting equilibrium find the distance fallen by C.

[Lond. *G* II 1959]

Suppose N is the normal reaction at each ring, μ the coefficient of friction and α the inclination of the tangent at A to the horizontal. Considering the equilibrium of the rings and the chain, and resolving vertically $2N = 2wl$ or $N = wl$. The ring at A is acted upon by the reaction of the rod, with components N and μN, and the tension T of the string at A.

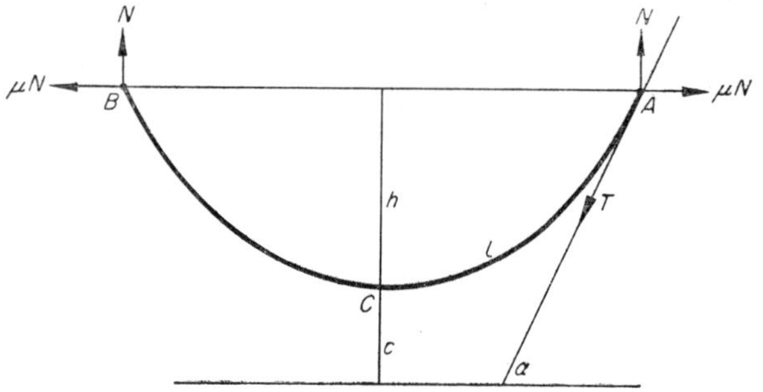

Fig. 118

Hence

$$T \cos \alpha = \mu wl, \qquad T \sin \alpha = wl$$

giving

$$\tan \alpha = 1/\mu = 2\sqrt{2}. \text{ Hence the angle } \alpha \text{ is known.}$$

Applying

$$s = c \tan \psi \text{ to the point } A,$$
$$l = c \tan \alpha, \qquad c = l\mu = l\sqrt{2}/4.$$

Again applying $y = c \sec \psi$ to the point A

$$h + c = c \sec \alpha$$

giving

$$h = c(\sec \alpha - 1) = \frac{l\sqrt{2}}{4}[\sqrt{(1+8)} - 1] = \frac{l\sqrt{2}}{2}.$$

When the weight is attached to C, the two portions AC and BC will now lie on different catenaries. Suppose that the catenary AC is produced as in the figure and that the usual axes are taken. Let the tension at C be T_1 acting at angle ψ_1, and tension at A be T_2 at an angle ψ_2. (Fig. 119).

Considering the system consisting of the chain, the rings and the weight at C and resolving vertically, the normal reaction on each ring

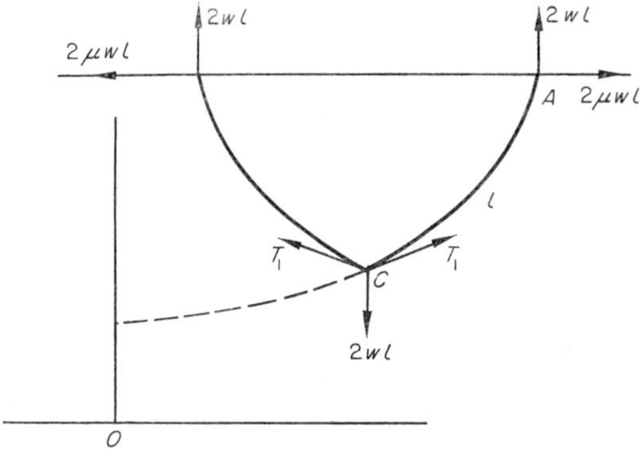

Fig. 119

is obtained as $2wl$. The frictional component of the reaction is then $2\mu wl$. Considering the ring at A

$$T_2 \cos \psi_2 = 2\mu wl, \qquad T_2 \sin \psi_2 = 2wl,$$

giving

$$\tan \psi_2 = 1/\mu = 2\sqrt{2}, \ \sec \psi_2 = 3, \text{ as before.}$$

Considering the particle at C,

$$2\,T_1 \sin \psi_1 = 2\,wl.$$

Considering the chain AC,

$$T_1 \cos \psi_1 = T_2 \cos \psi_2 = 2\mu wl.$$

Hence

$$\tan \psi_1 = 1/(2\mu) = \sqrt{2}, \qquad \sec \psi_1 = \sqrt{3}.$$

Applying $s = c \tan \psi$ to the points A and C, and subtracting

$$l = c\,(\tan \psi_2 - \tan \psi_1) = c\sqrt{2}, \text{ or } c = l/\sqrt{2}.$$

Applying $y = c \sec \psi$ to A and C and subtracting, the depth of C below the rod is obtained as

$$c\,(\sec \psi - \sec \psi_1) = (3 - \sqrt{3})\,l/\sqrt{2}.$$

Hence the distance fallen by C is

$$\frac{l}{\sqrt{2}}(3 - \sqrt{3}) - \tfrac{1}{2}\,l\sqrt{2} = \tfrac{1}{2}\,l\,(2\sqrt{2} - \sqrt{6}).$$

Example 3. A uniform flexible inextensible chain of length $2l$ and of weight $2wl$ hangs over two small smooth pegs at the same level and at a distance $2a$ apart. Show that, for equilibrium to be possible, the chain must hang symmetrically over the pegs, the two straight portions being equal in length, and show further that the parameter c of the catenary hanging between the pegs must satisfy the equation

$$l = ce^{a/c}.$$

Deduce that there are two positions of equilibrium if $l > ea$, one if $l = ea$, and none if $l < ea$. [Oxf. *I* 1956]

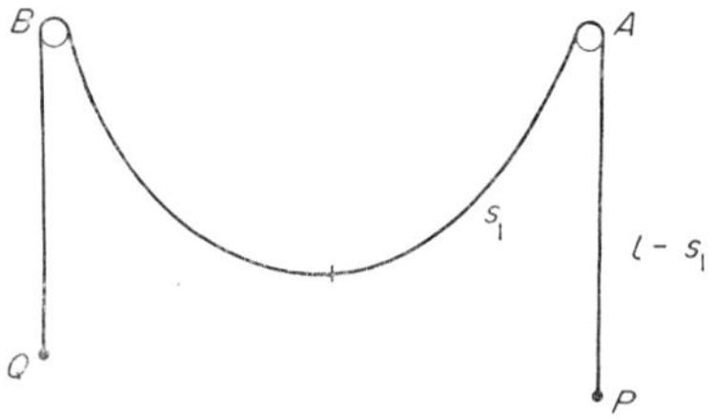

Fig. 120

If P and Q are the free ends of the chain, it may be shown that they lie on the directrix of the catenary. The pulley at A being smooth, the tension on either side of it is the same. If this tension is T_1, then just on the right of A, T_1 balances the weight of the portion AP hanging vertically, and hence $T_1 = w \,.\, AP$. Just on the left of A, the tension is given by the formula $T = wy$, and hence $T_1 = wy_1$ where y_1 is the height of A above the directrix. Therefore $AP = y_1$, and hence P lies on the directrix. Similarly Q lies on the directrix. Because of this property that the free ends lie on the directrix, the directrix is also called "no tension level". The portions AP and BQ being thus of the same length, it follows that the string will hang symmetrically.

Applying $y = c \cosh x/c$, $s = c \sinh x/c$ to the point on the catenary,

$$l - s_1 = c \cosh a/c, \qquad s_1 = c \sinh a/c.$$

Hence

$$l = c\,(\cosh a/c + \sinh a/c) = c\mathrm{e}^{a/c}.$$

This equation for c in terms of l and a cannot be solved algebraically. Writing $l/c = X$, the equation becomes

$$\mathrm{e}^X = mX$$

where $m = l/a$ is known when l and a are given numerically. An approximate solution may be found with the help of tables of the exponential function. Alternatively one may use a graphical method. If the curve

$$Y = \mathrm{e}^X$$

and the straight line

$$Y = mX$$

are drawn, the x-coordinates of the points of intersection will give the values of l/c. There are two, one or no points of intersection according as the gradient m of the straight line is $\gtreqless$ the gradient of the tangent to the curve from O. The point of contact of the tangent is seen to be $(1, \mathrm{e})$ and the gradient of this tangent is e. Hence there are two, one or no catenaries according as $m \gtreqless \mathrm{e}$, that is

$$l \gtreqless a\mathrm{e}.$$

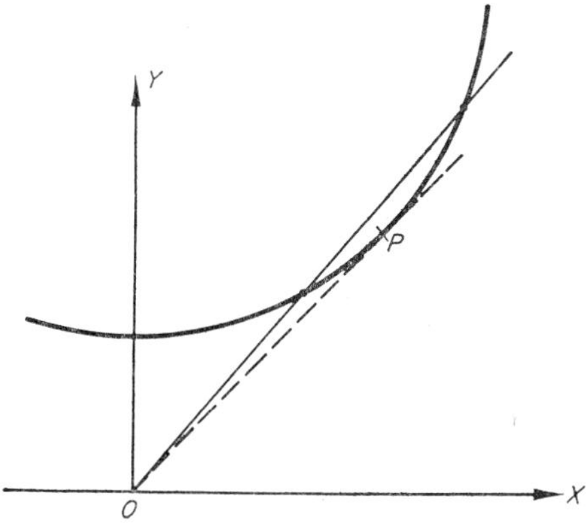

Fig. 121

Example 4. A uniform heavy string of given length l has its ends attached to points A and B which are such that the point B is at a horizontal distance a and a vertical distance b from A. Obtain an equation for the parameter of the catenary, and indicate how it may be solved.

Let C be the lowest point of the catenary when produced. Referred to the usual axes, let the coordinates of A be (α, β), then the coordinates of B are $(\alpha + a, \beta + b)$. Let the arc distance CA be s.

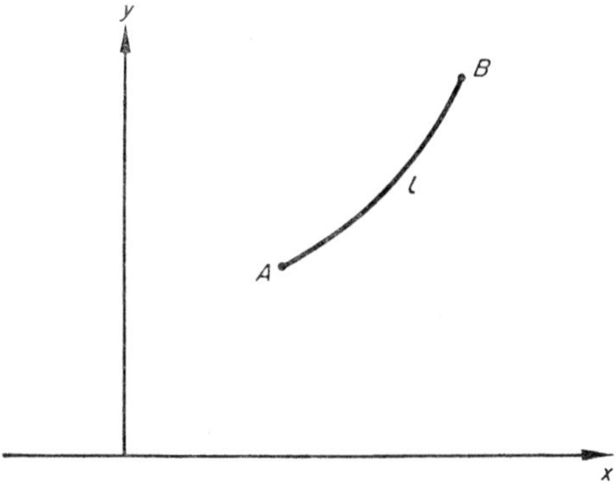

Fig. 122

Applying $y = c \cosh x/c$ and $s = c \sinh x/c$ for the points A and B

$$\beta = c \cosh \alpha/c, \qquad \beta + b = c \cosh (\alpha + a)/c$$
$$s = c \sinh \alpha/c, \qquad s + l = c \sinh (\alpha + a)/c.$$

Hence

$$l = c\,[\sinh (\alpha + a)/c - \sinh \alpha/c]$$
$$b = c\,[\cosh (\alpha + a)/c - \cosh \alpha/c].$$

Squaring and subtracting,

$$l^2 - b^2 = c^2\,[-1 - 1 + 2 \cosh a/c]$$
$$= 4\,c^2 \sinh^2 (a/2c).$$

Taking positive square root, as c is positive,

$$2c \sinh \frac{a}{2c} = \sqrt{(l^2 - b^2)}.$$

Given a, b and l, this equation may be used to determine c.

The equation cannot be solved algebraically. A graphical solution may be obtained as follows:

Put $a/2c = X$. Then X is a positive solution of

$$\sinh X = mX$$

where $m = \sqrt{(l^2 - b^2)}/a$ is a known constant.

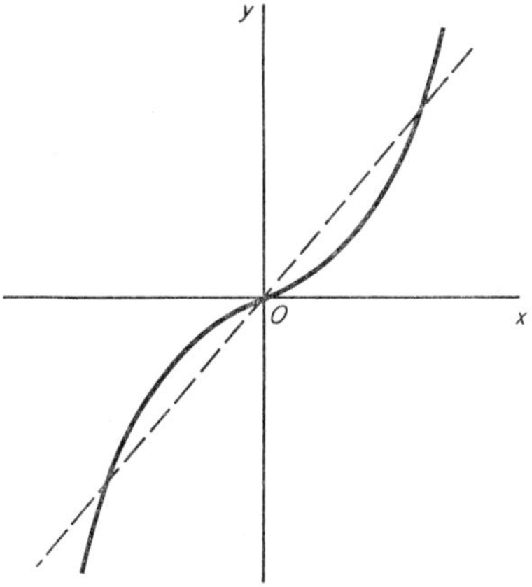

Fig. 123

If the curve

$$Y = \sinh X$$

and the straight line

$$Y = mX$$

are drawn, the x-coordinates of the points of intersection will give the solutions. When $m > 1$ there are two points of intersection, one of which gives a positive value for X. It may be noted that the condition $m > 1$ is equivalent to $\sqrt{(l^2 - b^2)} > a$, or $l > \sqrt{(a^2 + b^2)}$, that is, the length of the chain should be greater than the chord AB. This condition obviously has to be satisfied.

If an approximate value for X is known, a more accurate value may be obtained as follows:

Suppose X_0 is the approximate value. Putting $X = X_0 + \epsilon$, where ϵ is small,

$$\sinh (X_0 + \epsilon) = m (X_0 + \epsilon)$$

i.e.

$$\sinh X_0 + \epsilon \cosh X_0 = m (X_0 + \epsilon),$$

neglecting ϵ^2 and higher powers of ϵ. Hence

$$\epsilon = (mX_0 - \sinh X_0)/(\cosh X_0 - m).$$

$X_0 + \epsilon$ is a better approximation than X_0.

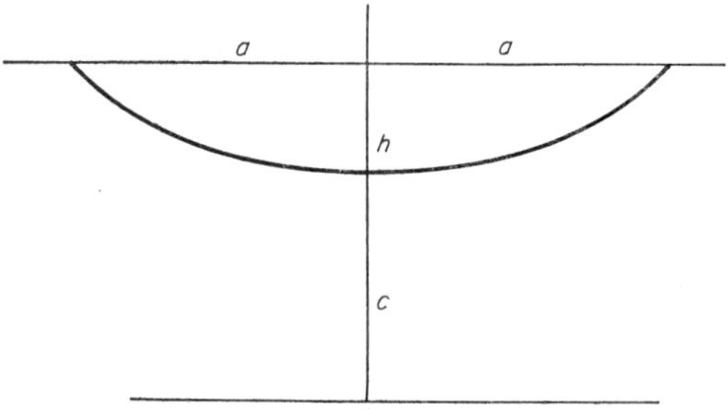

Fig. 124

Example 5. A telegraph wire, made of uniform material of weight w per unit length, hangs between two posts on the same level at distance $2a$ apart. If the small sag in the middle is h, show that the tension at its ends is approximately

$$\frac{1}{2} wa \left(\frac{a}{h} + \frac{7}{3}\frac{h}{a}\right).$$

Applying $y = c \cosh x/c$ to one of the points of suspension (Fig. 124)

$$c + h = c \cosh a/c$$

or

$$c (\cosh a/c - 1) = h.$$

h and a being known, an approximate solution may be obtained graphically as in the previous example. Alternatively, one may use a property that has been discussed earlier concerning a light string, namely that the parameter c is very large. Hence a/c is small, and one may solve for c by the method of approximations.

$$c\left[1 + \frac{a^2}{2c^2} + \frac{a^4}{24c^4} + \ldots \quad -1\right] = h,$$

i.e.

$$\frac{a^2}{2c} + \frac{a^4}{24c^3} + \ldots = h. \tag{i}$$

For a first approximation, the term $a^4/24c^3$ and terms having higher powers of (a/c) may be neglected compared to $a^2/2c$. Hence

$$\frac{a^2}{2c} = h \text{ or } c = \frac{a^2}{2h}.$$

The tension at the ends is $w(h + c)$. To distinguish between the tensions at different points of the strings, c has to be determined to an order of approximation which includes terms of order h.

To proceed to the next approximation, it is convenient to write (1) in the the following form, after multiplying by c/h and transposing sides.

$$c = \frac{a^2}{2h} + \frac{a^4}{24hc^2} + \ldots. \tag{iii}$$

When writing in this way it is readily seen that the first approximation is obtained by neglecting all the terms on the right hand side except the first. A second may be obtained by retaining the term $a^4/24hc^2$ and by substituting in it the value of c determined by the first approximation. Thus

$$c = \frac{a^2}{2h} + \frac{a^4}{24h} \cdot \left(\frac{2h}{a^2}\right)^2 = \frac{a^2}{2h} + \frac{1}{6}h.$$

Still better approximations may be obtained by retaining further terms in equation (iii). However, for the particular purpose indicated in the question, this approximation is sufficient.

8.3. Parabolic chain, suspension bridge

Suppose a light string hanging under gravity from two fixed points is loaded so that the weight of any element is proportional to the horizontal projection of that element. It may be shown that the string will hang in the form of a parabola.

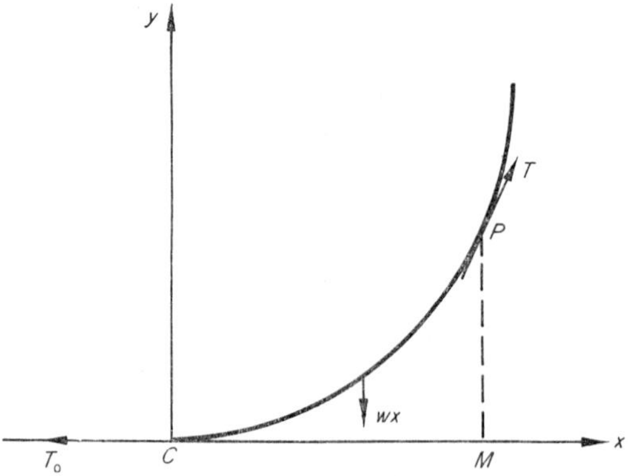

Fig. 125

If C is the lowest point of the chain consider the equilibrium of the portion CP. The forces acting on CP are the tension T_0 at C, tension T at P along the tangent at T and making an angle ψ with the horizontal, and the weight wx. Then

$$T \cos \psi = T_0$$
$$T \sin \psi = wx.$$

Hence

$$\tan \psi = \frac{wx}{T_0} \text{ or } \frac{\mathrm{d}y}{\mathrm{d}x} = \frac{w}{T_0} x.$$

Integrating

$$y = \frac{1}{2} \frac{w}{T_0} x^2 + \text{const.}$$

If the origin is taken at the lowest point C, then the constant of integration is zero, and the equation is

$$x^2 = \frac{2\,T_0}{w}\,y,$$

which is the equation of a parabola, with its axis vertical and vertex at C, the lowest point of the string. This may be used to discuss the case of a suspension bridge. In such a chain, there are two chains

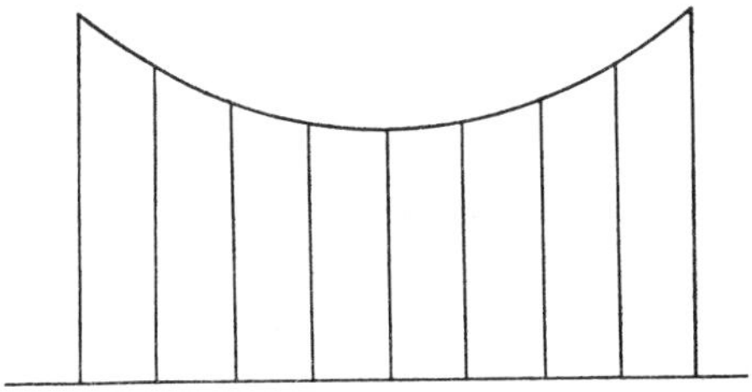

Fig. 126

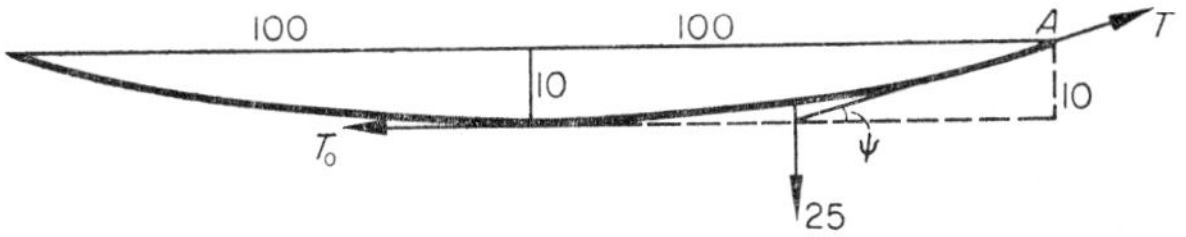

Fig. 127

hung up which are parallel to each other, their ends attached to firm supports. From different points on these chains hang vertical chains or rods which carry the roadway (Fig. 126). These vertical chains or rods are spaced at equal horizontal distances. The weight of the chains and the rods being negligible compared to that of the roadway, the vertical rods carry equal portions of the roadway. Hence this is approximately a case of uniform horizontal loading, and the chains will assume parabolic shapes.

Example. In a suspension bridge of 200 ft span and 10 ft dip the whole weight supported is $\frac{1}{2}$ ton per horizontal foot. Find the tension in each chain at the points of support.

Load carried by both chains is 100 tons. Each chain carries 50 tons. Consider the half chain OA (Fig. 127).

$$T \cos \psi = T_0, \; T \sin \psi = 25 \text{ also } \tan \psi = \frac{1}{5}.$$

Hence

$$T = 25\sqrt{26} \text{ tons wt.}$$

8.4. Catenary of uniform strength

This form of catenary is designed to have variable cross-section such that the stress (or tension per unit area of cross-section) is constant along the whole length of the chain. Portions of the chain subject to larger tensions are relatively thicker, and hence the chain is more durable this way. If τ is the constant stress, and α the cross-section, $T = \alpha\tau$. The weight w per unit length is given by $w = \alpha\rho$ where ρ is the density of the material, and therefore

$$T = \lambda w$$

where $\lambda = \tau/\rho$ is a constant.

The equations of equilibrium are

$$T \cos \psi = T_0$$

$$T \sin \psi = \int_0^s w \, ds = \frac{1}{\lambda} \int_0^s T \, ds.$$

Hence

$$\frac{d}{ds}(T \sin \psi) = \frac{1}{\lambda} T, \text{ or } \frac{d}{ds}(T_0 \tan \psi) = \frac{T_0}{\lambda} \sec \psi.$$

i.e.

$$\sec^2 \psi \frac{d\psi}{ds} = \frac{1}{\lambda} \sec \psi \text{ or } \frac{ds}{d\psi} = \lambda \sec \psi.$$

Integrating

$$s = \lambda \log(\sec \psi + \tan \psi) + D,$$

where the constant of integration is 0 if s is measured from the lowest point, that is, $s = O$ when $\psi = O$.

$$dx = ds \cos \psi = \lambda \, d\psi, \qquad x = \lambda\psi + E,$$

where $E = O$, taking $x = O$ when $\psi = O$.

$$dy = ds \sin \psi = \lambda \tan \psi \, d\psi, \qquad y = \lambda \log \sec \psi + F,$$

where $F = O$ taking $y = O$ when $\psi = O$. Thus the equation of the curve is

$$y = \lambda \log \sec x/\lambda.$$

The curve is symmetrical about the y-axis.

When

$$\frac{x}{\lambda} \to \frac{\pi}{2}, \qquad y \to \infty.$$

The curve has asymptotes $x = \pm \pi\lambda/2$. The maximum span is $\pi\lambda$.

Since $T = T_0 \sec \psi$, $\rho = \lambda \sec \psi$,

$$T = T_0\rho/\lambda.$$

Hence T and w are proportional to the radius of curvature.

Example. A chain of length l hangs in a catenary of uniform strength between two supports at the same horizontal level at a distance a apart. Find an equation for the parameter λ.

If ψ is the inclination at a support,

$$\frac{a}{2} = \lambda\psi, \qquad \frac{l}{2} = \lambda \log (\sec \psi + \tan \psi).$$

Hence

$$\sec \frac{a}{2\lambda} + \tan \frac{a}{2\lambda} = e^{l/2\lambda}.$$

Dividing

$$\sec^2 \frac{a}{2\lambda} - \tan^2 \frac{a}{2\lambda} = 1$$

by each side of this equation

$$\sec \frac{a}{2\lambda} - \tan \frac{a}{2\lambda} = e^{-l/2\lambda}.$$

Therefore

$$\sec \frac{a}{2\lambda} = \cosh \frac{l}{2\lambda}, \qquad \tan \frac{a}{2\lambda} = \sinh \frac{l}{2\lambda}.$$

$$\tanh\left(\frac{l}{4\lambda}\right) = \frac{e^{l/2\lambda} - 1}{e^{l/2\lambda} + 1} = \frac{\sec(a/2\lambda) + \tan(a/2\lambda) - 1}{\sec(a/2\lambda) + \tan(a/2\lambda) + 1}$$

$$= \frac{1 + \sin(a/2\lambda) - \cos(a/2\lambda)}{1 + \sin(a/2\lambda) + \cos(a/2\lambda)} = \tan(a/4\lambda).$$

This equation gives the parameter λ.

8.5. General equations of equilibrium of a string in one plane under given forces

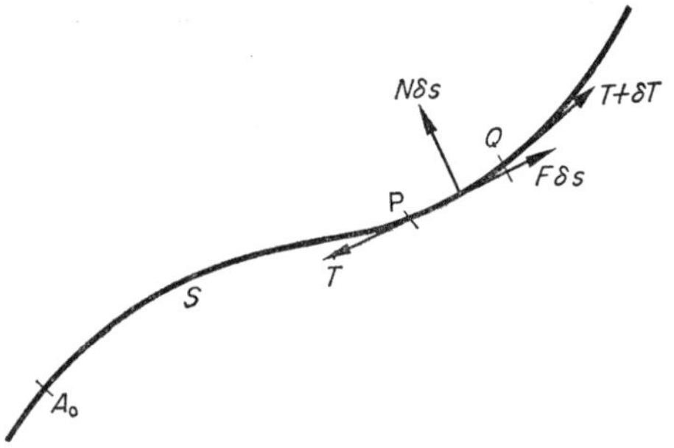

Fig. 128

Let A_0 be a given point on a string, and P a variable point on it where $A_0P = s$. Consider the equilibrium of an element PQ of length δs. If T is the tension at P, inclined at an angle ψ to the x-axis, then tension at Q is $T + \delta T$ inclined at angle $\psi + \delta\psi$. The components of these tensions along and perpendicular to the tangent at P are

$$(T + \delta T)\cos\delta\psi - T \text{ and } (T + \delta T)\sin\delta\psi$$

respectively. Hence, approximating by retaining terms of first order only, these reduce to

$$\delta T \text{ along the tangent} \tag{1}$$

and

$$T\delta\psi \text{ along the normal.} \tag{2}$$

Suppose the external forces acting on the element PQ are $F\delta s$ along the tangent and $N\delta s$ along the normal, that is, F and N are components along the tangent and normal of the external force per unit length. The equations of equilibrium of the element PQ are

$$\delta T + F\delta s = 0$$
$$T\delta\psi + N\delta s = 0,$$

which may be written, by proceeding to the limit $\delta s \to 0$,

$$\frac{dT}{ds} + F = 0 \tag{3}$$

$$\frac{T}{\rho} + N = 0, \tag{4}$$

where $\rho = ds/d\psi$ is the radius of curvature of the curve at P. The equations for the common catenary, catenary of uniform strength and other cases considered above may be obtained as particular cases of these by substituting the appropriate values of F and N. A few further cases of interest will be discussed below. It is convenient to write the equations for the element in each case, rather than to remember (3) and (4).

String on a Rough Curve

(i) **Light string in limiting equilibrium on a rough curve**

Consider an element PQ of length δs. Forces acting, besides the tensions at P and Q, are the normal and frictional components of reaction, $N\delta s$ and $\mu N\delta s$ respectively.

Resolving along the tangent

$$\delta T - \mu N\delta s = 0.$$

Resolving along the normal

$$T\delta\psi - N\delta s = 0.$$

Hence

$$\frac{dT}{d\psi} - \mu T = O.$$

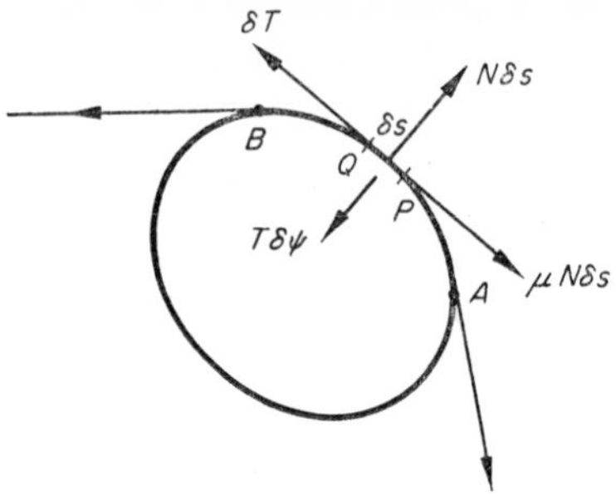

Fig. 129

Integrating

$$T = Ce^{\mu\psi}.$$

If A and B are the points where the string leaves the curve, and α, β are the values of ψ at these points, then

$$\frac{T_B}{T_A} = e^{\mu(\beta-\alpha)}.$$

That is, the tension increases along the string, in the sense in which it is about to slip, by an exponential factor involving the change in angle of the direction of the string. This factor can be quite large and explains why it is possible to withstand a considerable force by winding a rope round a support. For example if the coefficient of friction is $\frac{1}{2}$, a force F exerted at one end of the string can withstand a force $Fe^{2\pi} = 535F$ if the rope is coiled twice round the post, and a force $Fe^{3\pi} = 12{,}400F$ if coiled three times.

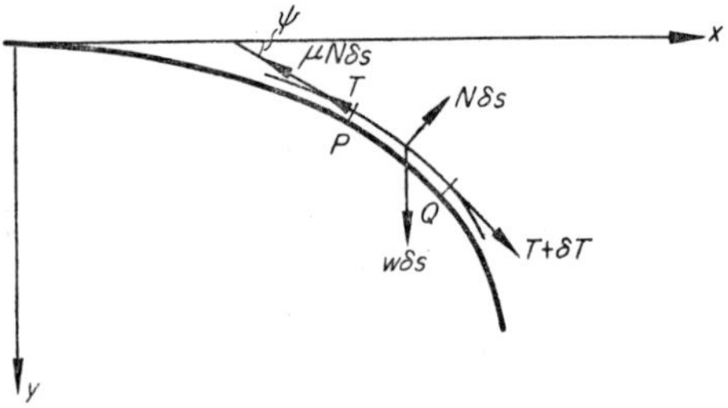

Fig. 130

(ii) Heavy string on a rough curve in a vertical plane

Suppose the string is about to slip downwards along the curve. The forces on the element PQ are shown in the figure (Fig. 130).

Resolving tangentially and normally

$$\delta T - \mu N \delta s + w \delta s \sin \psi = O$$
$$T \delta \psi - N \delta s + w \delta s \cos \psi = O.$$

Proceeding to the limit $\delta s \to O$

$$\frac{dT}{ds} - \mu N + w \sin \psi = O$$
$$\frac{T}{\rho} - N + w \cos \psi = O.$$

Eliminating N, and rearranging,

$$\frac{dT}{d\psi} - \mu T = w \frac{ds}{d\psi} (\mu \cos \psi - \sin \psi).$$

Integrating

$$Te^{-\mu\psi} = C + \int w\rho (\mu \cos \psi - \sin \psi) e^{-\mu\psi} d\psi$$

or

$$[Te^{-\mu\psi}]_A^B = \int_A^B w\rho (\mu \cos \psi - \sin \psi) e^{-\mu\psi} d\psi,$$

where A, B are any two points of the string.

Given the intrinsic equation of the curve, ρ is known as a function of ψ, and if w is also known, the integral may be evaluated. The following integrals are often of use.

$$\int e^{-\mu\psi} \sin a\psi \, d\psi = \frac{-e^{-\mu\psi}}{a^2 + \mu^2} (a \cos a\psi + \mu \sin a\psi).$$

$$\int e^{-\mu\psi} \cos a\psi \, d\psi = \frac{e^{-\mu\psi}}{a^2 + \mu^2} (a \sin a\psi - \mu \cos a\psi).$$

If $w = O$, that is, if the string is light, the result of integrating the equation of equilibrium is the same as that given in (1).

If $\mu = 0$ and w a constant,

$$\frac{dT}{ds} = -w \sin \psi = -w \frac{dy}{ds}$$

Integrating

$$T = -wy + \text{const.}$$

or

$$T_1 - T_2 = -w(y_1 - y_2).$$

The difference between the tensions at two points of a heavy uniform string on a smooth curve is proportional to the difference in levels. The reaction N may be obtained from the remaining equation, namely

$$N = T/\rho + w \cos \psi.$$

Example 1. A rough rigid wire is in the form of a catenary of parameter c. It is placed in a vertical plane with the vertex of the catenary upwards and the directrix horizontal. A heavy uniform string of length c is placed on top of the wire with one end at the vertex of the catenary and is just on the point of motion. Show that the coefficient of friction must be

$$(\log 4)/\pi.$$

[Lond. *S* 1949]

Using the same Fig. 130, the equations of equilibrium are

$$\delta T - \mu N \delta s + w \delta s \sin \psi = 0$$
$$T \delta \psi - N \delta s + w \delta s \cos \psi = 0,$$

where $s = c \tan \psi$ is the intrinsic equation of the catenary. Hence the equation for T is

$$\frac{dT}{d\psi} - \mu T = wc \sec^2 \psi (\mu \cos \psi - \sin \psi).$$

The free ends of the chain are when $\psi = 0$ and $\psi = \pi/4$. At these points the tension vanishes.

$$[Te^{-\mu\psi}]_0^{\pi/4} = wc \int_0^{\pi/4} (\mu \sec \psi - \sec \psi \tan \psi) e^{-\mu\psi} d\psi.$$

$$\int \sec\psi e^{-\mu\psi}\,d\psi = \frac{e^{-\mu\psi}}{-\mu}\sec\psi + \int \frac{e^{-\mu\psi}}{\mu}\sec\psi\tan\psi\,d\psi,$$

integrating by parts.

Therefore

$$\int^{\pi/4} (\mu\sec\psi - \sec\psi\tan\psi)\,e^{-\mu\psi}\,d\psi = \left[-\frac{1}{\mu}e^{-\mu\psi}\sec\psi\right]_0^{\pi/4}.$$

Hence

$$[e^{-\mu\psi}\sec\psi]_0^{\pi/4} = 0,$$

i.e.

$$e^{-\pi\mu/4}\sqrt{2} - 1 = 0, \text{ or } e^{\pi\mu/4} = \sqrt{2},$$

i.e.

$$\mu = \frac{2}{\pi}\log 2 = (\log 4)/\pi.$$

Variable Chain Hanging under Gravity

The following example illustrates the features of this type of chain.

Example. A chain, of variable weight w per unit length, hangs under gravity in the form of part of the cycloid

$$x = a(\theta + \sin\theta), \qquad y = a(1 - \cos\theta)$$

with the axis vertical and vertex downwards.

(i) Determine how w should vary with θ in order that the chain may hang freely in this form.

(ii) If the chain is uniform, of weight w per unit length, and its shape is maintained in the cycloidal form above by the application of a distribution of horizontal force X per unit length, show that $X = w\tan\frac{1}{2}\theta$.

[*CCS* (*H*) 1956]

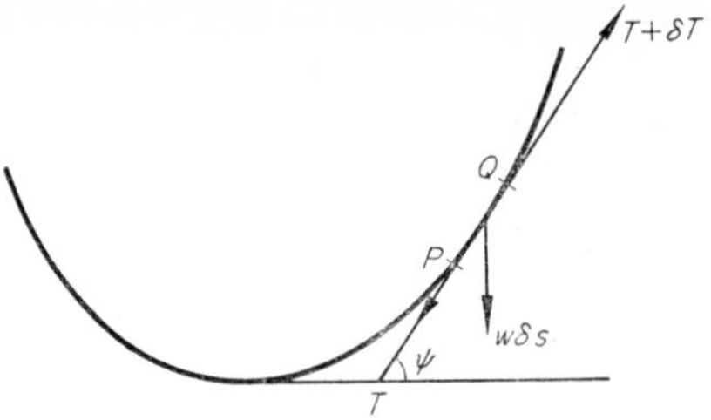

Fig. 131

It is convenient first to find the intrinsic equation of the cycloid.

$$\tan\psi = \frac{dy}{dx} = \frac{\sin\theta}{1+\cos\theta} = \tan\frac{\theta}{2}, \qquad \psi = \frac{\theta}{2}.$$

$$ds = \frac{dy}{\sin\psi} = \frac{a\sin\theta}{\sin\psi}\,d\theta = 4a\cos\psi\,d\psi.$$

Integrating

$$s = 4a\sin\psi,$$

the constant of integration vanishing if s is measured from the lowest point.

In case (1), considering the equilibrium of the element PQ,

$$\delta T - w\delta s\sin\psi = O$$
$$T\delta\psi - w\delta s\cos\psi = O.$$

Hence

$$\frac{1}{T}\frac{dT}{d\psi} = \tan\psi.$$

Integrating

$$\log T = \log\sec\psi + \text{const.}$$

or

$$T = T_0\sec\psi.$$

$$w = T\sec\psi\frac{d\psi}{ds} = \frac{T_0}{4a}\sec^3\psi.$$

In case (ii), where w is a constant, and a horizontal force $X\delta s$ acts on PQ,

$$\delta(T\cos\psi) + X\delta s = O$$
$$\delta(T\sin\psi) - w\delta s = O.$$

Integrating the last equation

$$T\sin\psi = ws, \text{ or } T = 4\,aw.$$

Hence

$$X = \frac{-\mathrm{d}}{\mathrm{d}s}(T\cos\psi) = -\frac{1}{4a\cos\psi}\frac{\mathrm{d}}{\mathrm{d}\psi}(4aw\cos\psi) = w\tan\psi$$
$$= w\tan\theta/2.$$

8.6. Elastic strings

For the light elastic strings that were considered earlier, Hooke's Law was used to connect the tension and the extension of the whole string, with the assumption that the tension was the same at all points of the string and so was the extension, which is the ratio of the increment in length to the unstretched length. In the case of a heavy elastic string this assumption cannot be made. However, Hooke's law may be applied to each small element of the string.

The equations of equilibrium for the stretched state of an elastic string may be applied as for inextensible strings. It must be noted, however, that after the string is stretched, the line density, that is, the mass per unit length, is unknown. For example, the string may be uniform before stretching, but may not be uniform after stretching. Thus one deals with this additional unknown factor when dealing with elastic strings. But there is the additional information given by Hooke's law, and so there are enough equations in all to solve for the unknowns.

The following example illustrates the method of solution:

Example. A uniform extensible string, of natural length l, weight W, and modulus of elasticity λ, hangs vertically from one end and carries a weight W' at the other end. Show that the string stretches a distance

$$\frac{l}{\lambda}\left(\frac{1}{2}W + W'\right).$$

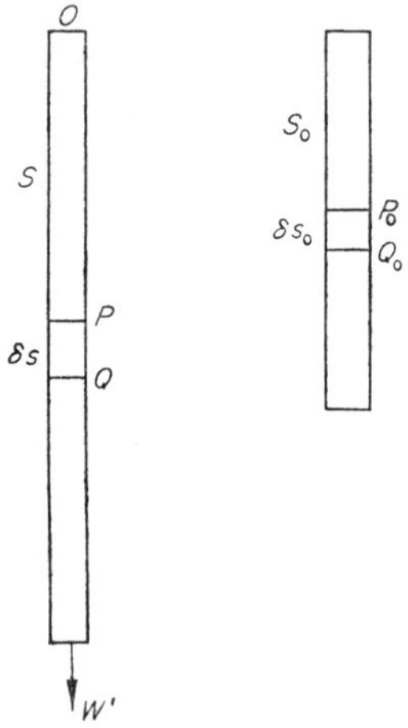

Fig. 132

Suppose PQ is an element of length δs in the stretched state, where $OP = s$. Let P_0Q_0 be the unstretched part which becomes PQ on stretching, where $OP_0 = s_0$, $P_0Q_0 = \delta s_0$. The weight of PQ is the same as that of P_0Q_0 which is $(W/l)\,\delta s_0$, since it is given that the unstretched string is uniform. Let T be the tension at P, and $T + \delta T$ the tension at Q. The equation of equilibrium of PQ gives

$$T = T + \delta T + \frac{W}{l}\,\delta s_0. \tag{i}$$

Also, Hooke's law applied to PQ gives

$$T = \lambda\,\frac{\delta s - \delta s_0}{\delta s_0} \quad \text{or} \quad \frac{ds}{ds_0} = 1 + \frac{T}{\lambda}. \tag{ii}$$

From (i),

$$\frac{dT}{ds_0} = -\frac{W}{l}.$$

Hence using (ii)

$$\frac{d^2s}{ds_0{}^2} = -\frac{W}{\lambda l}. \tag{iii}$$

Integrating

$$\frac{ds}{ds_0} = -\frac{W}{\lambda l} s_0 + C.$$

When $s_0 = l$, $T = W'$, and hence from (ii) and (iv),

$$1 + \frac{W'}{\lambda} = -\frac{W}{\lambda} + C \text{ or } C = 1 + (W + W')/\lambda.$$

Integrating (iv),

$$s = -\frac{1}{2}\frac{W}{\lambda l} s_0^2 + \left(1 + \frac{W + W'}{\lambda}\right) s_0 + D.$$

When $s_0 = O$, $s = O$, and hence $D = O$. Therefore when $s_0 = l$,

$$s = -\frac{1}{2}\frac{Wl}{\lambda} + \left(1 + \frac{W + W'}{\lambda}\right) l = l + \frac{l}{\lambda}\left(\frac{1}{2} W + W'\right).$$

Hence the string stretches by the amount $l(\frac{1}{2} W + W')/\lambda$.

8.7. Three-dimensional problems

So far the problems considered were two-dimensional. Suppose the figure (Fig. 133) shows a string in space, with A_0 a fixed point on it and $A_0P = s$, $PQ = \delta s$, position vector of P is $\mathbf{r} = (x, y, z)$ and $\mathbf{F}(s) = (X, Y, Z)$ is force per unit length acting at P. The forces acting on the element PQ are (i) tension at Q: $\mathbf{T} + \delta\mathbf{T}$, (ii) tension at P: $\mathbf{T}$, (iii) external force $\mathbf{F}\delta s$. Hence the equation of equilibrium is

$$\delta\mathbf{T} + \mathbf{F}\delta s = \mathbf{O}.$$

Dividing by δs and proceeding to the limit $\delta s \to O$,

$$\frac{\mathrm{d}\mathbf{T}}{\mathrm{d}s} + \mathbf{F} = \mathbf{O}.$$

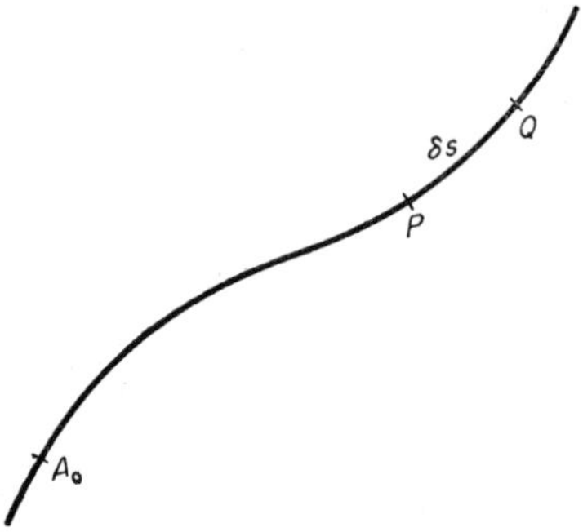

Fig. 133

Let **t**, **n**, **b** denote unit vectors at P along the curve's tangent, principal normal and binormal respectively. The equations of equilibrium may be written

$$\frac{\mathrm{d}}{\mathrm{d}s}(T\mathbf{t}) + \mathbf{F} = \mathbf{O} \tag{1}$$

or

$$\frac{\mathrm{d}T}{\mathrm{d}s}\mathbf{t} + \frac{T}{\rho}\mathbf{n} + \mathbf{F} = \mathbf{O}, \tag{2}$$

using

$$\frac{\mathrm{d}\mathbf{t}}{\mathrm{d}s} = \frac{1}{\rho}\mathbf{n}$$

where ρ is the radius of curvature at P. If $F_{\mathbf{t}}$, $F_{\mathbf{n}}$, $F_{\mathbf{b}}$ denote the components of **F** along the three directions equation (2) written in terms of components give

$$\frac{\mathrm{d}T}{\mathrm{d}s} + F_{\mathbf{t}} = O, \tag{3}$$

$$\frac{T}{\rho} + F_{\mathbf{n}} = O, \tag{4}$$

$$F_b = O. \tag{5}$$

Thus the external force is perpendicular to the binormal at P. The osculating plane at a point of the string contains the external force vector at that point.

The equation (1) may also be integrated giving

$$T\mathbf{t} + \int \mathbf{F}\, ds = \mathbf{k} \tag{6}$$

where $\mathbf{k}$ is a constant vector with components (k_1, k_2, k_3). On eliminating T one obtains the differential equation of the curve in which the string lies, and in terms of scalar quantities the equation is

$$\frac{k_1 - \int X\, ds}{\dfrac{dx}{ds}} = \frac{k_2 - \int Y\, ds}{\dfrac{dy}{ds}} = \frac{k_3 - \int Z\, ds}{\dfrac{dz}{ds}}. \tag{7}$$

The tension T is obtained by integrating (3), thus deriving

$$T = \text{const.} - \int (X\, dx + Y\, dy + Z\, dz).$$

If the external forces are conservative, there may be defined a potential energy function V such that

$$F = -\text{ grad } V, \text{ or } X = -\frac{\partial V}{\partial x}, \; Y = -\frac{\partial V}{\partial y}, \; Z = -\frac{\partial V}{\partial z}.$$

Then
$$T = C + V.$$

On the surface defined by $V + C = O$, the tension is zero. This surface is called no-tension level surface. Any free end of the string will be on this surface. The string must lie on the side of the surface such that $V + C > O$. Substituting $T = C + V$ in $T/\rho + F_n = O$ gives the differential equation of the curve.

String on a Given Smooth Surface $\phi(x, y, z) = O$

Let $\mathbf{n}_1$ be a unit vector along normal to the surface and $\mathbf{N}$ the normal reaction due to the surface. Then $\mathbf{n}_1 \propto \text{grad } \phi$. If the string is light and no other external forces act besides the reaction of the surface, equation of equilibrium gives

$$\frac{dT}{ds}\mathbf{t} + \frac{T}{\rho}\mathbf{n} + N\mathbf{n}_1 = \mathbf{O}.$$

Taking scalar product with **t**,

$$\frac{dT}{ds} = O \text{ or } T = \text{constant } C.$$

Substituting

$$\frac{T}{\rho}\mathbf{n} + N\mathbf{n}_1 = O$$

gives $\mathbf{n}_1 = \pm\,\mathbf{n}$ and $N = T/\rho$. In terms of scalars, the condition $\mathbf{n}_1 = \pm\,\mathbf{n}$ is

$$\frac{d^2x}{ds^2}\bigg/\frac{\partial\phi}{\partial x} = \frac{d^2y}{ds^2}\bigg/\frac{\partial\phi}{\partial y} = \frac{d^2z}{ds^2}\bigg/\frac{\partial\phi}{\partial z}.$$

The curve of the string is such that its principal normal coincides with the normal to the surface. Any element AB of the curve is the shortest distance on the surface between A and B. Such a curve is called a *geodesic*.

For example, a light string on a smooth sphere lies on a great circle and the normal reaction is $N = T/a$.

For a string on a given smooth surface, and acted upon by conservative forces **F** per unit length and normal reaction N,

$$\frac{dT}{ds}\mathbf{t} + \frac{T}{\rho}\mathbf{n} + N\mathbf{n}_1 + \mathbf{F} = \mathbf{O}.$$

Taking scalar product with **t**,

$$\frac{dT}{ds} + \mathbf{F}\,.\,\mathbf{t} = O.$$

Hence integrating

$$T = C - \int \mathbf{F}\,.\,d\mathbf{s} = C + V.$$

Again, taking scalar product with $\mathbf{t} \times \mathbf{n}_1$,

$$\frac{T}{\rho}\mathbf{b}\,.\,\mathbf{n}_1 + [\mathbf{F}, \mathbf{t}, \mathbf{n}_1] = O.$$

Substituting $T = C + V$, there is obtained the differential equation of the curve in which the string lies.

Exercises 8

1. A uniform flexible string AB, of length $2l$ and weight $2lw$, is attached at its ends A and B to small rings which slide on a rough horizontal rail. Prove that the equation of the curve in which the string hangs in equilibrium can be written in the form $y/c = \cosh x/c$.

If the weights of the rings are $2lw$ and $3lw$, respectively, and if the coefficient of friction between either ring and the rail is $\frac{1}{4}$, prove that the greatest value that the distance between the rings can have when the string hangs in equilibrium is $3/2\ l \log 3$. [Camb. *MT* 1958]

2. A heavy rod AB of length $2a$ can turn freely about its fixed end A and to the other end B is attached a heavy chain which hangs from a point C on the same level as A. If the rod and the chain are of the same uniform weight per unit length and in the position of equilibrium the rod is inclined at an angle $\pi/6$ to the vertical whilst the tangent at B to the chain is horizontal, show that the tangent at C to the chain makes an angle $\cos^{-1}(1/4)$ to the horizontal and find the length of the chain. [Lond. *G* 1936]

3. The ends of a uniform heavy chain of length $2l$ can slide on a fixed rough horizontal rod. Show that, if the angle of friction between the rod and the chain is λ, the least possible depth of the mid-point of the chain below the rod is

$$l \tan\left(\frac{\pi}{4} - \frac{\lambda}{2}\right),$$

and find the corresponding distance between the two ends.

[Camb. *MT* 1952]

4. One end of a uniform rough string of length l is fastened to a point A, at a height h above a table, and part of the string rests on the table in a vertical plane through A. If μ is the coefficient of friction, show that the greatest length which can lie on the table is the smaller root of the quadratic equation

$$\xi^2 - 2(l + \mu h)\,\xi + l^2 - h^2 = O.$$

5. Show that if T and T_0 are the tension in a catenary of parameter c at a point of height y above the directrix and the horizontal tension, $cT = yT_0$.

A heavy string of length $2l$ hangs symmetrically over two small smooth pegs A and B at the same level and distant $2a$ from each other and also across a small smooth peg C which is equidistant from A and B. Show that, if the constant c of the catenary is given, there are two possible positions for C, provided that $l > c(2\alpha - 1)^{1/2}$, and that the mean distance of the two positions of C from AB is

$$l(\alpha - 1)^2/2\alpha(2\alpha - 1) \text{ where } \alpha = e^{a/c}.$$

[Lond. *S* 1926]

6. A perfectly flexible uniform heavy chain has one end fixed at a point A and the other end at a point B, which is higher than A. If the inclination of the chain at A to the horizontal is 30° and the lowest point of the chain divides its

length in the ratio 1 : 3, show that the inclination of the chain at B to the horizontal is 60° and that AB is inclined to the horizontal at an angle

$$\cot^{-1} [\tfrac{1}{4} (3 + \sqrt{3}) \log (3 + 2\sqrt{3})].$$

[Lond. *S* 1935]

7. A uniform heavy flexible string AB, of length $2l$, has its ends A, B attached to light rough rings which can slide on a fixed horizontal rod. The coefficient of friction between the rings and the rod is $1/\sqrt{3}$. Show that when equilibrium is limiting at both ends the depth of the mid-point M of AB below the rod is $l/\sqrt{3}$.

If a particle of the same weight as the string is now attached to M and the string takes up a new symmetrical position of limiting equilibrium, show that M falls a distance $l(3 - \sqrt{7})/\sqrt{3}$. [Lond. *G* 1955]

8. A uniform flexible chain of length $2l$ and weight $2W$ has small rings attached to its ends, each ring being of weight $W/3$. The rings are threaded one on each of two fixed smooth wires OA, OB which are in a vertical plane and make equal angles $\pi/4$ with the downward vertical. If the system hangs in equilibrium, prove that the tangents at the ends of the chain are inclined at the angle $\tan^{-1} (\frac{3}{4})$ to the horizontal, and that the sag of the chain is $l/3$. Find the depth of the rings below O. [Lond. *G* 1957]

9. A uniform heavy flexible string hangs freely under gravity from two points A and B, the lowest point of the string is below A, and the vertical distance below A and B is k times the length of the string ($k < 1$). If α and β are the angles which the string makes with the downward vertical at A and B respectively, prove that

$$(1 - k) \tan \tfrac{1}{2}\alpha = (1 + k) \tan \tfrac{1}{2}\beta.$$

[Lond. *G* 1959]

10. A uniform heavy chain of length $2l$ is stretched between two supports at the same horizontal level. The lowest point of the chain is at a depth h below the supports. Prove that the centre of gravity of the chain is at a depth

$$\frac{h^2 + l^2}{4h} - \frac{(l^2 - h^2)^2}{8h^2 l} \sinh^{-1} \frac{2hl}{l^2 - h^2}$$

below the supports. [Lond. *G* 1958]

11. A uniform string, of length $2L$, hangs at rest over two smooth pegs A and B, whose horizontal and vertical distances apart are $2a$, $2h$. Show that the ends of the string are in the same horizontal line and that if a/u is the parameter c of the catenary formed by the portion of the string between the pegs, then

$$L^2 e^{-2u} = a^2 u^{-2} + h^2 \operatorname{cosec}^2 u.$$

[Oxf. *I* 1957]

12. A uniform rod, of length $2a$ and weight $2wa$, hangs from a pivot A at one end and a uniform chain also of length $2a$ and weight $2wa$, hangs from a second pivot B on the same level as A and at a distance less than $4a$ from it. The lower

end of the chain and the rod are now joined together and the whole hangs in equilibrium. Prove that if the rod makes an angle θ with the horizontal, then the inclination of the chain to the horizontal at its lower end is $2 \tan^{-1} (\tan^3 \frac{1}{2}\theta)$.
[Lond. *S* 1939]

13. The ends of a uniform heavy flexible string of length $2l$ are attached to two small light rings which are free to slide on a smooth circular wire of radius $a(a > l)$ fixed in a vertical plane. If the string is in equilibrium with the rings at the same horizontal level and at a non-zero distance $2d$ apart, prove that

$$(a^2 - d^2)^{1/2} = d \sinh \frac{(a^2 - d^2)^{1/2}}{l}$$

and find the depth of the lowest point of the string below the level of the rings.
[Lond. *G* 1956]

14. A uniform chain of length and weight W hangs vertically from one end which is attached to a fixed point, and carries a particle of weight P at its other end. The particle is now pulled aside by a horizontal force until a new position of equilibrium is attained. If X be the magnitude of the horizontal force in this position, show that the depth of the particle below the level of the point of support is

$$(l/W)\{\sqrt{[X^2 + (P + W)]^2} - \sqrt{[X^2 + P]^2}\}.$$

[Cey. *G* 1944]

15. A smooth ring of weight w is fastened to one end of a uniform heavy string of length $2l$ and weight w per unit length. The ring is free to slide on a smooth vertical rod and the string passes over a smooth pulley at a distance a from the rod. Prove that the parameter c of the catenary in which the part of the string between the pulley and the ring lies is given by

$$e^{a/c} = \frac{3l}{c}\left[\sqrt{\left(1 + \frac{l^2}{c^2}\right)} - \frac{l}{c}\right].$$

Show that this equation will certainly have no real roots if $3l < ae$.
[Oxf. *I* 1951]

16. Two smooth perpendicular wires, OA and OB, are fixed in a vertical plane with O uppermost, OA and OB being inclined, respectively, at angles α and $\frac{1}{2}\pi - \alpha$ to the downward vertical. A uniform inextensible string of length l has light rings attached to its ends, which slides freely on OA and OB. Find the parameter of the catenary in which the string hangs in equilibrium, and show that the distance from O of the ring on OA is

$$l \cos \alpha \{\cos \alpha - \sin \alpha + \sin^2 \alpha \log [(\sec \alpha + \tan \alpha)(\operatorname{cosec} \alpha + \cot \alpha)]\}.$$

[Oxf. *I* 1958]

17. A heavy uniform chain of length $2l$ is suspended between two supports in the same horizontal line distant $2a$ apart; the sag in the middle is k. Prove that the span is given in terms of the length and sag by the formula

$$2a = \frac{l^2 - k^2}{k} \log \left(\frac{l + k}{l - k}\right).$$

If a smooth horizontal table is placed at a depth b below the supports so that a length $2x$ of the chain rests on the table, prove that x satisfies the equation

$$2b\,(a-x) = (l+b-x)(l-b-x)\log\frac{l+b-x}{l-b-x},$$

provided $k > b > l - a$. [Lond. *S* 1946]

18. A flexible cable hangs from two points under the influence of its own weight and an applied continuous vertical load. Prove that the horizontal component H of the tension is constant and that a point (x, y) on the cable satisfies the differential equation

$$\frac{\mathrm{d}}{\mathrm{d}s}\left(\frac{\mathrm{d}y}{\mathrm{d}x}\right) = \frac{w}{H}$$

where s is the arc length along the cable and w is the total load per unit length (including the weight of the cable).

Integrate the equation in the cases of

(i) a weightless cable supporting a load uniformly distributed on a horizontal line (a suspension bridge);

(ii) a uniform cable hanging freely under its own weight.

Find the tension as a function of the x-coordinate at an arbitrary point in both cases.

[Oxf. *I* 1960]

20. A non-uniform flexible chain hangs in the form of a smooth curve from two points at the same horizontal level, which are at a distance l apart, with its lowest point at O; the curve is referred to horizontal and upward vertical axes Ox, Oy respectively. The tension T and mass per unit length m vary continuously along the chain, and have values T_0 and m_0 respectively at O. Show that

$$T = T_0\sqrt{(1+p^2)}, \qquad m = \frac{cm_0}{\sqrt{(1+p^2)}}\frac{\mathrm{d}p}{\mathrm{d}x}$$

where $p = \mathrm{d}y/\mathrm{d}x$ and $c = T_0/(m_0 g)$.

(i) The ratio $\gamma = T/(mg)$ measures the stress. If this is constant along the chain, show that the curve has equation

$$y = c\log\sec\frac{x}{c},$$

and that the span $l < \pi\gamma$.

(ii) If m is constant along the chain ($m = m_0$), show that the curve has equation

$$y = c\left(\cosh\frac{x}{c} - 1\right),$$

and that the stress $\gamma = c\cosh(x/c)$. If the maximum permitted value of γ is γ_1, show that the maximum value L of the span is obtained by eliminating c from the equations

$$\cosh(L/2c) = \gamma_1/c, \qquad \sinh(L/2c) = 2\gamma_1/L.$$

[Oxf. *I* 1956]

21. Two smooth circular cylinders of radius a are fixed with their axes parallel and in the same horizontal plane, their distance apart of the axes being $2b$ ($> 2a$). A uniform heavy chain of length $2l$ lies symmetrically across the cylinders with the ends hanging freely. If ϕ be the angle subtended at the centre of one of the cylinders by that portion of the chain in contact with it, prove that

$$b + a\cos\phi = (a\sin\phi + l - a\phi)\cot\tfrac{1}{2}\phi \log\tan\tfrac{1}{4}\phi.$$

[Oxf. *I* 1957]

22. An endless uniform belt of weight w per unit length hangs over a vertical smooth circular wheel of radius a so as to be in contact with three-quarters of the circumference, the rest hanging freely. Prove that the tension in the belt at the point where it leaves the wheel is $wa/\log(1+\sqrt{2})$, and find the pressure per unit length of the wheel on the belt at this point. [Oxf. *I* 1955]

23. The portion of the rough spiral curve $s = ae^{k\psi}$, which lies between $\psi = \pi/2$ and $\psi = 3\pi/2$ is held in a vertical plane so that the point $\psi = \pi$ is uppermost. A uniform chain partly lies along the curve from one end of the portion to the other and partly hangs vertically from the end $\psi = \pi/2$. If the hanging portion of the chain is on the point of moving upwards show that, at any point in contact with the spiral, the tension T satisfies the equation

$$\frac{dT}{d\psi} - \mu T = wak(\sin\psi - \mu\cos\psi)\,e^{k\psi},$$

where w is the weight per unit length of the chain and μ is the coefficient of friction between the chain and the curve.

Deduce that if $k > 2\mu$, the length of the vertical portion is

$$\frac{ak(k-2\mu)}{(k-\mu)^2+1}\,e^{k\pi/2}\{1 + e^{\pi(k-\mu)}\}.$$

[Lond. *S* 1936]

24. A uniform heavy string rests on the upper surface of a rough vertical circle of radius a, part of it hanging vertically. Prove that, if the end on the circle be at an angular distance θ ($\theta < \pi/2$) from the vertical on the side remote from the hanging portion, the greatest length that can hang vertically is

$$a\{\sin 2\lambda - e^{\mu(\pi/2+\theta)}\cos(\theta + 2\lambda)\}.$$

[Lond. *S* 1943]

25. Using polar coordinates (r, θ) find the equation of equilibrium of a string under the action of any forces in a plane in the form

$$\frac{d}{ds}\left(T\frac{dr}{ds}\right) - rT\left(\frac{d\theta}{ds}\right)^2 + R = O, \qquad \frac{d}{ds}\left(r^2 T\frac{d\theta}{ds}\right) + r\theta = O$$

and prove that, if the only force acting in the string is towards the pole and of magnitude $\phi(r)$ per unit length at the point (r, θ) then the differential equation of the curve in which it lies assumes the form

$$cu^2\left(\frac{d^2u}{d\theta^2} + u\right) = \left\{u^2 + \left(\frac{du}{d\theta}\right)^2\right\}^{1/2}\phi\left(\frac{1}{u}\right) \text{ where } u = \frac{1}{r}.$$

In the latter case, if the curve of the string is the equiangular spiral $r = ae^{m\theta}$ prove that $\phi(r)$ varies inversely as the square of r and the tension in the string inversely as r. [Lond. *S* 1943]

26. A uniform string of weight w per unit length rests in equilibrium on the upper surface of a rough right circular cylinder of radius a with axis horizontal. The string lies in a plane perpendicular to the axis of the cylinder, and the coefficient of friction between the cylinder and the string is μ. The tension at a point P of the string where the tangent is inclined to the horizontal at angle θ is denoted by T. Obtain equations for the equilibrium of the element P, assuming that the string is in limiting equilibrium with a tendency to slip in the direction which would increase θ, and establish the result

$$\frac{dT}{d\theta} - \mu T = wa(\mu \cos\theta - \sin\theta).$$

One end of the string is level with the axis of the cylinder, and the other end hangs freely a distance l below in the other side. Show that friction is sufficient to maintain equilibrium if

$$l < \frac{2\mu a}{1+\mu^2}(1 + e^{\mu\pi}).$$

[Oxf. *I* 1956]

27. Prove that a fixed chain can hang freely in the form of a parabola if its line density is such that the mass of any element is proportional to the length of the horizontal projection of that element.

A portion of such a chain is placed on a rough parabolic curve, whose plane is vertical and vertex upwards, tangent at the vertex being horizontal. One end of the chain is at this vertex and no part of the chain hangs freely. Prove that if the tangent at the lower end of the chain makes an angle ψ with the horizontal, the chain will be in limiting equilibrium if

$$e^{\mu\psi} = \sec\psi$$

μ being the coefficient of friction. [Oxf. *II* (*A*) 1936]

28. A smooth elastic string of normal length l, unstretched line-density ρ and modulus λ rests in a vertical plane on a horizontal circular cylinder of radius a with axis perpendicular to the plane of the string. If $\lambda = 2\rho g a$ and the ends of the string are at the same horizontal level as the axis of the cylinder, show that

$$l = 2\sqrt{2}\, a \log(1 + \sqrt{2}).$$

[Oxf. *I* 1960]

29. A uniform heavy string is in contact with a smooth fixed surface. Prove that the tension at any point is wz where w is the weight per unit length and z the height of P above a certain fixed plane.

A uniform heavy string lies on a smooth fixed sphere of radius a and the tension at any point of P is $wa\cos\theta$ where θ is the co-latitude of P measured from the highest point of the sphere. Prove that, if the arc s of the curve is measured from a point Q of maximum depth of the chain, the equation to the curve takes the form

$$\cos 2\theta = \cos 2\alpha \cos (2s/a)$$

where α is co-latitude of Q and $\pi/4 < \alpha < \pi/2$. [Oxf. *II* 1934]

30. The points A, B are the ends of a diameter of a right circular section of radius a of a smooth circular cylinder with its axis vertical. The ends of a light string of length s in contact with the cylinder are attached to A and B and a weight W is attached to the mid-point C of the string. Show that each part of the string forms a helix and that the tension of the string is equal to

$$Ws/2(s^2 - a^2\pi^2)^{1/2}.$$

[Lond. *S* 1926]

31. A necklace consists of n equal particles, each of weight W, strung at equal intervals on a light inextensible string of length l whose ends are joined together. It is placed in equilibrium round the top of a smooth sphere of radius a, so that the particles lie on a horizontal circle of radius r. Prove that

$$r = a \sin \left(\frac{l}{2na}\right) \operatorname{cosec} \frac{\pi}{n},$$

and that the tension in the string is equal to

$$\frac{W}{4} \sin \frac{l}{na} \operatorname{cosec} \frac{\pi}{n} \Big/ \left(\cos^2 \frac{l}{2na} - \cos^2 \frac{\pi}{n}\right)^{1/2}.$$

[Cey. *S* 1944]

Chapter 9

Elastic Beams

9.1. Introduction

THERE was considered in Chapter 6 the internal forces within rods and beams. This study was based on the assumption that these bodies are rigid bodies. In practice however all bodies do undergo deformations, even if slight, and it is important to take these into account. Beams, such as girders, are an important part of structural design, and it is necessary to know the extent of the deformations which the different parts of the structure are likely to undergo when subjected to loading, and also whether the forces that come into action within the body are within the margin of safety for the material to bear.

In Chapter 8 there were considered the conditions of equilibrium of perfectly flexible strings and chains. In this chapter we consider the equilibrium of beams which have a high degree of inflexibility. When one takes into account the very slight bending of these beams and uses the theory of elasticity, the indeterminate problems, briefly mentioned in § 6.5, become determinate.

A body is said to be elastic if it undergoes deformations when acted upon by external forces but regains its shape when the forces are withdrawn. The general deformation of an elastic body is expressed in terms of a *strain tensor*, and the internal elastic forces by a *stress tensor*. Each tensor may be expressed in matrix notation by nine elements in three rows and columns, and the components of the two tensors are connected by a relationship which is a generalized form of Hooke's law.

A discussion of the general theory of elasticity is outside the scope of this book. It is, however, of interest to discuss one or two cases which may be treated by elementary methods.

Extension of a Bar

Suppose a straight bar is acted upon by external forces applied at points on it in the direction of the bar, a point O of the bar being fixed. The shearing stress and bending moment vanish at each point but these will be a tension T. If A is the cross-sectional area of the bar, the stress or force per unit area is $\tau = T/A$, assuming that the stress is uniformly distributed over the cross-section.

The deformation of the bar will consist of a change in length. The elongation per unit length at any point of the bar is called the strain at that point. At a point P of the bar, let $OP = x$ in the unstretched state, and $OP = x + \xi(x)$ in the stretched state, where ξ is a function of x that requires to be determined. Let Q be a neighbouring point to P so that $OQ = x + \delta x$ in the unstretched state. Then after stretching

$$OQ = x + \delta x + \xi(x + \delta x) = x + \xi(x) + \delta x + \frac{d\xi}{dx}\delta x$$

to first order. Hence the length PQ after stretching is

$$\delta x + \frac{d\xi}{dx}\delta x,$$

so that the increment per unit length is $d\xi/dx$. Thus the strain is

$$e = \frac{d\xi}{dx}.$$

The stress and strain which do not vanish in this case are the tensile stress and tensile strain, these being the components along the line of the rod.

Hooke's law, when stated in terms of these quantities, is that *stress is proportional to strain.* That is,

$$\tau/e = \text{const.}$$

The constant is denoted by E and is called Young's modulus. Its value depends on the material. For india rubber E is about 2×10^7 dynes per cm^2 and for steel 2×10^{12} dynes per cm^2. E is very large for the materials that are used in structures. From Hooke's law one obtains

$$\frac{T}{A} = E\frac{d\xi}{dx}.$$

(The limit within which Hooke's law applies for a body is called the elastic limit. Certain materials like cement or cast-iron do not obey Hooke's law.)

If we take the particular case of a vertical bar, of natural length and weight w per unit unstretched length, and suspended from one end, if x is measured from the point of suspension, the tension T at the point satisfies

$$T = A(l - x)\,w.$$

Hence

$$E\frac{d\xi}{dx} = (l - x)\,w.$$

Integrating and using $\xi = O$ when $x = O$

$$\xi = \frac{w}{E}(lx - \tfrac{1}{2}x^2).$$

Thus ξ is determined for all points of the bar.

9.2. Bending of beams

Bernoulli–Euler Law

This is a simple approximate rule for the bending moment of a thin beam that is only slightly flexible, namely that the bending moment of a thin straight beam is directly proportional to the curvature of the central line of the beam, that is,

$$M \propto 1/\rho, \tag{1}$$

where ρ is the radius of curvature. For a beam that has a curvature

$1/\rho_0$ before bending, the bending moment that comes into being when the beam is bent is

$$M \propto (1/\rho - 1/\rho_0). \tag{2}$$

The following is a rough justification of formula (1) for a straight beam. For simplicity, the consideration is limited to a beam which has a central longitudinal plane of symmetry. Suppose bending takes place in planes parallel to this plane of symmetry. We assume

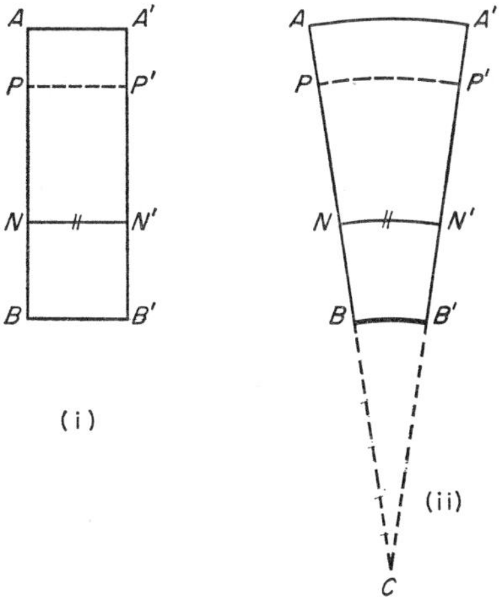

Fig. 134

that two normal plane sections of the beam, originally parallel, remain plane after bending and intersect in a line whose direction is independent of the particular sections. Adjacent sections are taken as congruent before bending.

Figure 134 (i) shows a longitudinal section parallel to the plane of bending of the beam between two adjacent cross-sections before bending, and Fig. 134(ii) the same after bending. The planes of the cross-sections after bending are inclined at an angle θ and intersect in a line C. If P and P' are corresponding points on the two cross-sections before bending, the straight line PP' may be assumed to deform into a circular arc of centre C. Suppose that the arc PP'

meets orthogonally the planes of section. This implies that there is no shearing of adjacent cross-sections.

It is seen that longitudinal fibres in the upper part of the beam near AA' are elongated, while those on the lower part near BB' are contracted. It is reasonable to infer that there is a line NN' which is neither elongated or contracted. In any cross-section of the beam, the points N for different longitudinal sections lie on a line called the *neutral line* of that section. This line is parallel to the line C. The neutral lines of the different cross-sections all lie on a *neutral surface.*

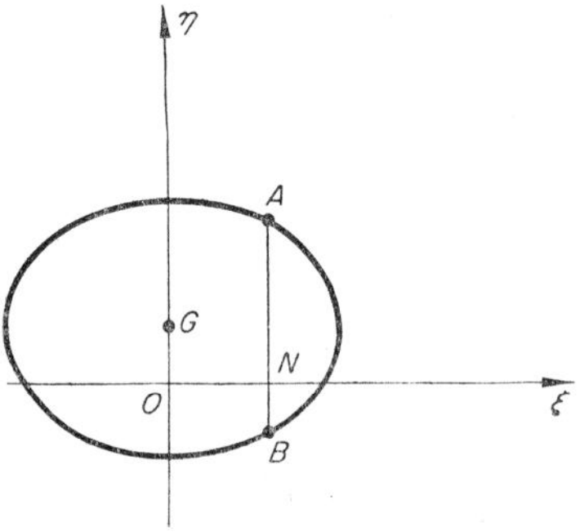

Fig. 135

Figure 135 shows a cross-section of the beam containing the line AB. The area of the cross-section has a line of symmetry, and the centroid G of the section lies on it. Let axes $O\xi$, $O\eta$ be taken in the plane of the section, with $O\xi$ along the neutral line of the section and $O\eta$ along the line of symmetry. If P has coordinates (ξ, η), then in Fig. 134(ii), $CN = \rho$, $CP = \rho + \eta$ and arc PP' is $(\rho + \eta)\,\theta$. Natural length of $PP' = NN' = \rho\theta$. Hence the extension of PP' is

$$\frac{PP' - NN'}{NN'} = \frac{(\rho + \eta)\,\theta - \rho\theta}{\rho\theta} = \frac{\eta}{\rho}.$$

Therefore the tensile stress at $P(\xi, \eta)$ is $E\eta/\rho$. Taking an area δA of the section at P, the force on this element is $E\eta\delta A/\rho$ parallel to the length of the beam. Hence the forces on a normal section are a system of parallel forces $(E\eta/\rho)\,\delta A$ acting on area δA about the point (ξ, η). The centroid G of the section has coordinates of the form $(O, \bar{\eta})$. Transferring each force to act at G by the introduction of a couple, the system is equivalent to a force

$$T = \frac{E}{\rho}\int \eta \, \mathrm{d}A = \frac{E}{\rho} A\bar{\eta} \tag{3}$$

acting at G in the direction of the beam, and couples

$$M_\xi = \frac{E}{\rho}\int \eta(\eta - \bar{\eta})\,\mathrm{d}A \tag{4}$$

$$M_\eta = -\frac{E}{\rho}\int \xi\eta \, \mathrm{d}A, \tag{5}$$

the axes of the couples being parallel to the ξ- and η-axes respectively. ρ has been taken to be the radius of curvature of NN' and is the same for all points N on the neutral line of one cross-section.

The forces acting on the section are equivalent to the tension T, and the bending moment which is the resultant of M_ξ and M_η. There is no shearing force, this being a consequence of the assumption that there is no shearing strain. Owing to symmetry $M_\eta = O$, and

$$M_\xi = \frac{E}{\rho}\int (\eta - \bar{\eta})^2\,\mathrm{d}A + \frac{E}{\rho}\,\bar{\eta}\int (\eta - \bar{\eta})\,\mathrm{d}A = \frac{EI}{\rho},$$

where the integral $\int (\eta - \bar{\eta})\,\mathrm{d}A$ vanishes, and I is the moment of inertia of the section of the line through G parallel to the ξ-axis.

If further the beam is such that there is no tension in the beam, i.e. $T = O$, then $\bar{\eta} = O$ and G lies on the neutral line of the section. Hence we have the result that if the bar is unstressed, i.e. the resultant stress across every cross-section is zero, and the rod is slightly bent by the applying couples, the centroids of the cross-sections lie on a central line which undergoes no extension. ρ is the radius of curvature at G of this line of centroids, and the bending moment at G is

$$M = \frac{E}{\rho}\int \eta^2\,\mathrm{d}A = \frac{EI}{\rho}. \tag{6}$$

EI is called the flexural rigidity of the beam. When the beam is of uniform cross-section, *EI* is often replaced by a single symbol *K*. When a beam is subjected to known loads, the bending moment can be calculated at various points of the beam. The relationship may then be used to find the shape of the beam.

The beam being only slightly flexible, the amount of bending is small, and the expression for M may be simplified further. If the axis of x is taken along the beam and the axis of y perpendicular to it, $\mathrm{d}y/\mathrm{d}x$ is small, and $(\mathrm{d}y/\mathrm{d}x)^2$ may be neglected in comparison with unity. Hence the equation (6) may be written

$$M = \pm \frac{K \dfrac{\mathrm{d}^2 y}{\mathrm{d}x^2}}{\left[1 + \left(\dfrac{\mathrm{d}y}{\mathrm{d}x}\right)^2\right]^{3/2}} = \pm K \frac{\mathrm{d}^2 y}{\mathrm{d}x^2}. \qquad (7)$$

Care has to be taken over the sign of the expression. Suppose the beam is horizontal, and bending is in the vertical plane. The axis of x is horizontal, and the axis of y is taken vertically downwards rather than upwards since the sag of the beam is then given by a positive expression. If the curve is as in Fig. 136(*a*), $\mathrm{d}^2y/\mathrm{d}x^2$ is positive, but M is negative, because if we consider the portion of the

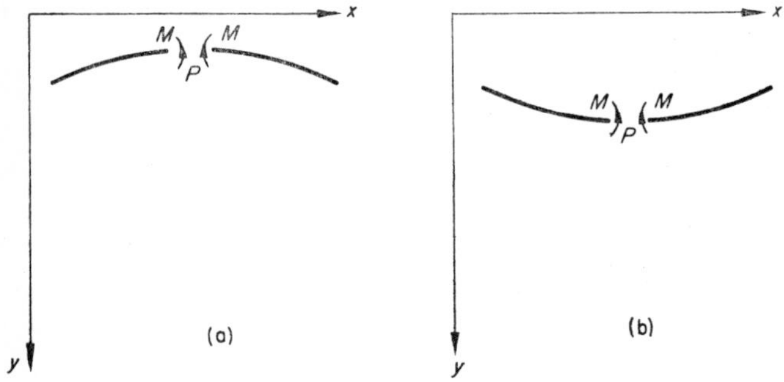

Fig. 136

beam to the left of P, from the way it is bent, it is seen that M is negative, and so in this case

$$M = - K \frac{d^2y}{dx^2}.$$

In case (b), d^2y/dx^2 is negative, M is positive, and so

$$M = - K \frac{d^2y}{dx^2}$$

in this case also.

Example 1. A uniform beam AC, of length $2l$ and of weight $2w$ rests on three supports A, B, C at the same level where B is the midpoint of AC. Assuming that the vertical deflection at all points is small, show that the reaction at B is equal to five-eighths of the weight of the beam. [Camb. *MT* 1953]

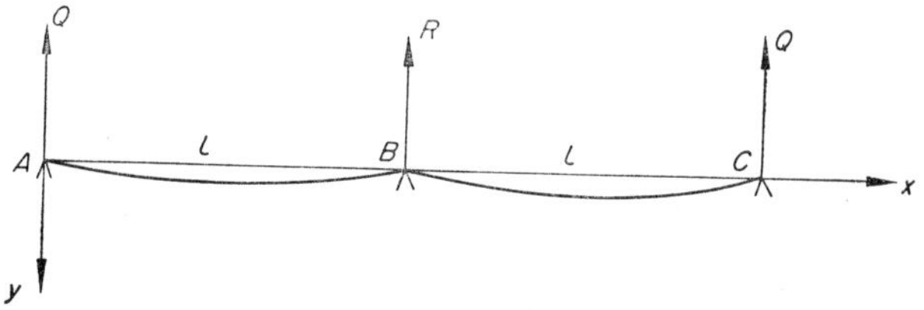

Fig. 137

There being symmetry, let the reactions at A and C be Q and at B be R. Then $2Q + R = W = 2wl$.

If P is a point between A and B and $AP = x$, then $0 < x < l$, and

$$- K \frac{d^2y}{dx^2} = M = Qx - \tfrac{1}{2} wx^2.$$

Integrating

$$- K \frac{dy}{dx} = \tfrac{1}{2} Qx^2 - \tfrac{1}{6} wx^3 + C.$$

Integrating again,

$$- Ky = \tfrac{1}{6} Qx^3 - {}^{1}\ wx^4 + Cx + D.$$

At A, $y = O$, that is, $y = O$ when $x = O$. Hence $D = O$. At B where $x = l$, then $y = O$ and $dy/dx = O$ by symmetry.

Hence

$$\tfrac{1}{6} Ql^3 - \tfrac{1}{24} wl^4 + Cl = O$$
$$\tfrac{1}{2} Ql^2 - \tfrac{1}{6} wl^3 + C = O.$$

Solving, $Q = \tfrac{3}{8} wl$, and $R = 2\,wl - 2\,Q = \tfrac{5}{8} W$.

Example 2. A uniform rod AB of length $2a$ and weight w per unit length is clamped horizontally at the end A. Find the deflection at B.

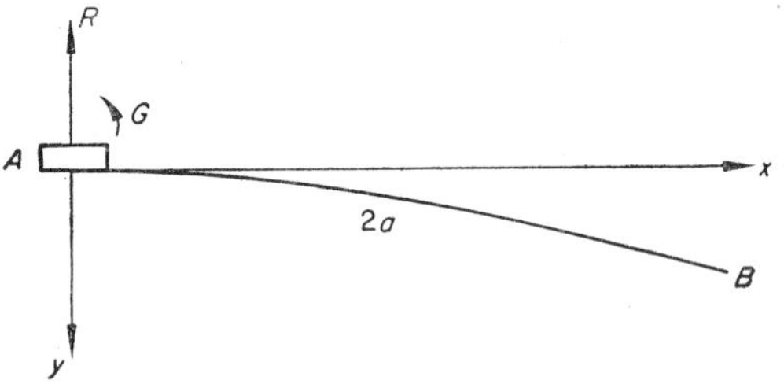

Fig. 138

The force at the support at A will consist of a force, R say, and a couple G. Resolving vertically and taking moments about A, $R = 2\,wa$ and $G = 2\,wa^2$. If P is a point of the beam at distance x from A, the bending moment at P is

$$M = -\,2\,wa^2 + 2\,wax - \tfrac{1}{2}\,wx^2.$$

Hence the differential equation of the curve in which the rod lies is

$$K\frac{d^2y}{dx^2} = 2\,wa^2 - 2\,wax + \tfrac{1}{2}\,wx^2.$$

Integrating

$$K\frac{dy}{dx} = w\,(2\,a^2x - ax^2 + \tfrac{1}{6}\,x^3) + C.$$

Since when $x = O$, $dy/dx = O$, hence $C = O$.
Integrating again,

$$Ky = w\,(a^2x^2 - \tfrac{1}{3}\,ax^3 + \tfrac{1}{24}\,x^4) + D.$$

Again $D = O$, since $y = O$ when $x = O$. The deflection at B is the value of y when $x = 2a$, and hence is

$$\frac{w}{K}\,a^4\,(4 - \tfrac{1}{3}\,.\,8 + \tfrac{1}{24}\,.\,16) = \frac{2\,wa^4}{K}.$$

Example 3. A beam of length l and weight w per unit length has its ends clamped horizontally in the same straight line. If y denotes the vertical deflection (assumed small) at distance x from one end, show that

$$K\,\frac{d^4y}{dx^4} = w.$$

Determine the shearing force at all points along the beam and show that the maximum deflection is

$$wl^4/(384\,K).$$

[Lond. *G II* 1957]

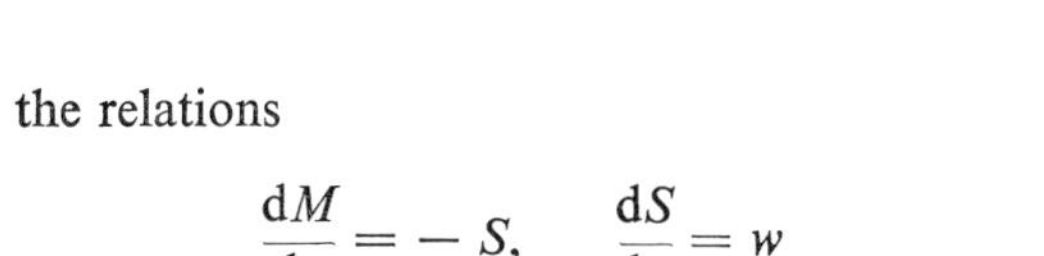

Fig. 139

We use the relations

$$\frac{dM}{dx} = -\,S, \qquad \frac{dS}{dx} = w$$

of Chapter 6. Eliminating S between these two equations

$$\frac{d^2M}{dx^2} = -\,w.$$

Substituting

$$M = -K\frac{d^2y}{dx^2},$$

there is obtained

$$K\frac{d^4y}{dx^4} = w.$$

The solution of this differential equation is of the form

$$Ky = \tfrac{1}{24}wx^4 + Ax^3 + Bx^2 + Cx + D.$$

Since $y = O$ when $x = O$ and $x = l$,

$$D = O, \qquad \tfrac{1}{24}wl^4 + Al^2 + Bl^2 + Cl = O.$$

$dy/dx = O$ when $x = O$ and $x = l$. Hence

$$C = O, \qquad \tfrac{1}{6}wl^3 + 3\,Al^2 + 2\,Bl = O.$$

Solving,

$$A = -\tfrac{1}{12}wl, \qquad B = \tfrac{1}{24}wl^2, \qquad C = O, \qquad D = O.$$

Hence one obtains

$$Ky = \tfrac{1}{24}wx^2(x - l)^2.$$

The shearing stress at any point of the beam is given by

$$S = -\frac{dM}{dx} = K\frac{d^3y}{dx^3} = wx + 6\,A = w\,(x - \tfrac{1}{2}l).$$

The maximum deflection is when $dy/dx = O$, that is, when $x = l/2$. Hence the maximum deflection is

$$\frac{1}{24}\frac{w}{K}(\tfrac{1}{2}l)^4 = \frac{wl^4}{384\,K}.$$

Example 4. A uniform elastic beam of weight W and length $2a$ rests on knife-edges at its ends and at its middle point, the ends being in the same horizontal line. The displacement of the beam is everywhere small. Show that if all three reactions are equal, the depth of the middle support below the other two is $7\,Wa^3/144\,EI$, where EI is the flexural rigidity of the beam.

The middle support is now raised so as to be at the same level as the other two. Find the reactions at the three supports.

[Lond. *G II* 1960]

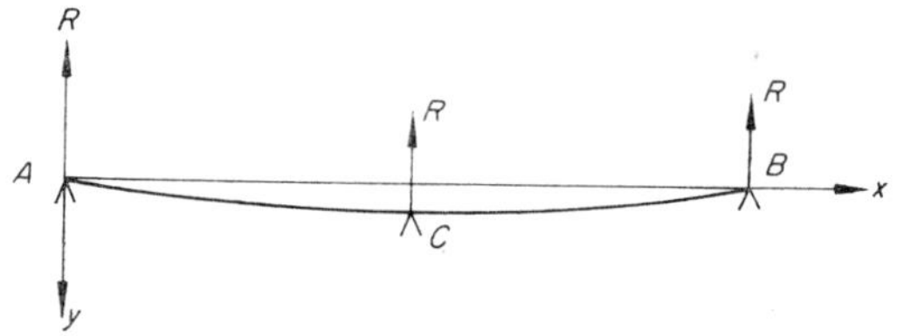

Fig. 140

When the three reactions are equal, each is $\frac{1}{3}W$. At a point P between A and C where $AP = x$, $O < x < a$,

$$M = Rx - \tfrac{1}{2}wx^2 = W\left(\frac{1}{3}x - \frac{1}{4}\frac{x^2}{a}\right).$$

Hence the differential equation of the curve is

$$EI\frac{d^2y}{dx^2} = W\left(-\frac{1}{3}x + \frac{1}{4}\frac{x^2}{a}\right).$$

Integrating

$$EI\frac{dy}{dx} = W\left(-\frac{1}{6}x^2 + \frac{1}{12}\frac{x^3}{a}\right) + C.$$

When $x = a$, $dy/dx = O$ by symmetry. Hence $C = \frac{1}{12}Wa^2$. Integrating again,

$$EI\,y = W\left(-\frac{1}{18}x^3 + \frac{1}{48}\frac{x^4}{a} + \frac{1}{12}a^2x\right) + D.$$

When $x = O$, $y = O$ and hence $D = O$. The depth of the middle support below the other two is the value of y when $x = a$ and hence is

$$\frac{Wa^3}{EI}\left(-\frac{1}{18} + \frac{1}{48} + \frac{1}{12}\right) = \frac{7}{144}\frac{Wa^3}{EI}.$$

The second part of the question is the same as in example 1 above. The reaction at each end support is $3W/16$, and at the middle support $5W/8$.

Example 5. The cross-section of a beam AB of length l is a circle whose area is $\pi a^2 x/l$, x being measured from the end A. The end B is clamped horizontally and the beam bends slightly under its own weight. Show that the displacement of A is

$$2\,\rho g l^4/9\,Ea^2$$

where E is Young's modulus and ρ the density.

Consider the section at a point P where $AP = x$

$$I = (\pi a^2 x/l)(\tfrac{1}{4}\,a^2 x/l) = \tfrac{1}{4}\,\pi a^4 x^2/l^2.$$

Expressing the bending moment at P,

$$-\tfrac{1}{4}\,E\pi a^4 x^2/l^2\,\frac{d^2y}{dx^2} = -\int_0^x (x-\xi)\,\frac{\pi a^2}{l}\,\rho g\xi\,d\xi$$

$$= -\frac{\pi a^2 \rho g}{l}\,(\tfrac{1}{2}\,x^3 - \tfrac{1}{3}\,x^3).$$

Hence

$$E\,\frac{d^2y}{dx^2} = \frac{2l}{3a^2}\,\rho g x.$$

The boundary conditions are that when $x=l$, $y=O$ and $dy/dx=O$. Integrating and using boundary condition

$$E\,\frac{dy}{dx} = \frac{l}{3a^2}\,\rho g\,(x^2 - l^2).$$

Integrating again

$$Ey = \frac{l\rho g}{3a^2}\,[\tfrac{1}{3}\,(x^3 - l^3) - l^2\,(x - l)].$$

The displacement of B is the value of y when $x = O$ and is

$$2\,\rho g l^4/9\,Ea^2.$$

9.3. The equation of three moments

If A_1, A_2, A_3 are three successive points of support in the same horizontal line of a uniformly loaded beam, and the bending moments at these points are M_1, M_2, M_3, Clapeyron's equation of three moments states that

$$aM_1 + 2(a+b)\,M_2 + bM_3 = -\tfrac{1}{4}\,w(a^3+b^3) \qquad (1)$$

where $A_1A_2 = a$, $A_2A_3 = b$, and w is the load per unit length.

Let S_1 denote the shearing stress at A_1 as we approach A_1 from the left, and S_1' as we approach from the right. There is a discontinuity in shearing stress, equal to the reaction at the support.

A_1 is taken as origin, $A_1A_2A_3$ as x-axis, and Oy vertically downwards.

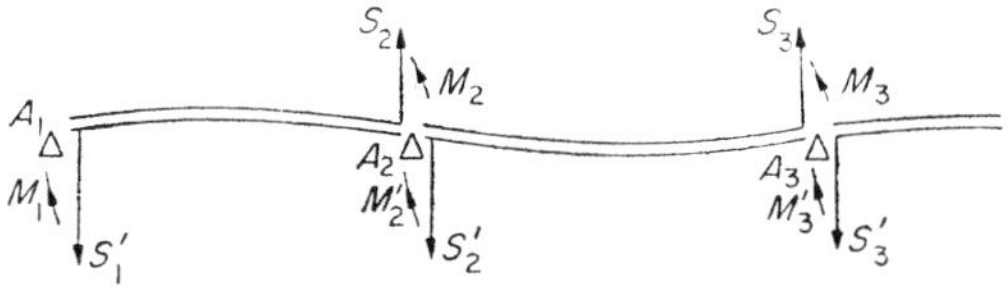

Fig. 141

Taking moments about A_2 for the equilibrium of A_1A_2

$$M_2 - M_1 + aS_1' + \tfrac{1}{2}\,wa^2 = O. \qquad (2)$$

Taking moments about A_3 for the equilibrium of A_2A_3,

$$M_3 - M_2 + bS_2' + \tfrac{1}{2}\,wb^2 = O. \qquad (3)$$

Also resolving vertically,

$$S_2 - S_1' = wa, \qquad S_3 - S_2' = wb. \qquad (4)$$

At a point P in A_1A_2 distant x from A_1, $0 < x < a$,

$$-K\frac{d^2y}{dx^2} = M = M_1 - S_1'\,x - \tfrac{1}{2}\,wx^2. \qquad (5)$$

Integrating

$$-K\frac{dy}{dx} = M_1x - \tfrac{1}{2}\,S_1'x^2 - \tfrac{1}{6}\,wx^3 + C.$$

$$-Ky = \tfrac{1}{2}\,M_1x^2 - \tfrac{1}{6}\,S_1'x^3 - \tfrac{1}{24}\,wx^4 + Cx + D.$$

$y = O$ when $x = O$ and also when $x = a$. Hence

$$D = O, \qquad \tfrac{1}{2}\,M_1a^2 - \tfrac{1}{6}\,S_1'a^3 - \tfrac{1}{24}\,wa^4 + Ca = O.$$

Hence

$$-K\frac{dy}{dx} = M_1(x - \tfrac{1}{2}a) - S_1'(\tfrac{1}{2}x^2 - \tfrac{1}{6}a^2) - w(\tfrac{1}{6}x^3 - \tfrac{1}{24}a^3)$$

$$= M_1(x - \tfrac{1}{2}a) + (M_2 - M_1 + \tfrac{1}{2}wa^2)\left(\frac{1}{2}\frac{x^2}{a} - \frac{1}{6}a\right) - $$

$$- w(\tfrac{1}{6}x^3 - \tfrac{1}{24}a^3)$$

substituting for S_1'. Therefore the gradients of A_1A_2 at A_1 and A_2 are given by

$$-K\left(\frac{dy}{dx}\right)_{A_1} = -\tfrac{1}{2}M_1a - \tfrac{1}{6}(M_2 - M_1 + \tfrac{1}{2}wa^2)a + \tfrac{1}{24}wa^3$$

$$= -\tfrac{1}{3}M_1a - \tfrac{1}{6}M_2a - \tfrac{1}{24}wa^3, \qquad (6)$$

$$-K\left(\frac{dy}{dx}\right)_{A_2} = \tfrac{1}{2}M_1a + \tfrac{1}{3}(M_2 - M_1 + \tfrac{1}{2}wa^2)a - \tfrac{1}{8}wa^3$$

$$= \tfrac{1}{6}M_1a + \tfrac{1}{3}M_2a + \tfrac{1}{24}wa^3. \qquad (7)$$

From (6), by changing a to b, the suffix 1 to 2, and 2 to 3, one obtains that the gradient of A_2A_3 at A_2 is given by

$$-K\left(\frac{dy}{dx}\right)_{A_2} = -\tfrac{1}{3}M_2b - \tfrac{1}{6}M_3b - \tfrac{1}{24}wb^3. \qquad (8)$$

The expressions (7) and (8) should be equal, since the beam has no change of direction at A_2. Equating these one obtains

$$M_1a + 2M_2(a + b) + M_3b = -\tfrac{1}{4}w(a^3 + b^3).$$

By applying Clapeyron's equation, one may often obtain the bending moments at the supports, and then the reactions at the supports, being expressible in terms of the bending moments, would also be known. For example, the reaction at A_2 is

$$S_2 - S_2' = wa + (M_1 - M_2)/a - \tfrac{1}{2}wa +$$

$$+ (M_3 - M_2)/b + \tfrac{1}{2}wb. \qquad (9)$$

If A_1, A_2, A_3 are not in the same straight line, but A_2 is at a depth y_1 below A_2 and y_2 below A_3, the equation of moments may be shown to take the form

$$M_1a + 2\,M_2(a + b) + M_3b = -\tfrac{1}{4}\,w(a^3 + b^3) +$$
$$+\,6\,K\left(\frac{y_1}{a} + \frac{y_2}{b}\right). \qquad (10)$$

Example 1. Use the equation of three moments to solve example 1 of the previous section.

In the notation used in the equation of moments,

$$M_1 = M_3 = O, \qquad a = b = l.$$

Applying the equation to the supports at A, B, and C

$$O\,.\,l + 2\,M_2(l + l) + O\,.\,l = -\tfrac{1}{4}\,w(l^3 + l^3).$$

i.e.

$$M_2 = -\tfrac{1}{8}\,wl^2.$$

The reaction at B is, from equation (9),

$$wl + \tfrac{1}{8}\,wl - \tfrac{1}{2}\,wl + \tfrac{1}{8}\,wl + \tfrac{1}{2}\,wl = \tfrac{5}{4}\,wl = \tfrac{5}{8}\,W.$$

Example 2. A uniform girder AB, of weight W and length l, is clamped horizontally at A, and the other end B rests on a support at the same horizontal as A. Show that the bending moment and shearing stress at A are $\tfrac{1}{8}\,wl$ and $\tfrac{5}{8}\,W$ respectively.

Show also that the form of the beam is given by the equation

$$48\,Kly = Wx^2(l - x)(3l - 2x).$$

Let the reaction of the clamp at A consist of the force Q and couple G, and the reaction at B the force R. Then

$$Q + R - W = O$$
$$G - Rl + \tfrac{1}{2}\,Wl = O.$$

Fig. 142

To apply the equation of three moments, the clamping at A may be supposed to be done by fixing two points of the beam indefinitely close to A. Then, the equation of three moments may be applied to the two points at A and one point at B. Then in the above notation,

$$a = O, \qquad b = l, \qquad M_1 = O, \qquad M_2 = G, \qquad M_3 = O.$$

and

$$O + 2\,Gl + O = -\tfrac{1}{4}\,wl^3 \text{ or } G = -\tfrac{1}{8}\,wl^2 = -\tfrac{1}{8}\,Wl.$$

Hence

$$R = \tfrac{3}{8}\,W \text{ and } Q = \tfrac{5}{8}\,W.$$

The bending moment at A is G which has magnitude $\tfrac{1}{8}\,Wl$, and the shearing stress at A is $-Q$ and has magnitude $\tfrac{5}{8}\,W$.

Take now a point P on AP where $AP = x$, and suppose the deflection at P is y. The bending moment M at P is, by taking moments,

$$M = G + Qx - \tfrac{1}{2}\,wx^2.$$

Applying the equation (10) to the points A, A, P. Substituting $a = O$, $b = x$, $M_1 = O$, $M_2 = G$, $M_3 = M$, $y_1 = O$, $y_2 = -y$, we obtain

$$O + 2\,Gx + Mx = -\tfrac{1}{4}\,wx^3 - 6\,\frac{Ky}{x},$$

or

$$6\,Ky/x = \tfrac{1}{4}\,Wlx - (-\tfrac{1}{8}\,Wl + \tfrac{5}{8}\,Wx - \tfrac{1}{2}\,wx^2)\,x - \tfrac{1}{4}\,wx^3,$$

i.e.

$$\begin{aligned} 48\,Ky &= Wx^2(2\,x^2 - 5\,lx + 3\,l^2) \\ &= Wx^2(3\,l - 2\,x)(l - x). \end{aligned}$$

9.4. Long columns

Suppose a long thin weightless beam, whose length l is large compared to the dimensions of its cross-section, is clamped vertically at its lower end and carries a weight W at its upper end.

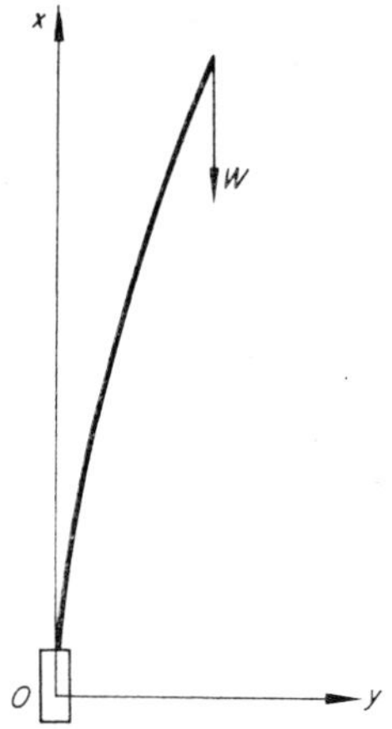

Fig. 143

Let us consider the possible positions of equilibrium. The axes of x and y are taken as shown in Fig. 143, and let c be the deflection at the upper end. At a point $P(x, y)$ of the rod, using the expressions for the bending moment

$$-K\frac{d^2y}{dx^2} = M = -W(c-y).$$

The solution of this equation is of the form

$$y = c + A\cos\alpha x + B\sin\alpha x$$

where A, B are arbitrary constants and $\alpha = \sqrt{(W/K)}$.

Using $y = O$ when $x = O$, and $y = c$ when $x = l$, the solution is

$$y = c\left[1 - \frac{\sin\alpha(l-x)}{\sin\alpha l}\right].$$

At the lower end, the column is clamped vertically, and hence $dy/dx = O$ when $x = O$. This gives

$$\cos\alpha l = O.$$

The smallest value of α satisfying this condition is $\alpha l = \pi/2$. This may be written

$$l = \tfrac{1}{2}\pi\sqrt{(K/W)} \text{ or } W = \frac{\pi^2}{4} K/l^2.$$

This implies that for a given K and W, there is a critical length $l_0 = \frac{1}{2}\pi\sqrt{(K/W)}$. If the beam has length $l < l_0$, then under the load W, the beam would remain vertical while contracting under the load. If l increases in value and begins to exceed l_0, then there is a possible position of equilibrium with the beam bent. It may be shown that in this case the bent position becomes the stable position, and the vertical position is unstable.

This result may also be expressed in terms of the values of the load. If K and l are given, then there exists a critical load

$$W_0 = \tfrac{1}{4}\pi^2 K/l^2$$

such that for loads $W < W_0$, the only equilibrium position is with the column vertical, and this position is stable. If W increases to a value just beyond W_0, there is also a bent position, which is the stable one.

Heavy Column

Suppose we now consider a thin uniform column, fixed vertically at the lowest point, and investigate the condition for the column not to give way under its weight.

Let the origin O be the upper end of the column, and axis Ox vertically downwards, Oy horizontal in the plane of deflection, the deflection being assumed small. Then taking moments about a point $P(x, y)$ of the beam

$$-K\frac{d^2y}{dx^2} = M = \int_0^x w(y-\eta)\,d\xi$$

Differentiating with respect to x,

$$\frac{d^3y}{dx^3} = -\frac{w}{K}\int_0^x \frac{dy}{dx}\,d\xi = -\frac{w}{K}x\frac{dy}{dx}.$$

Putting

$$\frac{dy}{dx} = p, \qquad \frac{w}{K} = \beta,$$

the equation is

$$\frac{d^2p}{dx^2} + \beta xp = O.$$

This equation may be reduced to a standard differential equation (Bessel's equation) by means of a transformation. Writing $\gamma = \frac{2}{3}\sqrt{\beta}$, $x = (u/\gamma)^{2/3}$, $p = (u/\gamma)^{1/3}v$, this differential equation becomes

$$\frac{d^2v}{du^2} + \frac{1}{v}\frac{dv}{du} + v\left(1 - \frac{1}{9u^2}\right) = O.$$

The solution is

$$v = AJ_{1/3}(u) + BJ_{-1/3}(u)$$

where $J_n(u)$ is Bessel's function of order n.

Hence

$$p = x^{1/2}\,[AJ_{1/3}(\gamma x^{3/2}) + BJ_{-1/3}(\gamma x^{3/2})].$$

At the highest point, the bending moment vanishes, and therefore $dp/dx = O$ when $x = O$. This may be shown to give $A = O$. Again $p = O$ when $x = l$, the column being fixed vertically at the lowest point. Hence

$$J_{-1/3}(\gamma l^{3/2}) = O.$$

This equation gives a value for l. It may be shown that an approximate solution is

$$1{\cdot}99\,(K/w)^{1/3}.$$

In this way, Bernoulli–Euler law for small flexure may be used for the investigations of many interesting problems. For more complicated problems, however, one has to utilize the theory of elasticity, and the reader is advised to refer to standard texts on elasticity.

9.5. Elastic energy of bending

The question of stability of the column considered in the previous section was briefly mentioned there. The conclusion stated there could be obtained by using the standard methods of investigating the stability of equilibrium, discussed in Chapter 7, provided the potential energy of the system is known. This energy may be obtained for a bent beam by calculating the work done against the stress couples in bending the beam.

Let PQ be an arc of length δs of the beam and ψ the angle between the tangents at its ends in the final bent position. For any intermediate position between the straight and final position, suppose the angle between the tangents at the ends of the same arc PQ is ϕ. The stress couple at P in this position is $K\rho = K\phi/\delta s$. When ϕ increases to $\phi + \delta\phi$, the work done against the couple is $(K\phi/\delta s)\,\delta\phi$. Thus as ϕ increases from O to ψ, work done on the arc PQ is

$$\delta W = (K/\delta s)\int_0^{\psi} \phi\,\mathrm{d}\phi = \tfrac{1}{2}\,K\psi^2/\delta s$$

$$= \tfrac{1}{2}\,(K/\rho^2)\,\delta s.$$

The work done for the whole beam is thus

$$\tfrac{1}{2}\int (K/\rho^2)\,\mathrm{d}s,$$

the integral being over the length of the beam.

We may interpret this integral as meaning that the elastic energy per unit length of beam is $\tfrac{1}{2}\,K/\rho^2$.

Example. A thin uniform beam of weight W, length l and flexural rigidity K is supported at its ends at the same level. Show that its elastic energy is

$$W^2l^3/(240\,K).$$

At a point P of the beam where $AP = x$,

$$K/\rho = M = \tfrac{1}{2}\,Wx - \frac{1}{2}\frac{W}{l}\,x^2.$$

The elastic energy per unit length s at P is

$$\tfrac{1}{2}\,K/\rho^2 = \tfrac{1}{2}\,M^2/K = \frac{1}{8}\frac{W^2}{K}\left(x - \frac{x^2}{l}\right)^2.$$

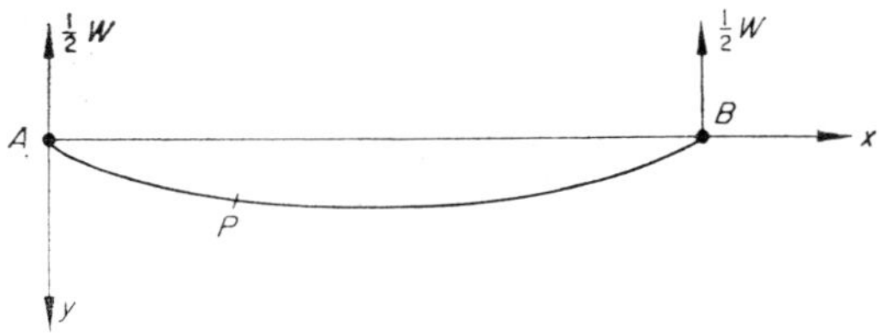

Fig. 144

Hence the total elastic energy is, taking $ds/dx = 1$ approximately,

$$\frac{1}{8}\frac{W^2}{K}\int_0^l (x - x^2/l)^2\, dx = \frac{1}{240}\frac{W^2 l^3}{K}.$$

Exercises 9

1. A uniform beam rests symmetrically over two supports at the same level. Prove that there will be no deflection at the midpoint if the ratio of the distance apart of the supports to the length of the beam is $6 - \sqrt{30} : 1$.
[Camb. *PM* 1947]

2. A straight uniform slightly elastic beam of weight W is clamped horizontally at one end. Find what weight must be hung from the middle point in order to double the sag at the free end. [Camb. *MT* 1960]

3. A uniform beam AC of length $2l$ and weight $2wl$ rests on three supports A, B, C at the same level, where B is the midpoint of AC. If the vertical deflection at all points is small, show that the radius of curvature of the beam at the midpoint of BC is twice the radius of curvature at B. [Camb. *MT* 1959]

4. A light uniform rod $ABCDE$ of length $4a$ rests on supports at the same level at B and D, where $AB = BC = CD = DE = a$, and the rod is slightly bent by equal weights W hung from A and E. Find the form of the rod, and show that the height of C above the level of B and D is three-eighths of the depth of A below the level of B and D. [Camb. *MT* 1956]

5. A light uniform bar AB of length l has a weight suspended from B. The bar is supported horizontally by a peg above the bar at A and by a second peg below the bar at a distance a from A. Assuming that bending is slight, show that the greatest deflection of the part of the bar between the pegs occurs at a point C at distance $a/\sqrt{3}$ from A.

Show further that the deflection at C will attain its greatest value if the second peg is placed at a point such that $a = \frac{2}{3}l$. [Camb. *MT* 1949]

6. A light uniform bar AB of length l is clamped horizontally at A and a

weight suspended from B produces a small deflection y at B. A peg is placed just beneath the bar at a distance a from A and is raised until A and B are at are at the same level. Show that the height h of the peg above AB is

$$h = \frac{a(4l - a)(l - a)^2}{2\,l^3\,(3\,l - a)}\,y.$$

[Camb. *MT* 1950]

7. A uniform beam AB of length $2l$ and weight w per unit length is clamped horizontally at one end A and as free at the other end B; the beam rests on a support at the midpoint C, the height of the support being adjusted and that B is on the same level as A. Find the height of the support at C above the level of A and prove that the pressure on it is $12/5\ wl$. [Lond. *S* 1943]

8. A uniform and slightly elastic rod, of length $4a$ and weight W, is placed symmetrically on two smooth supports (fixed at the same level) with each end at a distance a from the nearest support. If a load W' is hung from the middle point of the rod, show that the ends and the middle point will be below the level of supports if

$$3\,W < 48\,W' < 14\,W.$$

[Cey. *S* 1943]

9. A light uniform beam of length $2l$ is supported at its ends; the deflection at the centre is y_1 when a load rests on the centre, and is y_2 when the same load, divided into two equal halves, rests at the two points distant a from the centre. Prove that

$$y_2/y_1 = 1 - \frac{3}{2}\frac{a^2}{l^2} + \frac{1}{2}\frac{a^3}{l^3}.$$

[Lond. *S* 1936]

10. Four light beams AB, BC, CD, DA are loosely linked to form a rectangular framework; AD and BC are rigid, but AB and DC, which are of length l, are elastic with uniform flexural rigidity EI. When equal forces P act at the mid-points L and M of AB and DC in directions perpendicular to them, the elastic beams are slightly bowed outwards in a new equilibrium configuration. Calculate the increase in the distance LM, and show that the total elastic energy of the distorted system is

$$\frac{1}{48}\,P^2l^3/EI.$$

[Camb. *MT* 1954]

11. A uniform elastic beam AB of small cross-section, length l and weight wl, is in equilibrium, supported at its ends A, B with A, B in a horizontal line and subjected to small horizontal compressive forces of magnitude F at its ends. Show that the small downward deflection y at a point P distant x frow A is given by

$$\frac{d^2y}{dx^2} + \alpha^2 y = \frac{w\alpha^2}{2\,F}\,(x^2 - lx),$$

where α is a constant.

Determine the deflexion y as a function of x in the case

$$a = \tfrac{1}{2}\,\pi/l.$$

[Lond. *G II* 1959]

12. A uniform flexible beam of weight W and length $6a$ is placed on three narrow smooth rails P, Q, R, fixed at the same level at distances $PQ = 2a$, $QR = 4a$, P and R being under the ends of the rod. Show that the reactions on the rails are $\frac{1}{24}\,W$, $\frac{11}{16}\,W$, $\frac{13}{48}\,W$, respectively. [CCS (*H*) 1949]

13. A uniform beam of weight W and length $2a$ rests on two supports at its ends at the same level and a third support at its midpoint, at a height h above the level of those at the ends. Assuming that the flexural rigidity B is large, show that the pressure on the middle support is

$$\frac{5}{8}\,W + \frac{6\,Bh}{a^3},$$

and that the condition $16\,Bh < Wa^3$ is necessary. [CCS (*H*) 1952]

14. A light beam AB of length l has its ends clamped horizontally at the same level and a load W is placed at a point C of the beam, where

$$AC = a, \qquad CB = l - a = b.$$

Show that the reactions at the supports A and B are

$$W(2\,a + l)\,b^2/l^3 \text{ and } W(l + 2\,b)\,a^2/l^3$$

and the bending moments at A and B are

$$Wab^2/l^2 \text{ and } Wa^2b/l^2.$$

15. A horizontal beam is slightly bent under its own weight and external forces. Prove that the bending moment at any point is EI/R, where E is an elastic constant, I depends on the form of the section of the beam and R is the radius of curvature of the strained axis.

A beam of length l and of homogeneous material is built into a wall horizontally at one end. Its section is rectangular and of uniform depth but of variable breadth decreasing to zero at the free end. The breadth is such that the bending moment at any section per unit area of the section is constant. Show that the strained axis is an arc of a circle and that the bending moment is $A \sinh kx$ where x is measured from the free end and A, k are constants.

[Lond. *S* 1945]

16. Show that, if a thin rod of length l and flexural rigidity B is set up vertically with its lowest point fixed and the rod passing through a smooth ring fixed at a vertical height $\frac{1}{2}l$ above the lowest point and carrying at the top a weight W, then the least value of l for which the rod bends under the load is the smallest root of the equation

$$\tan \tfrac{1}{2}\,Wl = nl,$$

where $n^2 = W/B$. [Camb. *MT*]

17. A uniform, light, flexible beam AB of length l is clamped vertically at its lower end B. If a load W is attached to the upper end, show that the critical value of W is $\frac{1}{4}\pi^2EI/l^2$.

Show that when W just exceeds this value the shape of the beam is

$$y^2 - c^2 = -(2\,EI/W)(1 - \cos\psi)$$

where c is the horizontal separation of the two ends and y the deflection from the vertical through A.

18. A light, uniform pole, of length l and constant flexural rigidity EI, is fixed vertically in the ground at its lower end A, and its upper end B is acted upon by a force T which makes an angle α with the downward vertical. The consequent small, horizontal deflexion of B is a. Taking the origin at A, measuring x vertically up and y horizontally, state the bending moment at any point $P(x, y)$ of the pole and show that $(D^2 + x^2)\,y = n^2a + n^2(l - x)\tan\alpha$, where $D \equiv \mathrm{d}/\mathrm{d}x$, and $EI\,n^2 = T\cos\alpha$.

Solve this differential equation and show that

$$na = \tan\alpha\,(\tan nl - nl).$$

[Lond. *S*]

Index